New Challenges Arising in Engineering Problems with Fractional and Integer Order

New Challenges Arising in Engineering Problems with Fractional and Integer Order

Editors

Haci Mehmet Baskonus
Luis Manuel Sánchez Ruiz
Armando Ciancio

MDPI • Basel • Beijing • Wuhan • Barcelona • Belgrade • Manchester • Tokyo • Cluj • Tianjin

Editors
Haci Mehmet Baskonus
Harran University
Turkey

Luis Manuel Sánchez Ruiz
Universitat Politecnica de Valencia
Spain

Armando Ciancio
University of Messina
Italy

Editorial Office
MDPI
St. Alban-Anlage 66
4052 Basel, Switzerland

This is a reprint of articles from the Special Issue published online in the open access journal *Fractal and Fractional* (ISSN 2504-3110) (available at: https://www.mdpi.com/journal/fractalfract/special_issues/EPFIO2020).

For citation purposes, cite each article independently as indicated on the article page online and as indicated below:

LastName, A.A.; LastName, B.B.; LastName, C.C. Article Title. *Journal Name* **Year**, *Volume Number*, Page Range.

ISBN 978-3-0365-1968-5 (Hbk)
ISBN 978-3-0365-1969-2 (PDF)

Contents

About the Editors

Haci Mehmet Baskonus is currently an Associate Professor at Harran University, Sanliurfa/Turkey. His research interests include the numerical solution of differential equations, fluid and heat mechanics, finite element method, analytical methods for nonlinear differential equations, mathematical physics, and numerical solutions of the partial differential equations (of course, ordinary, partial, fractional order) by using numerical, analytical and semi-analytical methods, along with computer programs such as Mathematica, Maple, etc. He is an active reviewer of a plethora of papers and books. He has supervised many students, such as PhD, MSc and undergraduate students, and has been the external evaluator for many PhD theses in various countries. He was previously a Visiting Professor at the University of Tuscia, Viterbo, Italy, and University of Cartagena, Cartagena, Spain (via ERASMUS), on several occasions, from 2017–2019. He has also served as an editor for many famous journals. He was awarded by Springer and JECRC University with the Title of "Young Distinguished Researchers Award" in 2019, due to his publications and achievements related to performing original research work with a high degree of quality, recognized internationally, significant and done in a consistent way, and for supervising graduate students with their thesis work. He has been assigned the role of academic advisor at the Yunnan Normal University, Kunming, China, for the period 2020–2021.

Luis Manuel Sánchez Ruiz has been affiliated with Universitat Politècnica de València, Spain, since 1980. He became a Full Professor of Mathematics in 2000, and before this, he was a Visiting Professor at the University of Florida, Gainesville, FL, USA, on several occasions from 1992–1999. He has published over 150 papers in scientific journals and conference proceedings, and more than 10 textbooks on Mathematics for Engineers. He is the editor of several scientific journals and serial books, and his research interests focus on functional analysis, pure and applied, and in engineering education. His supervised dissertations comprise all these fields and he has been a Board Member of several PhDs in Spain, Italy, the Czech Republic and India. His lecturing is focused mainly on electronic, design and aeronautic engineering. Former Vice President of SEFI, Prof. Sánchez Ruiz is a member of the UPV Aerospace Engineering Program Academic Board, and Consultant Professor at Northwestern Polytechnic University, Xi'an (China).

Armando Ciancio is currently an Associate Professor at University of Messina, Italy. He became a doctor of philosophy, in the cycle of doctorate in Mathematics model for Economy and finance at the Faculty of Economy of the University of Messina, in 2004. He is a member, as a researcher, of the National Group of Mathematical Physic, sec. 3, and of the Institute of Higher Mathematics (INdAM) of Italy. Research Interests: time series based on wavelets; analysis of solutions in the field of physical-mathematical models of rheological media; mathematical models in economics and finance; fractal distributions; physical-mathematical models for biological media and applications to biotechnological and medical sciences. It currently presents 53 scientific papers. He is also a member of Editorial Board della rivista "Differential Geometry-Dynamical System" (DGDS), Balkan Society of Geometry, Geometry Balkan Press.

fractal and fractional

Editorial

New Challenges Arising in Engineering Problems with Fractional and Integer Order

Haci Mehmet Baskonus [1,*], Luis Manuel Sánchez Ruiz [2] and Armando Ciancio [3]

1 Department of Mathematics and Science Education, Faculty of Education, Harran University, Sanliurfa 63100, Turkey
2 ETSID-Departamento de Matemática Aplicada & CITG, Universitat Politecnica de Valencia, E-46022 Valencia, Spain; lmsr@mat.upv.es
3 Department of Biomedical and Dental Sciences and Morphofunctional Imaging, University of Messina, 98125 Messina, Italy; aciancio@unime.it
* Correspondence: hmbaskonus@gmail.com

Mathematical models have been frequently studied in recent decades in order to obtain the deeper properties of real-world problems. In particular, if these problems, such as finance, soliton theory and health problems, as well as problems arising in applied science and so on, affect humans from all over the world, studying such problems is inevitable. In this sense, the first step in understanding such problems is the mathematical forms. Extracted results are generally in the form of numerical solutions, analytical solutions, approximate solutions and periodic properties. With the help of newly developed computational systems, experts have investigated and modeled such problems. Moreover, their graphical simulations also have been presented in the literature.

In response to the call for papers, 33 submissions were received. All submissions were reviewed by at least three experts in the field. Finally, 12 papers were accepted for publication in this special issue, all of which were of high quality and represented the areas covered by this Special Issue well. This corresponds to an acceptance rate of 36%.

This Special Issue is based on fractional differentiation and integration, both with respect to theoretical and numerical aspects including the integer order.

The published papers in this Special Issue were briefly studied as follows.

In [1], the solution of a fractional kinetic equation (FKE), associated with the incomplete I-function (IIF) by using the well-known integral transform (Laplace transform), was investigated. The FKE plays an important role in solving astrophysical problems. The solutions in terms of the IIF were represented. They presented some interesting corollaries by specializing the parameters of the IIF in the form of simpler special functions. The authors also mentioned a few known results that are very useful in solving physical or real-life problems. Finally, some graphical results were presented to demonstrate the influence of the order of the fractional integral operator on the reaction rate.

In [2], the Sumudu decomposition method (SDM), a way to find approximate solutions to two-dimensional fractional partial differential equations, was used. A numerical algorithm for solving a fractional Riccati equation was investigated. The authors formed a combination of the Sumudu transform method and the decomposition method. The fractional derivative was described in the Caputo sense.

According to [3], time scales have been the target of work for many mathematicians for more than a quarter century. They used the fractional maximal integrals to establish integral inequalities on time scales. Moreover, their findings showed that inequality is valid for discrete and continuous conditions.

In [4], obtaining approximate solutions for a fractional order Burgers' equation was been presented in a reproducing kernel Hilbert space (RKHS). Some special reproducing kernel spaces were identified according to the inner products and norms. Then, an iterative approach was constructed by using kernel functions. The convergence of this

Citation: Baskonus, H.M.; Sánchez Ruiz, L.M.; Ciancio, A. New Challenges Arising in Engineering Problems with Fractional and Integer Order. *Fractal Fract.* **2021**, *5*, 35. https://doi.org/10.3390/fractalfract5020035

Received: 8 April 2021
Accepted: 18 April 2021
Published: 19 April 2021

approach and its error estimates was given. The numerical algorithm for the method was presented. In addition, the numerical outcomes were shown with tables and graphics for some examples.

In [5], the authors solved economic models based on market equilibrium with a constant proportional Caputo derivative by using the Laplace transform. They proved the accuracy and efficiency of the method. They constructed the relations between the solutions of the problems and bivariate Mittag–Leffler functions.

In [6], the authors applied an integral transform-based technique to solve a fractional order Volterra-type integro-differential equation (FVIDE) involving the generalized Lorenzo–Hartely function and generalized Lauricella confluent hypergeometric function with several complex variables in the kernel. They also investigated and introduced the Elzaki transform of the Hilfer derivative, generalized Lorenzo–Hartely function and generalized Lauricella confluent hypergeometric function. In this article, they established three results that were present in the form of lemmas, which give us new results for the above-mentioned three functions. By using these results, they derived results that were given in the form of theorems.

In [7], a fractional predator–prey model with a harvesting rate was considered. Besides the existence and uniqueness of the solution to the model, the local stability and global stability were examined. A novel discretization depending on the numerical discretization of the Riemann–Liouville integral was introduced, and the corresponding numerical discretization of the predator–prey fractional model was obtained. The net reproduction number R0 was obtained for the prediction and persistence of the disease. The dynamical behavior of the equilibria was examined by using the stability criteria. Furthermore, numerical simulations of the model were performed. Their graphical representations supported the numerical discretizations, emphasized the effectiveness of our theoretical results and monitored the effect of an arbitrary order derivative.

In [8], the application of the $(m+1/G')$-expansion method to the (2+1)-dimensional hyperbolic nonlinear Schrödinger equation was investigated. With the help of the proposed method, the periodic and singular complex wave solutions to the considered for the model were derived. Various figures such as 3D and 2D surfaces with suitable parameter values were plotted.

In [9], fractional order derivatives for the management and simulation of a fractional order disorderly finance system were investigated. In the developed system, the authors added the critical minimum interest rate parameter in order to develop a new stable financial model. The new emerging paradigm on the demand for innovation, which is the gateway to the knowledge economy, was surveyed. The derivatives were characterized in the Caputo fractional and the Atangana–Baleanu sense. They proved the existence and uniqueness of the solutions with fixed point theorems and an iterative scheme.

In [10], a new reproducing kernel approach was developed to obtain a numerical solution for multi-order fractional nonlinear three-point boundary value problems. This approach was based on a reproducing kernel, which was constructed by shifted Legendre polynomials (L-RKM). In the problem considered, fractional derivatives with respect to α and β were defined in the Caputo sense. This method was applied to some examples that had exact solutions. In order to show the robustness of the proposed method, some examples were solved, and the numerical results were given in tabulated forms.

In [11], one of the special cases of an auxiliary method, named the Bernoulli sub-equation function method, was applied for the nonlinear modified alpha equation. The characteristic properties of these solutions, such as complex and soliton solutions, were extracted. Moreover, the strain conditions of the solutions were also reported in detail. Observing the figures plotted, by considering various values of the parameters of these solutions, the effectiveness of the approximation method used for the governing model was confirmed.

In [12], the authors proved the equivalence of the norm of the restricted centered fractional maximal diamond-α integral operator to the norm of the centered fractional maximal diamond-α integral operator Mca on the time scales in variable exponent Lebesgue spaces. This study considered problems such as the boundedness and compactness of the integral operators in relation to the time scales.

Funding: This research received no external funding.

Conflicts of Interest: The authors declare no conflict of interest.

References

1. Bansal, M.K.; Kumar, D.; Harjule, P.; Singh, J. Fractional Kinetic Equations Associated with Incomplete I-Functions. *Fractal Fract.* **2020**, *4*, 19. [CrossRef]
2. Baleanu, D.; Jassim, H.K. Exact Solution of Two-Dimensional Fractional Partial Differential Equations. *Fractal Fract.* **2020**, *4*, 21. [CrossRef]
3. Akın, L. On the Fractional Maximal Delta Integral Type Inequalities on Time Scales. *Fractal Fract.* **2020**, *4*, 26. [CrossRef]
4. Saldır, O.; Sakar, M.G.; Erdogan, F. Numerical Solution of Fractional Order Burgers' Equation with Dirichlet and Neumann Boundary Conditions by Reproducing Kernel Method. *Fractal Fract.* **2020**, *4*, 27. [CrossRef]
5. Karatas Akgül, E.; Akgül, A.; Baleanu, D. Laplace Transform Method for Economic Models with Constant Proportional Caputo Derivative. *Fractal Fract.* **2020**, *4*, 30. [CrossRef]
6. Singh, Y.; Gill, V.; Singh, J.; Kumar, D.; Nisar, K.S. On the Volterra-Type Fractional Integro-Differential Equations Pertaining to Special Functions. *Fractal Fract.* **2020**, *4*, 33. [CrossRef]
7. Yavuz, M.; Sene, N. Stability Analysis and Numerical Computation of the Fractional Predator–Prey Model with the Harvesting Rate. *Fractal Fract.* **2020**, *4*, 35. [CrossRef]
8. Durur, H.; Ilhan, E.; Bulut, H. Novel Complex Wave Solutions of the (2+1)-Dimensional Hyperbolic Nonlinear Schrödinger Equation. *Fractal Fract.* **2020**, *4*, 41. [CrossRef]
9. Farman, M.; Akgül, A.; Baleanu, D.; Imtiaz, S.; Ahmad, A. Analysis of Fractional Order Chaotic Financial Model with Minimum Interest Rate Impact. *Fractal Fract.* **2020**, *4*, 43. [CrossRef]
10. Sakar, M.G.; Saldır, O. A New Reproducing Kernel Approach for Nonlinear Fractional Three-Point Boundary Value Problems. *Fractal Fract.* **2020**, *4*, 53. [CrossRef]
11. Baskonus, H.M.; Ercan, M. Extraction Complex Properties of the Nonlinear Modified Alpha Equation. *Fractal Fract.* **2021**, *5*, 6. [CrossRef]
12. Akın, L. A New Approach for the Fractional Integral Operator in Time Scales with Variable Exponent Lebesgue Spaces. *Fractal Fract.* **2021**, *5*, 7. [CrossRef]

fractal and fractional

MDPI

Article

On the Volterra-Type Fractional Integro-Differential Equations Pertaining to Special Functions

Yudhveer Singh [1], Vinod Gill [2], Jagdev Singh [3], Devendra Kumar [4] and Kottakkaran Sooppy Nisar [5,*]

1. Amity Institute of Information Technology, Amity University Rajasthan, Jaipur 303002, Rajasthan, India; yudhvir.chahal@gmail.com
2. Department of Mathematics, Govt. P.G. College, Hisar 125001, Haryana, India; vinod.gill08@gmail.com
3. Department of Mathematics, JECRC University, Jaipur 303905, Rajasthan, India; jagdevsinghrathore@gmail.com
4. Department of Mathematics, University of Rajasthan, Jaipur 302004, Rajasthan, India; devendra.maths@gmail.com
5. Department of Mathematics, College of Arts and Sciences, Prince Sattam bin Abdulaziz University, Wadi Aldawaser 11991, Saudi Arabia

* Correspondence: n.sooppy@psau.edu.sa

Received: 7 May 2020; Accepted: 3 July 2020; Published: 9 July 2020

Abstract: In this article, we apply an integral transform-based technique to solve the fractional order Volterra-type integro-differential equation (FVIDE) involving the generalized Lorenzo-Hartely function and generalized Lauricella confluent hypergeometric function in terms of several complex variables in the kernel. We also investigate and introduce the Elazki transform of Hilfer-derivative, generalized Lorenzo-Hartely function and generalized Lauricella confluent hypergeometric function. In this article, we have established three results that are present in the form of lemmas, which give us new results on the above mentioned three functions, and by using these results we have derived our main results that are given in the form of theorems. Our main results are very general in nature, which gives us some new and known results as a particular case of results established here.

Keywords: Volterra-type fractional integro-differential equation; Hilfer fractional derivative; Lorenzo-Hartely function; generalized Lauricella confluent hypergeometric function; Elazki transform

---

1. Introduction

From last three decade the fractional calculus have experienced significant observation to solve the mathematics, science & engineering and mathematical physics problems [1–11]. Fractional calculus plays a vital role to derive the solution of various kinds of differential and integral equations of fractional order arising in fractal geometry, propagation of seismic waves and diffusion problems for these we can cite the following works mentioned in [2,4,11–14]. In this connection Boyadjiev et al. [15] studied the non-homogeneous fractional integro-differential equation of Volterra-type (FIDEV) and obtained the solution in closed form in terms of Kummer functions and incomplete gamma function (IGF). Al-shammery et al. [16] studied the unsaturated behavior of the freeelectron lesser (FEL) and developed an analytical and numerical treatment of fractional generalization of the FEL equation. Further, Al-Shammery et al. [17] studied the arbitrary order generalization of the FEL equation and expressed their solution in terms of Kummer confluent hypergeometric functions (KCHF) as well as analyzed the behavior of FEL and it is governed by first-order IDEV. After this Saxena and Kalla [18] further generalized the first-order IDEV, which was an extension of the work done by Al-Shammery et al. [16,17]. In continuation of solution of FIDEV Kilbas et al. [19] consecutively studied and further generalized the work done by Saxena and Kalla [18] and established the solution in terms of generalized Mittag-Leffler function. Motivated by current work done by several authors on significant generalization of FIDEV with the help of fractional operator, Saxena and Kalla [20] investigated the solution of Cauchy-type generalized FIDEV involving a generalized Lauricella CHF in the kernels. At the same time Srivastava and Saxena [21] further derived the solution of FIDEV by using multivariable CHF in the kernel. Recently, Singh et al. [22] derived the solution of FEL containing Hilfer-Prabhakar derivative operator by using Elzaki transform in terms of Mittag-Leffler type function. Many authors have been work in the solution of fractional differential and integral equations refer to the work mentioned in [16,23–33]. In the literature of fractional differentiations and integrations there are several integral transforms like Laplace, Fourier, Mellin, Sumudu etc. Recently Elzaki introduced a new integral transform whose name is Elzaki transform [34,35], which is a modified form of classical Laplace and Sumudu transform and have some quality features. Elzaki transform has been effectively used to solve the integral equations as well as ordinary and partial differential equations in fractional calculus [36].

Primarily our objective of this paper is to investigate the formulae of Elzaki transform of functions which have been mentioned earlier and these results will be used to solve the generalized fractional integro-differential equations established here.

2. Definitions and Preliminaries

In this portion, we study a few important fundamental definitions associated to fractional calculus, Elzaki transform and special function to understand the further results, lemmas and application.

2.1. Elzaki Transform

Let $h(t)$ belong to a class K, where $K = \{h(t)\ :\ 3\,N,\ \mathrm{p}_1,\ \mathrm{p}_2 > 0$ such that $|h(t)| < Ne^{\frac{|t|}{p_i}}$ if $t\,\epsilon\,(-i)^j x[0,\ \infty)\}$.

Elzaki transform [34,35] of function $h(t)$ introduced by Tarig M. Elzaki is defined as

$$E[\mathrm{h(t)}] = u\int_0^{\infty} e^{-\frac{t}{u}}h(t)dt = \mathrm{T}(u\ ),\ \mathrm{t} > 0,\ u\,\epsilon\,\left(-\mathrm{p}_1,\mathrm{p}_2\right). \tag{1}$$

Convolution Property

The Elzaki transform of the convolution of $f(t)$ *and* $g(t)$ is given by

$$E[(f * g)(t)] = \frac{1}{u}\,F(u)G(u), \tag{2}$$

where $F(u)$ *and* $G(u)$ are the Elzaki transform of $f(t)$ *and* $g(t)$ *resp.*, and

$$(f * g)(t) = \int_0^t f(t)g(t-u)du.$$

2.2. Generalized Lorenzo-Hartley Function

Generalized Lorenzo-Hartley [37] is defined as:

$$G_{\nu,\mu,\sigma}(a,\omega) = \sum_{J=0}^{\infty} \frac{(\sigma)_j\,(a)^j\,\omega^{(\sigma+j)\nu-\mu-1}}{\Gamma(j+1)\Gamma(\sigma+j)\nu-\mu},\ \Re(\sigma\nu-\mu) > 0. \tag{3}$$

2.3. *Hilfer Derivative Operator*

The Hilfer derivative [38] of order α is defined as:

$$D_{a+}^{\beta,\gamma} y(x) = \left(I_{a+}^{\gamma(1-\beta)} \frac{d}{dt} I_{a+}^{(1-\gamma)(1-\beta)} y \right)(x). \tag{4}$$

2.4. *Generalized Lauricella Confluent Hypergeometric Function*

A special case of generalized Lauricella function in several complex variables, proposed by Srivastava and Daoust [39] (p. 454) in terms of a multiple series express in the following manner:

$$F^{\overbrace{0:1;\ldots;1}^{n}}_{\underbrace{1:0;\ldots;0}_{n}} \left[\begin{matrix} -:(\beta_1:1);\ldots;(\beta_n:1);- \\ \tau_1,\ldots,\tau_n \\ (\alpha:\delta_1,\ldots,\delta_n):-:- \end{matrix} \right] = \sum_{k_1,\ldots,k_n=0}^{\infty} \frac{(\beta_1)_{k_1}\cdots(\beta_n)_{k_n} {\tau_1}^{k_1}\ldots{\tau_n}^{k_n}}{\Gamma[\alpha+\delta_1 k_1+\ldots+\delta_n k_n](k_1)!\ \ldots\ (k_n)!}, \tag{5}$$

where $\alpha, \delta_j, \beta_j, \tau_j \in \mathbb{C}$ *and* $j = 1,\ldots,n$.

As per convergence condition mentioned by Srivastava and Doust [40] (p. 157) for the generalized Lauricella series in several variables, the series given in (5) converges for Re $(\delta_j) > 0$ *for* $j = 1,\ldots,n$.

3. Elzaki Transform of Generalized Lorenzo-Hartley Function, Hilfer Derivative & Generalized Lauricella Confluent Hypergeometric Function

In this portion, we introduce a formula of Elzaki transform of generalized Lorenzo-Hartely function, Hilfer derivative & generalized Lauricella confluent hypergeometric function.

Lemma 1. *The Elzaki transform of generalized Lorenzo-Hartely function is given by*

$$E\left[G_{v,\mu,\sigma}(a,\omega)\right] = u^{\sigma v-\mu+1}[1-(au^{v})]^{-\sigma}, \Re(\sigma v-\mu) > 0. \tag{6}$$

Proof. Elzaki transform of generalized Lorenzo-Hartely function defined by (3) is given by

$$E\left[G_{v,\mu,\sigma}(a,\omega)\right] = E\left[\sum_{J=0}^{\infty} \frac{(\sigma)_j\,(a)^j\,\omega^{(\sigma+j)v-\mu-1}}{\Gamma(j+1)\Gamma(\sigma+j)v-\mu}\right] = \sum_{J=0}^{\infty} \frac{(\sigma)_j\,(a)^j}{\Gamma(j+1)\Gamma(\sigma+j)v-\mu} E\left[\omega^{(\sigma+j)v-\mu-1}\right]. \tag{7}$$

Now, applying the formula of the Elazki transform in (7), we arrive at

$$E\left[G_{v,\mu,\sigma}(a,\omega)\right] = \sum_{J=0}^{\infty} \frac{u^{(\sigma+j)v-\mu+1}\,\Gamma(\sigma+j)\,(a)^j}{\Gamma(j+1)\,\Gamma(\sigma)}.$$

After this, we are rearranging the terms to convert the above equation in binomial function form

$$E\left[G_{v,\mu,\sigma}(a,\omega)\right] = u^{\sigma v-\mu+1} \sum_{J=0}^{\infty} \frac{\Gamma(\sigma+j)(au^{v})^j}{\Gamma(j+1)\,\Gamma(\sigma)}.$$

Finally, we get the desired result

$$E\left[G_{v,\mu,\sigma}(a,\omega)\right] = u^{\sigma v-\mu+1}[1-(au^{v})]^{-\sigma}.$$

□

Lemma 2. *The Elzaki transform of Hilfer derivative of fractional order defined in (4) is given by*

$$E\left[D_{a+}^{\beta,\gamma}y(x)\right](u) = u^{-\beta}E[y(x)](u) - u^{-\gamma(\beta-1)+1}\left(I^{(1-\beta)(1-\gamma)}y\right)(0+) \tag{8}$$

Proof. The Hilfer-derivative is defined as

$$D_{a+}^{\beta,\gamma}y(x) = \left(I_{a+}^{\gamma(1-\beta)}(D_{a+}^{\beta+\gamma-\beta\gamma}y)\right)(x). \tag{9}$$

Applying the integral operator (I_{a+}^{β}) on both side (see for instance [14]), we have

$$I_{a+}^{\beta}(D_{a+}^{\beta,\gamma}y)(x) = \left(I_{a+}^{\gamma(1-\beta)+\beta}(D_{a+}^{\beta+\gamma-\beta\gamma}y)\right)(x),$$

by using the definition of Riemann-Liouville integral operator [4]

$$\begin{aligned} &\frac{1}{\Gamma(\beta)}\int_a^t (t-x)^{\beta-1}(D_{a+}^{\beta,\gamma}y)(x)dx \\ &= y(x) - \sum_{k=0}^{n-1}\frac{(x-a)^{k-(n-\beta)(1-\gamma)}}{\Gamma[k-(n-\beta)(1-\gamma)+1]}\lim_{x\to a}\frac{d^k}{dx^k}\left(I_{a+}^{(n-\beta)(1-\gamma)}y\right)(x). \end{aligned} \tag{10}$$

Applying Elzaki transform and also using convolution property of Elzaki transform on above equation, we get

$$\begin{aligned} &\frac{1}{u\,\Gamma(\beta)}E\left[t^{\beta-1}\right]E\left[D_{a+}^{\beta,\gamma}y(x)\right](u) = \\ &E[y(x)](u) - \Sigma_{k=0}^{(n-1)}\left[\left\{\lim_{x\to a}\frac{d^k}{dx^k}\left(I_{a+}^{(n-\beta)(1-\gamma)}y\right)(x)\right\}E\left\{\frac{(x-a)^{k-(n-\beta)(1-\gamma)}}{\Gamma[k-(n-\beta)(1-\gamma)+1]}\right\}\right]. \end{aligned}$$

Using formula of Elzaki transform, we arrive at

$$\begin{aligned} &u^{\beta}\,E\left[D_{a+}^{\beta,\gamma}y(x)\right](u) = \\ &E[y(x)](u) - \sum_{k=0}^{n-1}\left[(u-a)^{k-(n-\beta)(1-\gamma)+2}\left\{\lim_{x\to a}\frac{d^k}{dx^k}\left(I_{a+}^{(n-\beta)(1-\gamma)}y\right)(x)\right\}\right]. \end{aligned} \tag{11}$$

Multiplying by $u^{-\beta}$ both side and taking $a = 0$ in Equation (11), we arrive at

$$\begin{aligned} &E\left[D_{0+}^{\beta,\gamma}y(x)\right](u) = \\ &u^{-\beta}E[y(x)](u) - \sum_{k=0}^{n-1}\left[(u)^{k-n+\gamma(n-\beta)+2}\left\{\lim_{x\to 0}\frac{d^k}{dx^k}\left(I_{0+}^{(n-\beta)(1-\gamma)}y\right)(x)\right\}\right], \end{aligned} \tag{12}$$

where $(n-1) < \beta \leq n$.

For $n = 1$, the above equation becomes

$$E\left[D_{0+}^{\beta,\gamma}y(x)\right](u) = u^{-\beta}E[y(x)](u) - (u)^{-\gamma(\beta-1)+1}\left(I_{0+}^{(1-\beta)(1-\gamma)}y\right)(0+).$$

This is the Elzaki transform formula of Hilfer-derivative. We use this result to solve fractional integro-differential equation. □

Lemma 3. *The Elzaki transform of generalized Lauricella confluent hypergeometric function in several complex variables defined in (5) is given by*

$$E^{-1}\left\{u^{\alpha+1}\prod_{j=1}^{n}\left(1-\tau_j u^{\delta_j}\right)^{-\beta_j}\right\}=\omega^{\alpha-1}F^{\overbrace{0:1;\ldots;1}^{n}}_{\underbrace{1:0;\ldots;0}_{n}}\left[\begin{array}{c}-:(\beta_1:1);\ldots;(\beta_n:1);-\\ \tau_1\omega^{\delta_1},\ldots,\tau_n\omega^{\delta_n}\\ (\alpha:\delta_1,\ldots,\delta_n):-:-\end{array}\right] \tag{13}$$

where $\alpha,\delta_j,\beta_j,\tau_j\in\mathbb{C}$, $\Re(u)>0$, $\max_{1\le j\le n}\left|\tau_j u^{\delta_j}\right|<1$, $\min_{1\le j\le n}\Re(\delta_j)>0$, $\Re(\alpha)>0$.

Proof. The Equation (13) can be easily solve by taking Elzaki transform of the function given in left hand side of (13), we have

$$E\left\{\omega^{\alpha-1}F^{\overbrace{0:1;\ldots;1}^{n}}_{\underbrace{1:0;\ldots;0}_{n}}\left[\begin{array}{c}-:(\beta_1:1);\ldots;(\beta_n:1);-\\ \tau_1\omega^{\delta_1},\ldots,\tau_n\omega^{\delta_n}\\ (\alpha:\delta_1,\ldots,\delta_n):-:-\end{array}\right]\right\}$$
$$=u\int_0^\infty\omega^{\alpha-1}\left(\sum_{k_1,\ldots,k_n=0}^{\infty}\frac{(\beta_1)_{k_1}\cdots(\beta_n)_{k_n}\tau_1k_1\ldots\tau_nk_n}{\Gamma[\alpha+\delta_1k_1+\ldots+\delta_nk_n](k_1)!\ldots(k_n)!}\right)e^{-\frac{\omega}{u}}d\omega,$$

interchanging the order of summations and integration, which is permissible under the conditions stated with Lemma 3, after rearrangement of the terms it is possible to express the above equation in the form

$$=u\left(\sum_{k_1,\ldots,k_n=0}^{\infty}\frac{(\beta_1)_{k_1}\cdots(\beta_n)_{k_n}}{\Gamma[\alpha+\delta_1k_1+\ldots+\delta_nk_n](k_1)!\ldots(k_n)!}\right)$$
$$\times\int_0^\infty\omega^{\alpha-1}\tau_1k_1\omega^{\delta_1k_1}\ldots\tau_nk_n\omega^{\delta_nk_n}e^{-\frac{\omega}{u}}d\omega,$$

and above equation can be written as

$$=\left(\sum_{k_1,\ldots,k_n=0}^{\infty}\frac{(\beta_1)_{k_1}\cdots(\beta_n)_{k_n}}{\Gamma[\alpha+\delta_1k_1+\ldots+\delta_nk_n](k_1)!\ldots(k_n)!}\right)E\left\{\tau_1k_1\ldots\tau_nk_n\,\omega^{\alpha+\delta_1k_1+\ldots+\delta_nk_n-1}\right\}. \tag{14}$$

Now, using the formula of the Elazki transform in (14), we have

$$E\left\{\omega^{\alpha-1}F^{\overbrace{0:1;\ldots;1}^{n}}_{\underbrace{1:0;\ldots;0}_{n}}\left[\begin{array}{c}-:(\beta_1:1);\ldots;(\beta_n:1);-\\ \tau_1\omega^{\delta_1},\ldots,\tau_n\omega^{\delta_n}\\ (\alpha:\delta_1,\ldots,\delta_n):-:-\end{array}\right]\right\}=$$
$$\sum_{k_1,\ldots,k_n=0}^{\infty}u^{\alpha+1}\frac{(\beta_1)_{k_1}\left(\tau_1u^{\delta_1}\right)^{k_1}}{(k_1)!}\cdots\frac{(\beta_n)_n\left(\tau_nu^{\delta_n}\right)^{k_n}}{(k_n)!}.$$

We express the above result in the form of product of binomial functions as

$$E\left\{\omega^{\alpha-1}F^{\overbrace{0:1;\ldots;1}^{n}}_{\underbrace{1:0;\ldots;0}_{n}}\left[\begin{array}{c}-:(\beta_1:1);\ldots;(\beta_n:1);-\\ \tau_1\omega^{\delta_1},\ldots,\tau_n\omega^{\delta_n}\\ (\alpha:\delta_1,\ldots,\delta_n):-:-\end{array}\right]\right\}=u^{\alpha+1}\left(1-\tau_1u^{\delta_1}\right)^{-\beta_1}\ldots\left(1-\tau_nu^{\delta_n}\right)^{-\beta_n}.$$

It can be written as

$$E\left\{\omega^{\alpha-1}F\overbrace{\underbrace{{}^{0:1;\ldots;1}_{1:0;\ldots;0}}_{n}}^{n}\left[\begin{array}{c} -:(\beta_1:1);\ldots;(\beta_n:1);- \\ \tau_1\omega^{\delta_1},\ldots,\tau_n\omega^{\delta_n} \\ (\alpha:\delta_1,\ldots,\delta_n):-:- \end{array}\right]\right\} = u^{\alpha+1}\prod_{j=1}^{n}\left(1-\tau_j u^{\delta_j}\right)^{-\beta_j}.$$

Finally, we arrive at the desired result. □

4. Solution of Generalized Fractional Integro-Differential Equations

Theorem 1. *Let us consider the following generalized fractional integro-differential equation of Volterra-type:*

$$D_{0+}^{\beta,\gamma}[y(x)] = \rho f(x) + \lambda\int_0^x G_{\nu,\mu,\sigma}(a,\omega)y(x-\omega)d\omega, \tag{15}$$

where $\nu,\ \mu,\ \sigma,\ \lambda,\ \rho \in \mathbb{C},\ 0 \le x \le 1,\ \beta \in (0,1),\ \gamma \in [0,1]$ *and* $\Re(\nu) > 0,\ \Re(\mu) > 0, \Re(\nu-\mu) > 0,$ *with the initial condition* $\left(I_{0+}^{(1-\beta)(1-\gamma)}y\right)(0+) = C$, *and* $f(x)$ *is assumed to be continuous on every finite closed interval* $[0,\ X](0 < X < \infty)$, *has its solution given by*

$$y(x) = C\,\phi(x) + \rho\int_0^x f(\omega)\,\xi(x-\omega)d\omega, \tag{16}$$

where

$$\phi(x) = \sum_{m=0}^{\infty}\lambda^m G_{\nu,\,(\mu-\beta)m+\gamma(\beta-1)-\beta,\sigma m}\,(a,x), \tag{17}$$

and

$$\xi(x) = \sum_{m=0}^{\infty}\lambda^m G_{\nu,\,(\mu-\beta)m-\beta,\sigma m}\,(a,\ x). \tag{18}$$

Proof. Applying Elzaki transform on Equation (15) and using (6) and (8), we have

$$\begin{aligned} &u^{-\beta}\,Y(u) - u^{-\gamma(\beta-1)+1}\left(I^{(1-\beta)(1-\gamma)}y\right)(0+) \\ &= \rho\,F(u) + \lambda\tfrac{1}{u}\,Y(u)u^{\sigma\nu-\mu+1}[1-(au^{\nu})]^{-\sigma}. \end{aligned}$$

After rearranging the terms, the above equation can be written as

$$u^{-\beta}\,Y(u)\left[1-\frac{\lambda u^{\sigma\nu-\mu+\beta}}{[1-(au^{\nu})]^{\sigma}}\right] = \rho\,F(u) + C\,u^{-\gamma(\beta-1)+1},$$

it can be written as follow

$$Y(u) = u^{\beta}\rho\,F(u)\left[1-\frac{\lambda u^{\sigma\nu-\mu+\beta}}{[1-(au^{\nu})]^{\sigma}}\right]^{-1} + C\,u^{-\gamma(\beta-1)+\beta+1}\left[1-\frac{\lambda u^{\sigma\nu-\mu+\beta}}{[1-(au^{\nu})]^{\sigma}}\right]^{-1}.$$

By virtue of binomial formula, we get

$$Y(u) = u^{\beta}\rho\,F(u)\sum_{m=0}^{\infty}\frac{\lambda^m u^{(\sigma\nu-\mu+\beta)m}}{[1-(au^{\nu})]^{\sigma m}} + C\,u^{-\gamma(\beta-1)+\beta+1}\sum_{m=0}^{\infty}\frac{\lambda^m u^{(\sigma\nu-\mu+\beta)m}}{[1-(au^{\nu})]^{\sigma m}}. \tag{19}$$

Now, inverting the Elzaki transform, we have

$$y(x) = \rho\, E^{-1}\left[\sum_{m=0}^{\infty} \lambda^m u^{(\sigma\nu-\mu+\beta)m+\beta}[1-(au^{\nu})]^{-\sigma m} F(u)\right] + CE^{-1}\left[\sum_{m=0}^{\infty} \lambda^m u^{(\sigma\nu-\mu+\beta)m-\gamma(\beta-1)+\beta+1}[1-(au^{\nu})]^{-\sigma m}\right].$$

Again using binomial result, we arrive at

$$y(x) = \rho\, E^{-1}\left[\sum_{m=0}^{\infty} \lambda^m \left\{\sum_{j=0}^{\infty} \frac{(\sigma m)_j (a)^j u^{(\sigma m+j)\nu-[(\mu-\beta)m-\beta]+1-1}}{\Gamma(j+1)}\right\} F(u)\right] + CE^{-1}\left[\sum_{m=0}^{\infty} \lambda^m \left\{\sum_{j=0}^{\infty} \frac{(\sigma m)_j (a)^j u^{(\sigma m+j)\nu-[(\mu-\beta)m+\gamma(\beta-1)-\beta]+1}}{\Gamma(j+1)}\right\}\right].$$

This leads us to the following equation

$$y(x) = \rho \sum_{m=0}^{\infty} \lambda^m \left[\sum_{j=0}^{\infty} \frac{(\sigma m)_j (a)^j}{\Gamma(j+1)} E^{-1}\{\tfrac{1}{u}\, E\left(\frac{x^{(\sigma m+j)\nu-[(\mu-\beta)m-\beta]-1}}{\Gamma(\sigma m+j)\nu-[(\mu-\beta)m-\beta]}\right) E\,\{f(x)\}\}\right] + C\sum_{m=0}^{\infty} \lambda^m \left[\sum_{j=0}^{\infty} \frac{(\sigma m)_j (a)^j}{\Gamma(j+1)} \frac{x^{(\sigma m+j)\nu-[(\mu-\beta)m+\gamma(\beta-1)-\beta]-1}}{\Gamma(\sigma m+j)\nu-[(\mu-\beta)m+\gamma(\beta-1)-\beta]}\right]. \quad (20)$$

Now, we applying the convolution property of the Elzaki transform in (20) and using (3), we find that

$$y(x) = \rho \sum_{m=0}^{\infty} \lambda^m \left[\sum_{j=0}^{\infty} \frac{(\sigma m)_j (a)^j}{\Gamma(j+1)} \left\{\int_0^x f(\omega) \frac{(x-\omega)^{(\sigma m+j)\nu-[(\mu-\beta)m-\beta]-1}}{\Gamma(\sigma m+j)\nu-[(\mu-\beta)m-\beta]}\, d\omega\right\}\right] + C\sum_{m=0}^{\infty} \lambda^m G_{\nu,\,(\mu-\beta)m+\gamma(\beta-1)-\beta,\sigma m}\,(a,x),$$

or

$$y(x) = C\sum_{m=0}^{\infty} \lambda^m G_{\nu,\,(\mu-\beta)m+\gamma(\beta-1)-\beta,\sigma m}\,(a,x) + \rho\sum_{m=0}^{\infty} \lambda^m \left[\int_0^x f(\omega) \sum_{j=0}^{\infty} \frac{(\sigma m)_j (a)^j}{\Gamma(j+1)} \frac{(x-\omega)^{(\sigma m+j)\nu-[(\mu-\beta)m-\beta]-1}}{\Gamma(\sigma m+j)\nu-[(\mu-\beta)m-\beta]}\, d\omega\right].$$

Finally, we arrive at the solution given by (15)

$$y(x) = C\sum_{m=0}^{\infty} \lambda^m G_{\nu,\,(\mu-\beta)m+\gamma(\beta-1)-\beta,\sigma m}\,(a,x) + \rho\left[\int_0^x f(\omega) \sum_{m=0}^{\infty} \lambda^m G_{\nu,\,(\mu-\beta)m-\beta,\sigma m}\,(a,\, x-\omega) d\omega\right].$$

We can also display the above result in this way

$$y(x) = \mathrm{C}\,\phi(\mathrm{x}) + \rho \int_0^x f(\omega)\, \xi(x-\omega) d\omega. \quad (21)$$

Here $\phi(\mathrm{x})$ and $\xi(x-\omega)$ are given by Equations (17) and (18). □

Theorem 2. *Let us consider the following generalized fractional integro-differential equation of Volterra-type:*

$$D_{0+}^{\beta,\gamma}[y(x)] = \rho f(x) + \lambda \int_0^x \omega^{\alpha-1} y(x-\omega) F^{\overbrace{0:1;\ldots;1}^{n}}_{\underbrace{1:0;\ldots;0}_{n}}\left[\begin{matrix} -:(\beta_1:1);\ldots;(\beta_n:1);- \\ \tau_1\omega^{\delta_1},\ldots,\tau_n\omega^{\delta_n} \\ (\alpha:\delta_1,\ldots,\delta_n):-:- \end{matrix}\right] d\omega, \tag{22}$$

where $\lambda, \alpha, \rho, \beta_j, \delta_j, \tau_j \in \mathbb{C}$; $0 \le x \le 1$; $\max_{1\le j\le n}\left|\tau_j\omega^{\delta_j}\right| < \infty$; $\Re(\alpha) > 0$; $\beta \in (0,1)$, $\gamma \in [0,1]$; $\min_{1\le j\le n}\Re\left(\delta_j\right) > 0$ $(j = 1,\ldots,n)$, *with the initial condition* $\left(I_{0+}^{(1-\beta)(1-\gamma)}y\right)(0+) = C$, *and* $f(x)$ *is assumed to be continuous on every finite closed interval* $[0, X]\,(0 < X < \infty)$, *has its solution given by*

$$y(x) = \rho \int_0^x f(\omega)\,\varphi(x-\omega)\,d\omega + C\psi(x), \tag{23}$$

where

$$\varphi(x) = x^{\beta-1}\sum_{r=0}^{\infty}\lambda^r x^{(\alpha+\beta)r} F^{\overbrace{0:1;\ldots;1}^{n}}_{\underbrace{1:0;\ldots;0}_{n}}\left[\begin{matrix} -:(\beta_1 r:1);\ldots;(\beta_n r:1);- \\ \tau_1 x^{\delta_1},\ldots,\tau_n x^{\delta_n} \\ (\beta+(\alpha+\beta)r\ :\delta_1,\ldots,\delta_n):-:- \end{matrix}\right], \tag{24}$$

and

$$\psi(x) = x^{\beta-\gamma(\beta-1)-1}\sum_{r=0}^{\infty}\lambda^r x^{(\alpha+\beta)r} F^{\overbrace{0:1;\ldots;1}^{n}}_{\underbrace{1:0;\ldots;0}_{n}}\left[\begin{matrix} -:(\beta_1 r:1);\ldots;(\beta_n r:1);- \\ \tau_1 x^{\delta_1},\ldots,\tau_n x^{\delta_n} \\ ((\alpha+\beta)r+\beta-\gamma(\beta-1):\delta_1,\ldots,\delta_n):-:- \end{matrix}\right]. \tag{25}$$

Proof. Applying the Elzaki transform on Equation (22), we have

$$E\left\{D_{0+}^{\beta,\gamma}[y(x)]\right\} = \rho E[f(x)] + \lambda\, E\left\{\int_0^x \omega^{\alpha-1} F^{\overbrace{0:1;\ldots;1}^{n}}_{\underbrace{1:0;\ldots;0}_{n}}\left[\begin{matrix} -:(\beta_1:1);\ldots;(\beta_n:1);- \\ \tau_1\omega^{\delta_1},\ldots,\tau_n\omega^{\delta_n} \\ (\alpha:\delta_1,\ldots,\delta_n):-:- \end{matrix}\right] y(x-\omega)d\omega\right\}. \tag{26}$$

Now, using (8) & (13) in (26), we found that

$$u^{-\beta}Y(u)\left[1-\lambda u^{\alpha+\beta}\left\{\prod_{j=1}^{n}\left(1-\tau_j u^{\delta_j}\right)^{-\beta_j}\right\}\right] = \rho F(u) + u^{-\gamma(\beta-1)+1}.C, \tag{27}$$

where $Y(u)$ *and* $F(u)$ represent, respectively the Elzaki transform of the function $y(x)$ *and* $f(x)$.

Solving Equation (27), we find that

$$\begin{aligned} Y(u) &= \rho u^{\beta} F(u)\left[1-\lambda u^{\alpha+\beta}\left\{\prod_{j=1}^{n}\left(1-\tau_j u^{\delta_j}\right)^{-\beta_j}\right\}\right]^{-1} \\ &+ u^{\beta-\gamma(\beta-1)+1}.C\left[1-\lambda u^{\alpha+\beta}\left\{\prod_{j=1}^{n}\left(1-\tau_j u^{\delta_j}\right)^{-\beta_j}\right\}\right]^{-1}, \end{aligned} \tag{28}$$

where we have tacitly assumed that

$$\left|\lambda u^{\alpha+\beta}\left\{\prod_{j=1}^{n}\left(1-\tau_j u^{\delta_j}\right)^{-\beta_j}\right\}\right|<1, \tag{29}$$

by virtue of binomial formula, we obtain

$$\begin{aligned} Y(u) = \rho F(u) \sum_{r=0}^{\infty} \lambda^r u^{\beta+(\alpha+\beta)r}\left\{\prod_{j=1}^{n}\left(1-\tau_j u^{\delta_j}\right)^{-\beta_j r}\right\} \\ +C\sum_{r=0}^{\infty} \lambda^r u^{(\alpha+\beta)r+\beta-\gamma(\beta-1)+1}\left\{\prod_{j=1}^{n}\left(1-\tau_j u^{\delta_j}\right)^{-\beta_j r}\right\}. \end{aligned} \tag{30}$$

Now, inverting the Elzaki transform and using the formula defined in (13) once again, we find from (30) that

$$\begin{aligned} y(x) = \\ \rho\, E^{-1}\left[\sum_{r=0}^{\infty} \lambda^r\, E\left\{f(x) * x^{\beta+(\alpha+\beta)r-1} F^{\overbrace{0:1;\ldots;1}^{n}}_{\underbrace{1:0;\ldots;0}_{n}}\left[\begin{array}{c} -:(\beta_1 r:1);\ldots;(\beta_n r:1);- \\ \tau_1 x^{\delta_1},\ldots,\tau_n x^{\delta_n} \\ (\beta+(\alpha+\beta)r\ :\delta_1,\ldots,\delta_n):-:- \end{array}\right]\right\}\right] \\ +C\sum_{r=0}^{\infty} \lambda^r x^{(\alpha+\beta)r+\beta-\gamma(\beta-1)-1} F^{\overbrace{0:1;\ldots;1}^{n}}_{\underbrace{1:0;\ldots;0}_{n}}\left[\begin{array}{c} -:(\beta_1 r:1);\ldots;(\beta_n r:1);- \\ \tau_1 x^{\delta_1},\ldots,\tau_n x^{\delta_n} \\ (\alpha+\beta)r+\beta-\gamma(\beta-1):(\delta_1,\ldots,\delta_n):-:- \end{array}\right]. \end{aligned} \tag{31}$$

Using the convolution property of Elazki transform in the above equation, we have

$$\begin{aligned} y(x) = \\ \rho E^{-1}\left[\sum_{r=0}^{\infty} \lambda^r E\left\{\int_0^x f(\omega)(x-\omega)^{\beta+(\alpha+\beta)r-1} F^{\overbrace{0:1;\ldots;1}^{n}}_{\underbrace{1:0;\ldots;0}_{n}}\left[\begin{array}{c} -:(\beta_1 r:1);\ldots;(\beta_n r:1);- \\ \tau_1 (x-\omega)^{\delta_1},\ldots,\tau_n (x-\omega)^{\delta_n} \\ (\beta+(\alpha+\beta)r\ :\delta_1,\ldots,\delta_n):-:- \end{array}\right] d\omega\right\}\right] \\ +C\sum_{r=0}^{\infty} \lambda^r x^{(\alpha+\beta)r+\beta-\gamma(\beta-1)-1} F^{\overbrace{0:1;\ldots;1}^{n}}_{\underbrace{1:0;\ldots;0}_{n}}\left[\begin{array}{c} -:(\beta_1 r:1);\ldots;(\beta_n r:1);- \\ \tau_1 x^{\delta_1},\ldots,\tau_n x^{\delta_n} \\ (\alpha+\beta)r+\beta-\gamma(\beta-1):(\delta_1,\ldots,\delta_n):-:- \end{array}\right]. \end{aligned} \tag{32}$$

Finally, after little simplification, we find that

$$\begin{aligned} y(x) = \\ \rho\left[\left\{\int_0^x \sum_{r=0}^{\infty} \lambda^r f(\omega)(x-\omega)^{\beta+(\alpha+\beta)r-1} F^{\overbrace{0:1;\ldots;1}^{n}}_{\underbrace{1:0;\ldots;0}_{n}}\left[\begin{array}{c} -:(\beta_1 r:1);\ldots;(\beta_n r:1);- \\ \tau_1 (x-\omega)^{\delta_1},\ldots,\tau_n (x-\omega)^{\delta_n} \\ (\beta+(\alpha+\beta)r\ :\delta_1,\ldots,\delta_n):-:- \end{array}\right] d\omega\right\}\right] \\ +C\sum_{r=0}^{\infty} \lambda^r x^{(\alpha+\beta)r+\beta-\gamma(\beta-1)-1} F^{\overbrace{0:1;\ldots;1}^{n}}_{\underbrace{1:0;\ldots;0}_{n}}\left[\begin{array}{c} -:(\beta_1 r:1);\ldots;(\beta_n r:1);- \\ \tau_1 x^{\delta_1},\ldots,\tau_n x^{\delta_n} \\ (\alpha+\beta)r+\beta-\gamma(\beta-1):(\delta_1,\ldots,\delta_n):-:- \end{array}\right]. \end{aligned} \tag{33}$$

We see that the above expression can be demonstrated in the form (23). Therefore this completes the proof of Theorem 2. □

5. Conclusions

In this work, we have applied efficient and interesting transform (Elzaki transform) to obtain the close form solution of generalized fractional integro-differential equation of Volterra-type involving the generalized Lorenzo-Hartely function and generalized Lauricella series function in terms of function itself. We also derived novel results such as Elzaki transform of Hilfer-derivative, generalized Lorenzo-Hartely function as well as generalized Lauricella confluent hypergeometric function. If we assign particular value to the parameters involve in (16) and (23), then our results established here are particular cases of various results derived by numbers of authors. We can use this transform to solve numerous problems, such as problems occurring in mathematics can be solve without utilizing a novel frequency domain, ODE, Non-homogenous equations, fractional integral and differential equations, one of the important aspect of this transform is that it can change the system of equations (differential & Integral) into algebraic equations.

Author Contributions: Conceptualization, D.K. and J.S.; Formal analysis, V.G., D.K. and K.S.N.; Investigation, Y.S. and J.S.; Methodology, J.S.; Writing—original draft, Y.S., V.G., D.K. and K.S.N.; Writing—review & editing, J.S. and K.S.N. All authors have read and agreed to the published version of the manuscript.

Funding: This research received no external funding.

Acknowledgments: The author K.S. Nisar thanks to Deanship of Scientific Research (DSR), Prince Sattam bin Abdulaziz University, Saudi Arabia for providing facilities and support.

Conflicts of Interest: The authors declare no conflict of interest.

References

1. Miller, K.S.; Ross, B. *An Introduction to the Fractional Calculus and Fractional Differential Equations*; John Wiley & Sons, INC.: New York, NY, USA, 1993.
2. Oldham, K.; Spanier, J. *Fractional Calculus: Theory and Applications of Differentiation and Integration of Arbitrary Order*; Academic Press: New York, NY, USA, 1974.
3. Kilbas, A.A.; Srivastava, H.M.; Trujillo, J.J. *Theory and Applications of Fractional Differential Equations*; North.-Holland Mathematical Studies; Elsevier (North-Holland) Science Publisher: Amsterdam, The Netherlands; London, UK; New York, NY, USA, 2006; Volume 204.
4. Podlubny, I. *Fractional Differential Equations*; Academic Press: San Diego, CA, USA, 1999.
5. Gill, V.; Singh, J.; Singh, Y. Analytical solution of generalized space-time fractional advection-dispersion equation via coupling of Sumudu and Fourier transforms. *Front. Phys.* **2019**, *6*. [CrossRef]
6. Kumar, D.; Singh, J.; Tanwar, K.; Baleanu, D. A new fractional exothermic reactions model having constant heat source in porous media with power, exponential and Mittag-Leffler laws. *Int. J. Heat Mass Tran.* **2019**, *138*, 1222–1227. [CrossRef]
7. Gao, W.; Veeresha, P.; Prakasha, D.G.; Baskonus, H.M. Novel dynamical structures of 2019-n CoV with non operator via powerful computational technique. *Biology* **2020**, *9*, 107. [CrossRef]
8. Bhatter, S.; Mathur, A.; Kumar, D.; Singh, J. A new analysis of fractional Drinfeld–Sokolov–Wilson model with exponential memory. *Phys. A* **2020**, *537*, 122578. [CrossRef]
9. Singh, J.; Kumar, D.; Baleanu, D. A new analysis of fractional fish farm model associated with Mittag-Leffler type kernel. *Int. J. Biomath.* **2020**, *12*, 2050010. [CrossRef]
10. Kumar, D.; Singh, J.; Baleanu, D. On the analysis of vibration equation involving a fractional derivative with Mittag-Leffler law. *Math. Method App. Sci.* **2020**, *43*, 443–457. [CrossRef]
11. Hilfer, R. *Applications of Fractional Calculus in Physics*; World Scientific: Hackensack, NJ, USA, 2000.
12. Mainardi, F.; Tomirotti, M. Seismic pulse propagation with constant Q and stable probability distributions. *Ann. Geophys.* **1997**, *40*, 1311–1328.
13. Metzler, R.; Klafter, J. The random walk's guide to anomalous diffusion: A fractional dynamics approach. *Phys. Rep.* **2000**, *339*, 1–77. [CrossRef]
14. Samko, S.G.; Kilbas, A.A.; Marichev, O.I. *Fractional Integrals and Derivatives*; Theory and Applications, Gordon and Breach Science Publishers: Yverdon, Switzerland, 1993.

15. Boyadjiev, L.; Kalla, S.L.; Kajah, H.G. Analytical and numerical treatment of a fractional integro-differential equation of Volterra-type. *Math. Comput. Modelling.* **1997**, *25*, 1–9. [CrossRef]
16. Al-Shammery, A.H.; Kalla, S.L.; Khajah, H.G. A fractional generalization of the free electron laser equation. *Fract. Calc. Appl. Anal.* **1999**, *2*, 501–508.
17. Al-Shammery, A.H.; Kalla, S.L.; Khajah, H.G. On a generalized fractional integro-differential equation of Volterra-type. *Integral Transform. Spec. Funct.* **2000**, *9*, 81–90. [CrossRef]
18. Saxena, R.K.; Kalla, S.L. On a fractional generalization of the free electron laser equation. *Appl. Math. Comput.* **2003**, *143*, 89–97. [CrossRef]
19. Kilbas, A.A.; Saigo, M.; Saxena, R.K. Solution of Volterra integro-differential equations with generalized Mittag-Leffler functions in the kernels. *J. Integral Equ. Appl.* **2002**, *14*, 377–396. [CrossRef]
20. Saxena, R.K.; Kalla, S.L. Solution of Volterra-type integro-differential equations with a generalized Lauricella confluent hypergeometric function in the kernels. *Int. J. Math. Math. Sci.* **2005**, *8*, 1155–1170. [CrossRef]
21. Srivastava, H.M.; Saxena, R.K. Some Volterra-type fractional integro-differential equations with a multivariable confluent hypergeometric function in their kernel. *J. Integral Equ. Appl.* **2005**, *17*, 199–217. [CrossRef]
22. Singh, Y.; Gill, V.; Kundu, S.; Kumar, D. On the Elzaki transform and its application in fractional free electron laser equation. *Acta Univ. Sapientiae Math.* **2019**, *11*, 419–429. [CrossRef]
23. Singh, Y.; Kumar, D.; Modi, K.; Gill, V. A new approach to solve Cattaneo-Hristov diffusion model and fractional diffusion equations with Hilfer-Prabhakar derivative. *AIMS Math.* **2019**, *5*, 843–855.
24. Veeresha, P.; Prakasha, D.G.; Kumar, D.; Baleanu, D.; Singh, J. An efficient computational technique for fractional model of generalized Hirota-Satsuma coupled KdV and coupled mKdV equations. *J. Comput. Nonlin. Dyn.* **2020**, *15*, 071003. [CrossRef]
25. Saxena, R.K. Alternative derivation of the solution of certain integro-differential equations of volterra type. *Ganita Sandesh* **2003**, *17*, 51–56.
26. Singh, J.; Kumar, D.; Bansal, M.K. Solution of nonlinear differential equation and special functions. *Math. Methods Appl. Sci.* **2020**, *43*, 2106–2116. [CrossRef]
27. Srivastava, H.M. An integral equation involving the confluent hypergeometric functions of several complex variables. *Appl. Anal.* **1976**, *5*, 251–256. [CrossRef]
28. Chaurasia, V.B.L.; Singh, Y. New generalization of integral equations of Fredholm type using Aleph- function. *Int. J. Mod. Math. Sci.* **2014**, *9*, 208–220.
29. Gao, W.; Veeresha, P.; Prakasha, D.G.; Baskonus, H.M.; Yel, G. New numerical results for the time-fractional Phi-four equation using a novel analytic approach. *Symmetry* **2020**, *12*, 1–12. [CrossRef]
30. Gao, W.; Veeresha, P.; Prakasha, D.G.; Baskonus, H.M.; Yel, G. New approach for the model describing the deathly disease in pregnant women using Mittag-Leffler function. *Chaos Solitons Fractals* **2020**, *134*, 1–11. [CrossRef]
31. Li, M. Three classes of fractional oscillators. *Symmetry* **2018**, *10*, 40. [CrossRef]
32. Jain, R.; Tomar, D.S. An integro-differential equation of Volterra type with Sumudu transform. *Math. Aeterna* **2012**, *2*, 541–547.
33. Shrivastava, S.; Tomar, D.S.; Verma, A. Application of Sumudu transform to fractional integro-differential equations involving generalized R-function. *Ganita* **2019**, *69*, 09–13.
34. Elzaki, T.M. The new integral transform "ELzaki Transform" fundamental properties investigations and applications. *Glob. J. Pure Appl. Math.* **2011**, *7*, 57–64.
35. Elzaki, T.M. Application of new transform "Elzaki Transform" to partial differential equations. *Glob. J. Pure Appl. Math.* **2011**, *7*, 65–70.
36. Eslaminasab, M.; Abbasbandy, S. Study on usage of Elzaki transform for the ordinary differential equations with non-constant coefficients. *Int. J. Ind. Math.* **2015**, *7*, 277–281.
37. Garra, R.; Goreno, R.; Polito, F.; Tomovski, Z. Hilfer-Prabhakar derivatives and some applications. *Appl. Math. Comput.* **2014**, *242*, 576–589. [CrossRef]
38. Lorenzo, C.F.; Hartley, T.T. *Generalized Functions for the Fractional Calculus;* Technical report NASA/TP-1999-209424, NAS 1.60:209424, E-11944; NASA: Washington, DC, USA, 1999; pp. 1–17.

39. Srivastava, H.M.; Daoust, M.C. Certain generalized Neumann expansions associated with the Kampe de Feriet function. *Nederl. Akad. Wetensch. Proc. Ser. Indag Math.* **1969**, *31*, 449–457.
40. Srivastava, H.M.; Daoust, M.C. A note on convergence of Kampe de Feriet double hypergeometric series. *Math. Nachr.* **1972**, *53*, 151–159. [CrossRef]

fractal and fractional

MDPI

Article

A New Reproducing Kernel Approach for Nonlinear Fractional Three-Point Boundary Value Problems

Mehmet Giyas Sakar * and Onur Saldır

Faculty of Sciences, Department of Mathematics, Van Yuzuncu Yil University, 65080 Van, Turkey; onursaldir@yyu.edu.tr
* Correspondence: giyassakar@yyu.edu.tr; Tel.: +90-(432)-2251701-27895

Received: 30 June 2020; Accepted: 20 November 2020; Published: 24 November 2020

Abstract: In this article, a new reproducing kernel approach is developed for obtaining a numerical solution of multi-order fractional nonlinear three-point boundary value problems. This approach is based on a reproducing kernel, which is constructed by shifted Legendre polynomials (L-RKM). In the considered problem, fractional derivatives with respect to α and β are defined in the Caputo sense. This method has been applied to some examples that have exact solutions. In order to show the robustness of the proposed method, some examples are solved and numerical results are given in tabulated forms.

Keywords: shifted Legendre polynomials; reproducing kernel method; variable coefficient; Caputo derivative; three-point boundary value problem

1. Introduction

In this paper, a new iterative reproducing kernel approach will be constructed for obtaining the numerical solution of a multi-order fractional nonlinear three-point boundary value problem as follows:

$$a_2(\xi)\,{}^cD^{\alpha}z(\xi) + a_1(\xi)\,{}^cD^{\beta}z(\xi) + a_0(\xi)z(\xi) = g(\xi, z(\xi), z'(\xi)) \tag{1}$$

$$0 \le \xi \le 1,\ 1 < \alpha \le 2,\ 0 < \beta \le 1.$$

with the following boundary conditions,

$$z(0) = \gamma_0,\ z(\theta) = \gamma_1,\ z(1) = \gamma_2,\ \ 0 < \theta < 1. \tag{2}$$

Here, $a_0(\cdot), a_1(\cdot), a_2(\cdot) \in C^2(0,1)$ and $g(\cdot, z(\cdot), z'(\cdot)) \in L^2_{\rho}[0,1]$ are sufficiently smooth functions, ρ is a weighted function and it will be taken as $\rho = 1$ for Legendre polynomials. Fractional derivatives are also taken in the Caputo sense. Without loss of generality, we pay regards to $z(0) = 0$, $z(\theta) = 0$ and $z(1) = 0$. Because $z(0) = \gamma_0$, $z(\theta) = \gamma_1$ and $z(1) = \gamma_2$, boundary conditions can be easily reduced to $z(0) = 0$, $z(\theta) = 0$ and $z(1) = 0$.

Nonlinear fractional multi-point boundary value problems appear in a different area of applied mathematics and physics ([1–7] and references therein). Many important phenomena have been concerned in engineering and applied science, such as dynamical systems, fluid mechanics, control theory, oil industries, and heat conduction, and can be well-turned by fractional differential equations [8–10]. Some applications, qualitative behaviors of solutions and numerical methods to find approximate solutions have been investigated for differential equations with fractional order in [11–14].

More specfically, it is not easy to directly get exact solutions to most differential equations with fractional order. Hence, numerical techniques are largely utilized. Actually, in recent times, many efficient and convenient methods have been developed, such as the finite difference method [15], finite element method [16], homotopy perturbation method [17], Haar wavelet methods [18], collocation methods [19], homotopy analysis method [20], differential transform method [21], variational iteration method [22], reproducing kernel space method [23,24] and so on [25–32].

In 1908, Zaremba firstly introduced the reproducing kernel concept [33]. His researches regarded boundary value problems, which include the Dirichlet condition. The reproducing kernel method (RKM) produces a solution in convergent series form for many differential, partial and integro-differential equations. For more information, we refer to [34,35]. Recently, the RKM has been applied for a different type of problem. For example, fractional order nonlocal boundary value problems [36], Riccati differential equations [37], forced Duffing equations with a nonlocal boundary conditions [38], Burgers' equation with a fractional order Caputo derivative [39], time-fractional Kawahara equation [40], fractional order Boussinesq equation [41], nonlinear fractional Volterra integro-differential equations [42].

The Legendre reproducing kernel method is proposed for the fractional two-point boundary value problem of Bratu type equations [43]. The main motivation of this paper is to extend the Legendre reproducing kernel approach for solving multi-order fractional nonlinear three-point boundary value problems with a Caputo derivative.

The remainder part of the paper is prepared as follows: some fundamental definitions of fractional calculus and the theory of reproducing kernel with Legendre basis functions are given in Section 2. The structure of the solution with a Legendre reproducing kernel is demonstrated in Section 3. In order to show the effectiveness of the proposed method, some numerical findings are reported in Section 4. Finally, the last section contains some conclusions.

2. Preliminaries

In this section, several significant concepts, definitions, theorems, and properties that will be used in this research are provided.

Definition 1 ([8,12,13]). *Let $z(\xi) \in C[0,1]$ and $\xi \in [0,1]$. Then, the α order Riemann–Liouville fractional integral operator is given as:*

$$J^{\alpha} z(\xi) = \frac{1}{\Gamma(\alpha)} \int_{0}^{\xi} (\xi - s)^{\alpha - 1} z(s) ds,$$

here $\Gamma(.)$ is a Gamma function, $\alpha \geq 0$ and $\xi > 0$.

Definition 2 ([8,12,13]). *Let $z(\xi) \in AC[0,1]$ and $\xi \in [0,1]$. Then, the α order Caputo differential operator is given as:*

$${}^{c}D^{\alpha} z(\xi) = \frac{1}{\Gamma(a-\alpha)} \int_0^{\xi} \frac{z^{(a)}(s)}{(\xi - s)^{\alpha+1-a}} ds, \ a - 1 < \alpha \leq a, a \in \mathbb{N} \text{ and } \xi > 0.$$

Definition 3 ([26,43]). *In order to a construct polynomial type reproducing kernel, the first kind of shifted Legendre polynomials are defined over the interval $[0,1]$. For obtaining these polynomials, the following iterative formula can be given:*

$$\begin{aligned} P_0(\xi) &= 1, \\ P_1(\xi) &= 2\xi - 1, \\ &\vdots \\ (n+1)P_{n+1}(\xi) &= (2n+1)(2\xi-1)P_n(\xi) - nP_{n-1}(\xi),\ n = 1,2,\ldots \end{aligned}$$

The orthogonality requirement is

$$\langle P_n, P_m\rangle = \int_0^1 \rho_{[0,1]}(\xi)P_n(\xi)P_m(\xi)d\xi = \begin{cases} 0, & n \neq m, \\ 1, & n = m = 0, \\ \frac{1}{2n+1}, & n = m \neq 0, \end{cases} \tag{3}$$

here, the weighted function is taken as,

$$\rho_{[0,1]}(\xi) = 1. \tag{4}$$

Legendre basis functions can be established so that this basis function system satisfies the homogeneous boundary conditions as:

$$z(0) = 0 \ and \ z(1) = 0. \tag{5}$$

Equation (5) has an advantageous feature for solving boundary value problems. Therefore, these basis functions for $j \geq 2$ can be defined as;

$$\phi_j(\xi) = \begin{cases} P_j(\xi) - P_0(\xi), & j \text{ is even}, \\ P_j(\xi) - P_1(\xi), & j \text{ is odd}. \end{cases} \tag{6}$$

such that this system satisfies the conditions

$$\phi_j(0) = \phi_j(1) = 0. \tag{7}$$

It is worth noting that the basis functions given in Equation (6) are a complete system. For more information about orthogonal polynomials, please see [44–46].

Definition 4. *Let $\Psi \neq \emptyset$, and $\mathbb{H}$ with its inner product $\langle\cdot,\cdot\rangle_{\mathbb{H}}$ be a Hilbert space of real-valued functions on Ψ. Then, the reproducing kernel of $\mathbb{H}$ is $R : \Psi \times \Psi \to \mathbb{R}$ iff*

1. $R(\cdot,\xi) \in \mathbb{H}, \forall\xi \in \Psi$
2. $\langle\phi(\cdot), R(\cdot,\xi)\rangle_{\mathbb{H}} = \phi(\xi), \forall\phi \in \mathbb{H}, \forall\xi \in \Psi.$

The last condition is known as a reproducing property. Especially, for any x, $\xi \in \Psi$,

$$R(x,\xi) = \langle R(\cdot,x), R(\cdot,\xi)\rangle_{\mathbb{H}}.$$

If a Hilbert space satisfies the above two conditions then it is called a reproducing kernel Hilbert space. The uniqueness of the reproducing kernel with respect to the inner product can be shown by the use of the Riesz representation theorem [47].

Theorem 1. *Let $\{e_j\}_{j=1}^{n}$ be an orthonormal basis of n-dimensional Hilbert space $\mathbb{H}$, then*

$$R(x,\xi) = R_x(\xi) = \sum_{j=1}^{n} \bar{e}_j(x)e_j(\xi), \tag{8}$$

is a reproducing kernel of $\mathbb{H}$ [34,35].

Definition 5. *Let $\Omega_\rho^m[0,1]$ polynomials space be the pre-Hilbert space over $[0,1]$ with real coefficients and its degree $\leq m$ and inner product as:*

$$\langle z, v\rangle_{\Omega_\rho^m} = \int_0^1 \rho_{[0,1]}(\xi)z(\xi)v(\xi)d\xi, \quad \forall z, v \in \Omega_\rho^m[0,1], \tag{9}$$

with $\rho_{[0,1]}$ described by Equation (4), and the norm

$$\|z\|_{\Omega_\rho^m} = \sqrt{\langle z, z\rangle_{\Omega_\rho^m}}, \quad \forall z \in \Omega_\rho^m[0,1]. \tag{10}$$

With the aid of definiton of L^2 Hilbert space, $L_\rho^2[0,1] = \{g | \int_0^1 \rho_{[0,1]}(\xi)|g(\xi)|^2 d\xi < \infty\}$ for any fixed m, $\Omega_\rho^m[0,1]$ is a subspace of $L_\rho^2[0,1]$ and $\forall z, v \in \Omega_\rho^m[0,1]$, $\langle z, v\rangle_{\Omega_\rho^m} = \langle z, v\rangle_{L_\rho^2}$.

Theorem 2 ([43])**.** *$\Omega_\rho^m[0,1]$ Hilbert space is a reproducing kernel space.*

Definition 6. *Let*

$$^0\Omega_\rho^m[0,1] = \{z \mid z \in \Omega_\rho^m[0,1],\ z(0) = z(1) = 0\}.$$

One can easily demonstrate that $^0\Omega_\rho^m[0,1]$ is a reproducing kernel space using Equation (6). From Theorem 1, the kernel function $R_x^m(\xi)$ of $^0\Omega_\rho^m[0,1]$ can be written as

$$R_x^m(\xi) = \sum_{j=2}^{m} h_j(\xi)h_j(x). \tag{11}$$

here, $h_j(\xi)$ is complete system, which is easily obtained from the basis functions in Equation (6) with the help of the Gram-Schmidt orthonormalization process. Equation (11) is very useful for implementation. In other words, $R_x^m(\xi)$ and $\Omega_\rho^m[0,1]$ can be readily updated and re-calculated by increasing m.

3. Main Results

In this section, some important results related to the reproducing kernel method with shifted Legendre polynomials are presented. In the first subsection, the generation of reproducing kernel that satisfies three-point boundary value problems is presented. In the second subsection, the representation of a solution is given in $^\theta\Omega_\rho^m[0,1]$. Then, we will construct an iterative process for a nonlinear problem in the third subsection.

3.1. Generation of Reproducing Kernel for Three-Point Boundary Value Problems

In this subsection, we shall generate a reproducing kernel Hilbert space ${}^{\theta}\Omega_{\rho}^{m}[0,1]$ in which every functions satisfies $z(0) = 0$, $z(\theta) = 0$ and $z(1) = 0$ for $\theta \in (0,1)$. Namely, ${}^{\theta}\Omega_{\rho}^{m}[0,1]$ is defined as ${}^{\theta}\Omega_{\rho}^{m}[0,1] = \{z | z \in \Omega_{\rho}^{m}[0,1], z(0) = z(\theta) = z(1) = 0\}$.

Obviously, ${}^{\theta}\Omega_{\rho}^{m}[0,1]$ reproducing kernel space is a closed subspace of ${}^{0}\Omega_{\rho}^{m}[0,1]$. The reproducing kernel of ${}^{\theta}\Omega_{\rho}^{m}[0,1]$ can be given with the following theorem.

Theorem 3. *The reproducing kernel of* ${}^{\theta}\Omega_{\rho}^{m}[0,1]$ *is* ${}^{\theta}R_{x}^{m}(\xi)$:

$$ {}^{\theta}R_{x}^{m}(\xi) = R_{x}^{m}(\xi) - \frac{R_{x}^{m}(\theta)R_{\theta}^{m}(\xi)}{R_{\theta}^{m}(\theta)}. \tag{12} $$

Proof. Frankly, not all elements of ${}^{0}\Omega_{\rho}^{m}[0,1]$ vanish at θ. This shows that $R_{\theta}^{m}(\theta) \neq 0$. Hence, it can be easily seen that ${}^{\theta}R_{x}^{m}(\theta) = {}^{\theta}R_{\theta}^{m}(\xi) = 0$ and therefore ${}^{\theta}R_{x}^{m}(\xi) \in {}^{\theta}\Omega_{\rho}^{m}[0,1]$. For $\forall z(x) \in {}^{\theta}\Omega_{\rho}^{m}[0,1]$, clearly, $z(\theta) = 0$, it follows that

$$ \langle z(x), {}^{\theta}R_{x}^{m}(\xi)\rangle_{{}^{\theta}\Omega_{\rho}^{m}[0,1]} = \langle z(x), R_{x}^{m}(\xi)\rangle_{{}^{\theta}\Omega_{\rho}^{m}[0,1]} - \frac{R_{x}^{m}(\alpha)z(\theta)}{R_{\theta}^{m}(\theta)} = z(\xi). $$

Namely, ${}^{\theta}R_{x}^{m}(\xi)$ is a reproducing kernel of ${}^{\theta}\Omega_{\rho}^{m}[0,1]$. This completes the proof. □

3.2. Representation of Solution in ${}^{\theta}\Omega_{\rho}^{m}[0,1]$ Hilbert Space

In this subsection, the reproducing kernel method with Legendre polynomials is established for obtaining a numerical solution of a three-point boundary value problem. For Equations (1) and (2), the approximate solution shall be constructed in ${}^{\theta}\Omega_{\rho}^{m}[0,1]$. Firstly, we will define the linear operator L as follows,

$$ L : {}^{\theta}\Omega_{\rho}^{m}[0,1] \to L_{\rho}^{2}[0,1] $$

such that

$$ Lz(\xi) := a_2(\xi)\, {}^{c}D^{\alpha}z(\xi) + a_1(\xi)\, {}^{c}D^{\beta}z(\xi) + a_0(\xi)z(\xi). $$

Therefore, Equations (1) and (2) can be stated as follows

$$ \begin{cases} Lz = g(\xi, z(\xi), z'(\xi)) \\ z(0) = z(\theta) = z(1) = 0. \end{cases} \tag{13} $$

It can easily be shown that the linear operator L is bounded. We will obtain the representation solution of Equation (13) in the ${}^{\theta}\Omega_{\rho}^{m}[0,1]$ space. Let ${}^{\theta}R_{x}^{m}(\xi)$ be the polynomial form of the reproducing kernel in ${}^{\theta}\Omega_{\rho}^{m}[0,1]$ space.

Theorem 4 ([43]). *Let* $\{\xi_j\}_{j=0}^{m-2}$ *be any* $(m-1)$ *distinct points in open interval* $(0,1)$ *for Equations (1) and (2), then* $\psi_j^{m}(\xi) = L^{*}\, {}^{\theta}R_{\xi_j}^{m}(\xi) = L_x\, {}^{\theta}R_{x}^{m}(\xi)|_{x=\xi_j}$ *for* $m \geq 2$.

Theorem 5 ([43]). *Let* $\{\xi_j\}_{j=0}^{m-2}$ *be any* $(m-1)$ *distinct points in open interval* $(0,1)$ *for* $m \geq 2$, *then* $\{\psi_j^{m}\}_{j=0}^{m-2}$ *is complete in* ${}^{\theta}\Omega_{\rho}^{m}[0,1]$.

Theorem 5 indicates that in the Legendre reproducing kernel approach, using finite distinct points is enough. However, in the traditional reproducing kernel method needs a dense sequence on the interval. So, this new approach varies from the traditional method in [27,36–39,42].

The orthonormal system $\{\bar{\psi}_j^m\}_{j=0}^{m-2}$ of ${}^{\theta}\Omega_p^m[0,1]$ can be derived with the help of the Gram-Schmidt orthogonalization process using $\{\psi_j^m\}_{j=0}^{m-2}$,

$$\bar{\psi}_j^m(\xi) = \sum_{k=0}^{j} \beta_{jk}^m \psi_k^m(\xi), \tag{14}$$

here, β_{jk}^m shows the coefficients of orthogonalization.

Theorem 6. *Suppose that z_m is the exact solution of Equations (1) and (2) and $\{\xi_j\}_{j=0}^{m-2}$ shows any $(m-1)$ distinct points in open interval $(0,1)$ for $m \geq 2$; in that case, the approximate solution $z_m(\xi)$ can be expressed as*

$$z_m(\xi) = \sum_{j=0}^{m-2} \sum_{k=0}^{j} \beta_{jk}^m g(\xi_k, z_m(\xi_k), z_m'(\xi_k)) \bar{\psi}_j^m(\xi). \tag{15}$$

Proof. Since $z_m \in {}^{\theta}\Omega_p^m[0,1]$, from Theorem 5, the following equality can be written

$$z_m(\xi) = \sum_{i=0}^{m-2} \langle z_m(\xi), \bar{\psi}_j^m(\xi)\rangle_{{}^{\theta}\Omega_p^m} \bar{\psi}_j^m(\xi).$$

On the other part, using Theorem 4 and Equation (14), we obtain $z_m(\xi)$, which is the precise solution of Equation (10) in ${}^{\theta}\Omega_p^m[0,1]$ as,

$$\begin{aligned} z_m(\xi) &= \sum_{j=0}^{m-2} \langle z_m(\xi), \bar{\psi}_j^m(\xi)\rangle_{{}^{\theta}\Omega_p^m} \bar{\psi}_j^m(\xi) = \sum_{j=0}^{m-2} \langle z_m(\xi), \sum_{k=0}^{j} \beta_{jk}^m \psi_k^m(\xi)\rangle_{{}^{\theta}\Omega_p^m} \bar{\psi}_j^m(\xi) \\ &= \sum_{j=0}^{m-2} \sum_{k=0}^{j} \beta_{jk}^m \langle z_m(\xi), \psi_k^m(\xi)\rangle_{{}^{\theta}\Omega_p^m} \bar{\psi}_j^m(\xi) = \sum_{j=0}^{m-2} \sum_{k=0}^{j} \beta_{jk}^m \langle z_m(\xi), L^{*\theta} R_{\xi_k}^m(\xi)\rangle_{{}^{\theta}\Omega_p^m} \bar{\psi}_j^m(\xi) \\ &= \sum_{j=0}^{m-2} \sum_{k=0}^{j} \beta_{jk}^m \langle Lz_m(\xi), {}^{\theta} R_{\xi_k}^m(\xi)\rangle_{L_p^2} \bar{\psi}_j^m(\xi) = \sum_{j=0}^{m-2} \sum_{k=0}^{j} \beta_{jk}^m \langle g(\xi, z_m(\xi), z_m'(\xi)), {}^{\theta} R_{\xi_k}^m(\xi)\rangle_{L_p^2} \bar{\psi}_j^m(\xi) \\ &= \sum_{j=0}^{m-2} \sum_{k=0}^{j} \beta_{jk}^m g(\xi_k, z_m(\xi_k), z_m'(\xi_k)) \bar{\psi}_j^m(\xi). \end{aligned}$$

The proof is completed. □

Theorem 7. *If $z_m \in {}^{\theta}\Omega_p^m[0,1]$, then $|z_m^{(s)}(\xi)| \leq F\|z_m\|_{{}^{\theta}\Omega_p^m}$ for $s = 0,\ldots,m-1$ and $m \geq 2$, where F is a constant.*

Proof. We have $z_m^{(s)}(\xi) = \langle z_m(\cdot), \partial_\xi^s\, {}^{\theta}R_\xi^m(\cdot)\rangle_{{}^{\theta}\Omega_p^m}$ for any ξ, $x \in [0,1]$, $s = 0,\ldots,m-1$. From the expression of ${}^{\theta}R_\xi^m(x)$, it pursues that $\left\|\partial_\xi^s\, {}^{\theta}R_\xi^m(x)\right\|_{{}^{\theta}\Omega_p^m} \leq F_s$, $s = 0,\ldots,m-1$.

So,

$$\begin{aligned} |z_m^{(s)}(\xi)| &= |\langle z_m(\cdot), \partial_\xi^s \, {}^\theta R_\xi^m(\cdot) \rangle_{{}^\theta\Omega_\rho^m}| \\ &\le \|z_m\|_{{}^\theta\Omega_\rho^m[0,1]} \|\partial_\xi^s \, {}^\theta R_\xi^m\|_{{}^\theta\Omega_\rho^m} \\ &\le F_s \|z_m\|_{{}^\theta\Omega_\rho^m}, s = 0, \ldots, m-1. \end{aligned}$$

Therefore, $\|z_m^{(s)}\| \le \max\{F_0, \ldots, F_{m-1}\} \, \|z_m\|_{{}^\theta\Omega_\rho^m}$, $s = 0, \ldots, m-1$. □

Theorem 8. *The approximate solution z_m and its derivatives $z_m^{(s)}$, respectively, uniformly converge to the exact solution z and its derivatives $z^{(s)}$ ($s = 0, \ldots, m-1$).*

Proof. By using Theorem 7 for any $\xi \in [0,1]$ we get

$$\begin{aligned} |z_m^{(s)}(\xi) - z^{(s)}(\xi)| &= |\langle z_m(\cdot) - z(\cdot), \partial_\xi^s \, {}^\theta R_\xi^m(\cdot) \rangle|_{{}^\theta\Omega_\rho^m} \\ &\le \|\partial_\xi^s \, {}^\theta R_\xi^m\|_{{}^\theta\Omega_\rho^m} \|z_m - z\|_{{}^\theta\Omega_\rho^m} \\ &\le F_s \|z_m - z\|_{{}^\theta\Omega_\rho^m}, \ s = 0, \ldots, m-1. \end{aligned}$$

where $F_0, \ldots, F_{m-1}$ are positive constants. Therefore, if $z_m \to z$ in the norm of ${}^\theta\Omega_\rho^m[0,1]$ as $m \to \infty$, z_m and its derivatives $z_m', \ldots, z_m^{(m-1)}$, respectively, uniformly converge to z and its derivatives $z', \ldots, z^{(m-1)}$. This completes the proof. □

If the considered problem is linear, a numerical solution can be obtained directly from (15). However, for a nonlinear problem, the following iterative procedure can be constructed.

3.3. Construction of Iterative Procedure

In this subsection, we will use the following iterative sequence to overcome the nonlinearity of the problem, $y_{m,n}(\xi)$, inserting,

$$\begin{cases} Ly_{m,n}(\xi) = g\left(\xi, z_{m,n-1}(\xi), z'_{m,n-1}(\xi)\right) \\ z_{m,n}(\xi) = P_{m-1} y_{m,n}(\xi) \end{cases} \tag{16}$$

here, an orthogonal projection operator is defined as $P_{m-1} : {}^\theta\Omega_\rho^m[0,1] \to span\{\bar{\psi}_0^m, \bar{\psi}_1^m, \ldots, \bar{\psi}_{m-2}^m\}$ and $y_{m,n}(\xi) \in {}^\theta\Omega_\rho^m[0,1]$ shows the n-th iterative numerical solution of (16). Then, the following important theorem will be given for the iterative procedure.

Theorem 9. *If $\{\xi_j\}_{j=0}^{m-2}$ are distinct points in open interval $(0,1)$ for $m \ge 2$, then*

$$y_{m,n}(\xi) = \sum_{j=0}^{m-2} \sum_{k=0}^{j} \beta_{jk}^m g(\xi_k, z_{m,n-1}(\xi_k), z'_{m,n-1}(\xi_k)) \bar{\psi}_j^m(\xi). \tag{17}$$

Proof. Since $y_{m,n}(\xi) \in {}^{\theta}\Omega_{\rho}^{m}[0,1]$, $\{\bar{\psi}_j^m(\xi)\}_{j=0}^{m-2}$ is the complete orthonormal system in ${}^{\theta}\Omega_{\rho}^{m}[0,1]$,

$$
\begin{aligned}
y_{m,n}(\xi) &= \sum_{j=0}^{m-2} \langle y_{m,n}(\xi), \bar{\psi}_j^m(\xi) \rangle_{{}^{\theta}\Omega_{\rho}^{m}} \bar{\psi}_j^m(\xi) \\
&= \sum_{j=0}^{m-2} \langle y_{m,n}(\xi), \sum_{k=0}^{j} \beta_{jk}^m \psi_k^m(\xi) \rangle_{{}^{\theta}\Omega_{\rho}^{m}} \bar{\psi}_j^m(\xi) \\
&= \sum_{j=0}^{m-2} \sum_{k=0}^{j} \beta_{jk}^m \langle y_{m,n}(\xi), \psi_k^m(\xi) \rangle_{{}^{\theta}\Omega_{\rho}^{m}} \bar{\psi}_j^m(\xi) \\
&= \sum_{j=0}^{m-2} \sum_{k=0}^{j} \beta_{jk}^m \langle y_{m,n}(\xi), L^{*}\, {}^{\theta}R_{\xi_k}^m(\xi) \rangle_{{}^{\theta}\Omega_{\rho}^{m}} \bar{\psi}_j^m(\xi) \\
&= \sum_{j=0}^{m-2} \sum_{k=0}^{j} \beta_{jk}^m \langle L y_{m,n}(\xi), {}^{\theta}R_{\xi_k}^m(\xi) \rangle_{L_{\rho}^2} \bar{\psi}_j^m(\xi) \\
&= \sum_{j=0}^{m-2} \sum_{k=0}^{j} \beta_{jk}^m \langle g(\xi, z_{m,n-1}(\xi), z'_{m,n-1}(\xi)), {}^{\theta}R_{\xi_k}^m(\xi) \rangle_{L_{\rho}^2} \bar{\psi}_j^m(\xi) \\
&= \sum_{j=0}^{m-2} \sum_{k=0}^{j} \beta_{jk}^m g(\xi_k, z_{m,n-1}(\xi_k), z'_{m,n-1}(\xi_k)) \bar{\psi}_j^m(\xi).
\end{aligned}
$$

This completes the proof. □

Taking $z_{m,0}(\xi) = 0$ and define the iterative sequence

$$
z_{m,n}(\xi) = P_{m-1} y_{m,n}(\xi) = \sum_{j=0}^{m-2} \sum_{k=0}^{j} \beta_{jk}^m g(\xi_k, z_{m,n-1}(\xi_k), z'_{m,n-1}(\xi_k)) \bar{\psi}_j^m(\xi), \;\; n = 1, 2, \ldots \tag{18}
$$

Remark 1. *For obtaining homogeneous boundary conditions in Equation (2), if the $z(\xi) = v(\xi) + a\xi^2 + b\xi + c$ transformation is done, then coefficients can be found as $a = (\gamma_2 - \gamma_0)/(1 - \gamma_1)$, $b = \theta(\gamma_0 - \gamma_2)/(1 - \gamma_1)$, $c = \gamma_0$. Here, $v(\xi)$ is a new unknown variable, and $v(0) = v(\theta) = v(1) = 0$ homogeneous boundary conditions are also satisfied.*

4. Numerical Applications

In this section, some nonlinear three-point boundary value problems are considered to exemplify the accuracy and efficiency of the proposed approach. Numerical results, which are achieved by L-RKM, are shown with tables.

Example 1. *We consider the following multi-order fractional nonlinear three-point boundary value problem with a Caputo derivative:*

$$
{}^{c}D^{\alpha} z(\xi) + (\xi + 1)\, {}^{c}D^{\beta} z(\xi) + \xi z(\xi) - z^2(\xi) = f(\xi), \quad 1 < \alpha \leq 2. \quad 0 < \beta \leq 1. \tag{19}
$$

$$
z(0) = z(\frac{1}{2}) = z(1) = 0. \tag{20}
$$

here, $f(\xi)$ is a known function such that the exact solution of this problem is $z(\xi) = \xi(\xi - \frac{1}{2})(\xi - 1)$.

By using the proposed approach for Equations (19) and (20), and choosing nodal points as $\xi_j = \frac{j+0.3}{m}$, $j = 0, 1, 2, ..., m-2$, *the approximate solution* $z_{m,n}(\xi)$ *is computed by Equation (18). For Equations (19) and (20), a comparison of absolute errors for different* α, β *values are demonstrated in Tables 1 and 2 and a comparison of the exact solution and numerical solution for* $\alpha = 1.75$ *and* $\beta = 0.75$ *is given in Table 3.*

Table 1. Comparison of absolute error of Example 1 for various α, β ($m = 3, n = 3$).

x	$\alpha = 2, \beta = 1$	$\alpha = 1.9, \beta = 0.9$	$\alpha = 1.8, \beta = 0.8$	$\alpha = 1.7, \beta = 0.7$	$\alpha = 1.6, \beta = 0.6$
0	0	0	0	0	0
0.1	3.25×10^{-11}	6.08×10^{-11}	3.70×10^{-12}	4.45×10^{-10}	3.14×10^{-9}
0.2	5.45×10^{-11}	8.75×10^{-11}	4.93×10^{-12}	8.70×10^{-10}	5.51×10^{-9}
0.3	6.97×10^{-11}	9.00×10^{-11}	4.34×10^{-12}	1.32×10^{-9}	7.36×10^{-9}
0.4	8.17×10^{-11}	7.81×10^{-11}	2.55×10^{-12}	1.85×10^{-9}	8.96×10^{-9}
0.5	0	0	0	0	0
0.6	1.10×10^{-10}	5.14×10^{-11}	2.03×10^{-12}	3.36×10^{-9}	1.24×10^{-8}
0.7	1.34×10^{-10}	5.65×10^{-11}	3.56×10^{-12}	4.44×10^{-9}	1.49×10^{-8}
0.8	1.70×10^{-10}	8.70×10^{-11}	3.73×10^{-12}	5.80×10^{-9}	1.81×10^{-8}
0.9	2.21×10^{-10}	1.53×10^{-11}	1.89×10^{-12}	7.49×10^{-9}	2.25×10^{-8}
1	0	0	0	0	0

Table 2. Comparison of absolute error of Example 1 for various α, β ($m = 3, n = 5$).

x	$\alpha = 2, \beta = 1$	$\alpha = 1.9, \beta = 0.9$	$\alpha = 1.8, \beta = 0.8$	$\alpha = 1.7, \beta = 0.7$	$\alpha = 1.6, \beta = 0.6$
0	0	0	0	0	0
0.1	3.78×10^{-17}	1.33×10^{-16}	2.49×10^{-19}	4.86×10^{-15}	7.48×10^{-14}
0.2	5.27×10^{-17}	1.94×10^{-16}	3.36×10^{-19}	1.13×10^{-14}	1.36×10^{-13}
0.3	5.10×10^{-17}	2.03×10^{-16}	3.80×10^{-19}	1.99×10^{-14}	1.91×10^{-13}
0.4	3.91×10^{-17}	1.81×10^{-16}	5.20×10^{-19}	3.09×10^{-14}	2.43×10^{-13}
0.5	0	0	0	0	0
0.6	1.05×10^{-17}	1.36×10^{-16}	1.56×10^{-18}	6.18×10^{-14}	3.60×10^{-13}
0.7	6.65×10^{-18}	1.57×10^{-16}	2.74×10^{-18}	8.25×10^{-14}	4.36×10^{-13}
0.8	1.81×10^{-17}	2.34×10^{-16}	4.50×10^{-18}	1.07×10^{-14}	5.30×10^{-13}
0.9	5.14×10^{-17}	3.91×10^{-16}	7.02×10^{-18}	1.36×10^{-14}	6.48×10^{-13}
1	0	0	0	0	0

Table 3. Numerical results of Example 1 for $m = 5$, $n = 9$ values ($\alpha = 1.75$, $\beta = 0.75$).

x	Exact Sol.	Approximate Sol.	Absolute Error
0.0	0.00000000000000000000	0.00000000000000000000	0
0.1	0.03600000000000000000	0.03600000000000000018	1.80×10^{-20}
0.2	0.04800000000000000000	0.04800000000000000044	4.40×10^{-20}
0.3	0.04200000000000000000	0.04200000000000000061	6.10×10^{-20}
0.4	0.02400000000000000000	0.02400000000000000071	7.10×10^{-20}
0.5	0.00000000000000000000	0.00000000000000000000	0
0.6	−0.02400000000000000000	−0.02399999999999999899	1.01×10^{-19}
0.7	−0.04200000000000000000	−0.04199999999999999819	1.81×10^{-19}
0.8	−0.04800000000000000000	−0.04799999999999999694	3.06×10^{-19}
0.9	−0.03600000000000000000	−0.03599999999999999491	5.09×10^{-19}
1	0.00000000000000000000	0.00000000000000000000	0

Example 2. *We take care of the following multi-order fractional nonlinear three-point boundary value problem with a Caputo derivative*

$$\xi^2\, {}^cD^{\alpha}z(\xi) + (\xi^2-1)\, {}^cD^{\beta}z(\xi) + \xi^3 z(\xi) - z(\xi)z'(\xi) - z^3(\xi) = f(\xi), \quad 1<\alpha\le 2. \quad 0<\beta\le 1. \tag{21}$$

$$z(0) = z(\frac{3}{5}) = z(1) = 0. \tag{22}$$

Here, $f(\xi)$ *is a known function such that the exact solution of this problem is* $z(\xi) = \xi(\xi-\frac{3}{5})(\xi-1)$.

By using the proposed approach for Equations (21) and (22), and choosing the nodal points as $\xi_j = \frac{j+0.3}{m}$, $j = 0,1,2,\dots,m-2$, *the approximate solution* $z_{m,n}(\xi)$ *is computed by Equation (18). For (21) and (22), a comparison of absolute errors for different* α, β *values are demonstrated in Tables 4 and 5 and a comparison of the exact solution and numerical solution for* $\alpha = 1.75$ *and* $\beta = 0.75$ *is given in Table 6.*

Table 4. Comparison of absolute error of Example 2 for various α,β ($m=3, n=8$).

x	$\alpha=2,\beta=1$	$\alpha=1.9,\beta=0.9$	$\alpha=1.8,\beta=0.8$	$\alpha=1.7,\beta=0.7$	$\alpha=1.6,\beta=0.6$
0	0	0	0	0	0
0.1	5.00×10^{-11}	4.11×10^{-15}	2.78×10^{-13}	6.10×10^{-12}	1.40×10^{-12}
0.2	8.39×10^{-11}	3.45×10^{-15}	1.87×10^{-13}	1.17×10^{-11}	2.42×10^{-11}
0.3	1.06×10^{-10}	1.24×10^{-15}	1.87×10^{-13}	1.45×10^{-11}	7.08×10^{-11}
0.4	1.23×10^{-10}	9.21×10^{-15}	7.60×10^{-13}	1.20×10^{-11}	1.32×10^{-10}
0.5	1.39×10^{-10}	1.97×10^{-14}	1.44×10^{-12}	1.75×10^{-12}	2.02×10^{-10}
0.6	0	0	0	0	0
0.7	1.88×10^{-10}	4.52×10^{-14}	2.81×10^{-12}	5.17×10^{-11}	3.45×10^{-10}
0.8	2.31×10^{-10}	5.88×10^{-14}	3.32×10^{-12}	9.98×10^{-11}	4.05×10^{-10}
0.9	2.93×10^{-10}	7.18×10^{-14}	3.60×10^{-12}	1.65×10^{-10}	4.49×10^{-10}
1	0	0	0	0	0

Table 5. Comparison of absolute error of Example 2 for various α,β ($m=3, n=10$).

x	$\alpha=2,\beta=1$	$\alpha=1.9,\beta=0.9$	$\alpha=1.8,\beta=0.8$	$\alpha=1.7,\beta=0.7$	$\alpha=1.6,\beta=0.6$
0	0	0	0	0	0
0.1	3.49×10^{-13}	1.93×10^{-18}	4.48×10^{-16}	2.68×10^{-14}	4.75×10^{-15}
0.2	5.87×10^{-13}	8.32×10^{-19}	2.99×10^{-16}	5.58×10^{-14}	7.68×10^{-14}
0.3	7.47×10^{-13}	2.90×10^{-18}	3.06×10^{-16}	7.18×10^{-14}	2.25×10^{-13}
0.4	8.65×10^{-13}	8.81×10^{-18}	1.23×10^{-15}	6.00×10^{-14}	4.21×10^{-13}
0.5	9.76×10^{-13}	1.65×10^{-17}	2.34×10^{-15}	5.54×10^{-15}	6.45×10^{-13}
0.6	0	0	0	0	0
0.7	1.31×10^{-12}	3.55×10^{-17}	4.55×10^{-15}	2.91×10^{-13}	1.09×10^{-12}
0.8	1.61×10^{-12}	4.60×10^{-17}	5.37×10^{-15}	5.64×10^{-13}	1.29×10^{-12}
0.9	2.05×10^{-12}	5.65×10^{-17}	5.83×10^{-15}	9.39×10^{-13}	1.43×10^{-12}
1	0	0	0	0	0

Table 6. Numerical results of Example 2 for $m = 5, n = 9$ values ($\alpha = 1.75$, $\beta = 0.75$).

x	Exact Sol.	Approximate Sol.	Absolute Error
0.0	0.000000000000000000000	0.000000000000000000000	0
0.1	0.045000000000000000000	0.045000000000480782793	4.80×10^{-13}
0.2	0.064000000000000000000	0.064000000000580045412	5.80×10^{-13}
0.3	0.063000000000000000000	0.063000000000488602930	4.88×10^{-13}
0.4	0.048000000000000000000	0.048000000000398645450	3.98×10^{-13}
0.5	0.025000000000000000000	0.025000000000468872800	4.68×10^{-13}
0.6	0.000000000000000000000	0.000000000000000000000	0
0.7	−0.021000000000000000000	−0.020999999998651962040	1.34×10^{-12}
0.8	−0.032000000000000000000	−0.031999999998006864020	1.99×10^{-12}
0.9	−0.027000000000000000000	−0.026999999997598991320	2.40×10^{-12}
1	0.000000000000000000000	0.000000000000000000000	0

5. Conclusions

In this research, a novel numerical approach called L-RKM has been proposed and successfully implemented to find the approximate solution of a multi-order fractional nonlinear three-point boundary value problem with a Caputo derivative. For nonlinear problems, a new iterative process is proposed. Numerical findings show that the present approach is efficient and convenient for solving three-point boundary value problems with fractional order.

Author Contributions: Writing-original draft, M.G.S.; writing-review & editing, O.S. Both authors have read and agreed to the published version of the manuscript.

Funding: This research received no external funding.

Conflicts of Interest: The authors declare no conflict of interest.

References

1. Lin, Y.; Niu, J.; Cui, M. A numerical solution to nonlinear second order three-point boundary value problems in the reproducing kernel space. *Appl. Math. Comput.* **2012**, *218*, 7362–7368. [CrossRef]
2. Rehman, M.; Khan, R.A.; Asif, N.A. Three point boundary value problems for nonlinear fractional differential equations. *Acta Math.* **2011**, *31*, 1337–1346. [CrossRef]
3. Geng, F. Solving singular second order three-point boundary value problems using reproducing kernel Hilbert space method. *Appl. Math. Comput.* **2009** *215*, 2095–2102. [CrossRef]
4. Zhang, C.P.; Niu, J.; Lin, Y.Z. Numerical solutions for the three-point boundary value problem of nonlinear fractional differential equations. *Abstr. Appl. Anal.* **2012**, *2012*,1–16. [CrossRef]
5. Etemad, S.; Ntouyas, S.K.; Tariboon, J.Existence results for three-point boundary value problems for nonlinear fractional differential equations. *J. Nonlinear Sci. Appl.* **2016**, *9*, 2105–2116. [CrossRef]
6. Wu, B.; Li, X. Application of reproducing kernel method to third order three-point boundary value problems. *Appl. Math. Comput.* **2010**, *217*, 3425–3428. [CrossRef]
7. Ahmad, B.; Alghanmi, M.; Ntouyas, S.K.; Alsaedi, A. A study of fractional differential equations and inclusions involving generalized Caputo-type derivative equipped with generalized fractional integral boundary conditions. *AIMS Math.* **2018**, *4*, 26–42. [CrossRef]
8. Podlubny, I. *Fractional Differential Equations*; Academic Press: New York, NY, USA, 1999.
9. Lakshmikantham, V.; Leela, S.; Vasundhara Devi, J. *Theory of Fractional Dynamic Systems*; Cambridge Scientific Publishers: Cambridge, UK, 2009.
10. Hilfer, R. *Applications of Fractional Calculus in Physics*; World Scientific: Singapore, 2000.
11. Tarasov, V.E. *Fractional Dynamics: Application of Fractional Calculus to Dynamics of Particles, Fields and Media*; Springer: Berlin, Germany, 2010.

12. Diethelm, K. *The Analysis of Fractional Differential Equations. Lecture Notes in Mathematics*; Springer-Verlag: Berlin/Heidelberg, Germany, 2010.
13. Kilbas, A.A.; Srivastava, H.M.; Trujillo, J.J. *Theory and Applications of Fractional Differential Equations*; B.V, Elsevier Science: Amsterdam, The Netherlands, 2006.
14. Khalouta, A.; Kadem, A. A new numerical technique for solving Caputo time-fractional biological population equation. *AIMS Math.* **2019**, *4*, 1307–1319. [CrossRef]
15. Tadjeran, C.; Meerschaert, M.M. A second-order accurate numerical method for the two-dimensional fractional diffusion equation. *J. Comput. Phys.* **2007**, *220*, 813–823. [CrossRef]
16. Esen, A.; Tasbozan, O. Numerical solution of time fractional Burgers equation by cubic B-spline finite elements. *Mediterr. J. Math.* **2016**, *13*, 1325–1337. [CrossRef]
17. Sakar, M.G.; Uludag, F.; Erdogan, F. Numerical solution of time-fractional nonlinear PDEs with proportional delays by homotopy perturbation method. *Appl. Math. Model.* **2016**, *40*, 6639–6649. [CrossRef]
18. Saeed, U.; Rehman, M. Haar wavelet-quasilinearization technique for fractional nonlinear differential equations. *Appl. Math. Comput.* **2013**, *220*, 630–648. [CrossRef]
19. Pezza, L.; Pitolli, F. A multiscale collocation method for fractional differential problems. *Math. Comput. Simul.* **2018**, *147*, 210–219. [CrossRef]
20. Sakar, M.G.; Erdogan, F. The homotopy analysis method for solving the time-fractional Fornberg-Whitham equation and comparison with Adomian's decomposition method. *Appl. Math. Model.* **2013**, *37*, 1634–1641. [CrossRef]
21. Jafari, H.; Jassim, H.K.; Moshokoa, S.P.; Ariyan, V.M.; Tchier, F. Reduced differential transform method for partial differential equations within local fractional derivative operators. *Adv. Mech. Eng.* **2016**, *4*, 1–6. [CrossRef]
22. Sakar, M.G.; Saldır, O. Improving variational iteration method with auxiliary parameter for nonlinear time-fractional partial differential equations. *J. Optim. Theory Appl.* **2017**, *174*, 530–549. [CrossRef]
23. Xu, M.Q.; Lin, Y.Z. Simplified reproducing kernel method for fractional differential equations with delay. *Appl. Math. Lett.* **2016**, *52*, 156–161. [CrossRef]
24. Wang, Y.L.; Du, M.J.; Temuer, C.L.; Tian, D. Using reproducing kernel for solving a class of time-fractional telegraph equation with initial value conditions. *Int. J. Comput. Math.* **2018**, *95*, 1609–1621. [CrossRef]
25. Kadem, A.; Baleanu, D. Fractional radiative transfer equation within Chebyshev spectral approach. *Comput. Math. Appl.* **2010**, *59*, 1865–1873. [CrossRef]
26. Eldien, S.S.E.; Hafez, R.M.; Bhrawy, A.H.; Baleanu, D.; Kalaawy, A.A.E. New numerical approach for fractional variational problems using shifted Legendre orthonormal polynomials. *J. Optim. Theory Appl.* **2017**, *174*, 295–320. [CrossRef]
27. Sakar, M.G.; Akgül, A.; Baleanu, D. On solutions of fractional Riccati differential equations. *Adv. Differ. Equ.* **2017**, *39*, 1–10. [CrossRef]
28. Sakar, M.G.; Saldır, O.; Erdogan, F. A hybrid method for singularly perturbed convection–diffusion equation. *Int. J. Appl. Comput.* **2019**, *5*, 1–17. [CrossRef]
29. Erturk, V.S.; Momani, S.; Odibat, Z. Application of generalized differential transform method to multi-order fractional differential equations. *Commun. Nonlinear Sci. Numer. Simul.* **2008**, *13*, 1642–1654. [CrossRef]
30. Dabiri, A.; Butcher, E.A. Stable fractional Chebyshev differentiation matrix for the numerical solution of multi-order fractional differential equations. *Nonlinear Dyn.* **2017**, *90*, 185–201. [CrossRef]
31. Sakar, M.G.; Saldır, O; Akgül, A. A novel technique for fractional Bagley-Torvik equation. *Proc. Natl. Acad. Sci., India Sect. A Phys. Sci.* **2019**, *89*, 539–545. [CrossRef]
32. Khalegi, M.; Babolian, E.; Abbasbandy, S. Chebyshev reproducing kernel method: application to two-point boundary value problems. *Adv. Differ. Equ.* **2017**, *26*, 1–19.
33. Zaremba, S.Sur le Calcul Numérique des Fonctions Demandées Dans le probléme de Dirichlet et le Problème Hydrodynamique. *Bulletin International de l'Académie des Sciences de Cracovie* **1908**, 125–195.
34. Cui, M.; Lin, Y. *Nonlinear Numerical Analysis in the Reproducing Kernel Space*; Nova Science: New York, NY, USA, 2009.
35. Alpay, D. *Reproducing Kernel Spaces and Applications*; Springer: Berlin/Heidelberg, Germany, 2003.

36. Geng, F.; Cui, M. A reproducing kernel method for solving nonlocal fractional boundary value problems. *Appl. Math. Lett.* **2012**, *25*, 818–823. [CrossRef]
37. Sakar, M.G. Iterative reproducing kernel Hilbert spaces method for Riccati differential equation. *J. Comput. Appl. Math.* **2017**, *309*, 163–174. [CrossRef]
38. Geng, F.; Cui, M. New method based on the HPM and RKHSM for solving forced Duffing equations with integral boundary conditions. *J. Comput. Appl. Math.* **2009**, *233*, 165–172. [CrossRef]
39. Saldır, O.; Sakar, M.G.; Erdogan, F. Numerical solution of fractional order Burgers' equation with Dirichlet and Neumann boundary conditions by reproducing kernel method. *Fractal Fract.* **2020**, *4*, 27. [CrossRef]
40. Saldır, O.; Sakar, M.G.; Erdogan, F. Numerical solution of time-fractional Kawahara equation using reproducing kernel method with error estimate. *Comput. Appl. Math.* **2019**, *38*, 1–23. [CrossRef]
41. Sakar, M.G.; Saldır, O. A novel iterative solution for time-fractional Boussinesq equation by reproducing kernel method. *J. Appl. Math. Comput.* **2020**, *64*, 227–254. [CrossRef]
42. Jiang, W.; Tian, T. Numerical solution of nonlinear Volterra integro-differential equations of fractional order by the reproducing kernel method. *Appl. Math. Model.* **2015**, *39*, 4871–4876. [CrossRef]
43. Sakar, M.G.; Saldır, O.; Akgül, A. Numerical solution of fractional Bratu type equations with Legendre reproducing kernel method. *Int. J. Appl. Comput. Math.* **2018**, *126*, 1-14. [CrossRef]
44. Kaplan, W. *Advanced Calculus (5E)*; Pearson Education: New York, NY, USA, 2002.
45. Rainville, E.D. *Special Functions*; Chelsea Publishing Co.: New York, NY, USA, 1960.
46. Szegö, G. *Orthogonal Polynomials*; American Mathematical Society Colloquium Publications: Providence, RI, USA, 1939.
47. Aronszajn, N. Theory of reproducing kernels. *Trans. Am. Math. Soc.* **1950**, *68*, 337–404. [CrossRef]

fractal and fractional

MDPI

Article

Novel Complex Wave Solutions of the (2+1)-Dimensional Hyperbolic Nonlinear Schrödinger Equation

Hulya Durur [1], Esin Ilhan [2,*] and Hasan Bulut [3]

1 Department of Computer Engineering, Faculty of Engineering, Ardahan University, 75000 Ardahan, Turkey; hulyadurur@ardahan.edu.tr
2 Mucur Vocational School, Ahi Evran University, 40500 Kırşehir, Turkey
3 Department of Mathematics, Faculty of Science, Firat University, 23100 Elazig, Turkey; hbulut@firat.edu.tr
* Correspondence: eilhan@ahievran.edu.tr

Received: 18 June 2020; Accepted: 11 August 2020; Published: 16 August 2020

Abstract: This manuscript focuses on the application of the $(m+1/G')$-expansion method to the (2+1)-dimensional hyperbolic nonlinear Schrödinger equation. With the help of projected method, the periodic and singular complex wave solutions to the considered model are derived. Various figures such as 3D and 2D surfaces with the selecting the suitable of parameter values are plotted.

Keywords: the $(m+1/G')$-expansion method; the (2+1)-dimensional hyperbolic nonlinear Schrödinger equation; periodic and singular complex wave solutions; traveling waves solutions

---

1. Introduction

Most of the properties of nature and science explained by using nonlinear partial differential equations (NPDEs) are closely associated with the basic properties of applied sciences. Recently, NPDEs have been used to investigate properties of many real-world problems arising in fluid mechanics, population ecology, shallow-water wave propagation, plasma physics, solid-state physics, heat, quantum mechanics, optical fibers and biology. Moreover, their mathematical structures have also been presented to literature. Therefore, many effective methods such as $(m+G'/G)$-expansion method [1,2], $(1/G')$-expansion method [3–5], rational sine–cosine function method [6], F-expansion method [7], Clarkson–Kruskal (CK) direct method [8], (G'/G)-expansion method [9], Bäcklund transformation method [10], modified $\exp(-\Omega(\xi))$-expansion function [11], the Painlevé analysis [12], $(G'/G, 1/G)$-expansion method [13], modified Laplace decomposition method [14], Hirota bilinear method [15,16], homotopy analysis method [17], modified Kudryashov method [18], etc. [19–47] have been presented to the literature for observing of deeper properties of these models. In this sense, many detailed explanations of some methods with the regards of physical and mathematical properties have been presented by R. Conte and his team [48,49].

In this work, we consider the (2+1)-dimensional hyperbolic nonlinear Schrödinger equation (HNSE) [19]:

$$ih_y(x,y,t) + \frac{1}{2}\left[h_{xx}(x,y,t) - h_{tt}(x,y,t)\right] + \left|h(x,y,t)\right|^2 h(x,y,t) = 0, \tag{1}$$

where $h(x,y,t)$ is used to describe the complex field, x, y and t denote spatial and temporal variables, respectively. Nonlinear Schrödinger equations are mathematical models that correspond to basic physical phenomena that define the dynamics of optical strength propagation in single-mode optical fibers [43–46]. Many scientists have observed various properties of this model. Analytical properties to the Equation (1) have been obtained in [20], exact solutions Equation (1) using extended sinh–Gordon equation expansion method [21], via Adomian decomposition method [22], with the help of the first integral method [23] and many other properties such as instabilities of Schrödinger equation in [24] and also group-invariant solutions and conservation laws in [36].

In second section, we present the general properties of the $(m+1/G')$-expansion method. This method is an extended version of the classic $(1/G')$-expansion method. Specifically, when $m=0$, solutions produced in $(1/G')$-expansion method can be obtained. In third section, we apply the $(m+1/G')$-expansion method to the governing model to find many new periodic and singular complex wave solutions. In fourth section, we discuss some important properties of new findings. In fifth section, we introduce a conclusion about the findings and figures.

2. General Properties of $(m+1/G')$-Expansion Method

Consider the general form of NPDEs as:

$$P\Big(u, u_x, u_y, u_z, u_t, u_{xyzt}, \cdots\Big) = 0, \tag{2}$$

and using wave transformation given as:

$$\phi(x,y,t) = U(\xi),\ \xi = c_1 x + c_2 y + c_3 z + c_4 t, \tag{3}$$

where $c_i \neq 0,\ (i = 1,2,3,4)$. Using Equation (3) into Equation (2) yields a nonlinear ODE as following:

$$N\Big(U, U', U'', U^2, \cdots\Big) = 0. \tag{4}$$

The solution of Equation (4) may assumed in the following form according to projected method:

$$U(\xi) = \sum_{i=-n}^{n} a_i (m+F)^i = ma_0 + a_1(m+F) + a_2(m+F)^2 + \ldots + a_n(m+F)^n, \tag{5}$$

where $a_i, (\ i = 0,1,\cdots,n)$ are constants, m is nonzero and real constant. With the balancing principle, we find the value of n. Moreover, F is defined as following:

$$F = \frac{1}{G'(\xi)}, \tag{6}$$

and $G' = G'(\xi)$ provides the following second order linear ordinary differential equation:

$$G'' + (\lambda + 2m\mu)G' + \mu = 0, \tag{7}$$

where λ and μ are real constants and non zero to be determined later. Putting the Equation (5) into Equation (4) and using Equation (6), then collect all terms with the same order of the $(m+F)^n$, we obtain a system of algebraic equations for $c_i \neq 0,\ (i = 1,2,3,4), a_i, (\ i = 0,1,\cdots,n), \mu$ and λ. Finally, when we solve the system to find the value of $c_i \neq 0,\ (i = 1,2,3,4)$ and $a_i, (\ i = 0,1,\cdots,n)$, and inserting them into Equation (5), we can extract the periodic and singular complex wave solutions to the Equation (2).

3. Application of Projected Method

In this section, we apply the considered method to the Equation (1). Applying the following wave transformation defined as:

$$h(x,y,t) = e^{i\phi(x,y,t)} U(\xi),\ \xi = x - t\rho + y\tau,\ \phi(x,y,t) = ax + by + dt + \theta_0, \tag{8}$$

where $a,\ b,\ d,\ \rho,\ \tau,\ \theta_0$ are real constants with not zero. ρ is velocity, τ is the slope of the connector between the two stable states of the solution, a is the frequency, d is the phase, b is wavenumber, θ_0 is the center of phase. Considering Equation (8) into Equation (1), we have follows:

$$\left(-a^2-2b+d^2\right)U+2U^3-\left(-1+\rho^2\right)U''=0, \tag{9}$$

$$2\mathrm{i}(a+d\rho+\tau)U'=0. \tag{10}$$

From imaginary part, we get the following strain condition as:

$$a=-\rho-\tau. \tag{11}$$

Balancing in Equation (9), we get $n=1$. Taking this into Equation (5), we get the following solution form

$$U(\xi)=+a_{-1}(m+F)^{-1}+ma_0+a_1(m+F)^1. \tag{12}$$

Substituting Equation (12) into Equation (9), we get the following system of equations:

$$\begin{aligned}
&\left(m+\tfrac{1}{G'}\right)^0: && 2m^2\lambda^2a_{-1}-2m^2\lambda^2\rho^2a_{-1}+4m^3\lambda\mu a_{-1}-4m^3\lambda\rho^2\mu a_{-1}+2m^4\mu^2a_{-1}\\
& && -2m^4\rho^2\mu^2a_{-1}+2a_{-1}^3=0,\\
&\left(m+\tfrac{1}{G'}\right)^1: && -3m\lambda^2a_{-1}+3m\lambda^2\rho^2a_{-1}-3m^2\lambda\mu a_{-1}+3m^2\lambda\rho^2\mu a_{-1}+6a_{-1}^2a_0=0,\\
&\left(m+\tfrac{1}{G'}\right)^2: && -2ba_{-1}+d^2a_{-1}+\lambda^2a_{-1}-\lambda^2\rho^2a_{-1}-2m\lambda\mu a_{-1}+2m\lambda\rho^2\mu a_{-1}-2m^2\mu^2a_{-1}\\
& && +2m^2\rho^2\mu^2a_{-1}-(-d\rho-\tau)^2a_{-1}+6a_{-1}a_0^2+6a_{-1}^2a_1=0,\\
&\left(m+\tfrac{1}{G'}\right)^3: && \lambda\mu a_{-1}-\lambda\rho^2\mu a_{-1}-2ba_0+d^2a_0-(-d\rho-\tau)^2a_0+2a_0^3-m\lambda^2a_1+m\lambda^2\rho^2a_1\\
& && -m^2\lambda\mu a_1+\ m^2\lambda\rho^2\mu a_1+12a_{-1}a_0a_1=0,\\
&\left(m+\tfrac{1}{G'}\right)^4: && -2ba_1+d^2a_1+\lambda^2a_1-\lambda^2\rho^2a_1-2m\lambda\mu a_1+2m\lambda\rho^2\mu a_1-2m^2\mu^2a_1\\
& && +2m^2\rho^2\mu^2a_1\ -(-d\rho-\tau)^2a_1+6a_0^2a_1+6a_{-1}a_1^2=0,\\
&\left(m+\tfrac{1}{G'}\right)^5: && 3\lambda\mu a_1-3\lambda\rho^2\mu a_1+6a_0a_1^2=0,\\
&\left(m+\tfrac{1}{G'}\right)^6: && 2\mu^2a_1-2\rho^2\mu^2a_1+2a_1^3=0.
\end{aligned} \tag{13}$$

Solving this system, we can find the following cases of the solutions to the Equation (1).

Case 1. Selecting the following coefficients

$$\begin{gathered}
a_{-1}=0,a_1=\sqrt{-1+\rho^2}\mu,b=\tfrac{1}{4}\left(\left(1-\rho^2\right)\left(2d^2-(\lambda+2m\mu)^2\right)-4d\rho\tau-2\tau^2\right),\\
a_0=\tfrac{1}{2}\lambda\sqrt{\rho^2-1},
\end{gathered} \tag{14}$$

we have the following singular complex wave solution to the Equation (1):

$$h_1=\frac{1}{2}\mathrm{e}^{\mathrm{i}(dt-x(d\rho+\mu 1)+\frac{1}{4}y(\kappa-4\rho\tau-2\tau^2)+\theta_0)}\sqrt{\rho^2-1}\left(\lambda+2\mu\left(m+\frac{\lambda+2m\mu}{-\mu+\varpi\tau\mathrm{e}^{-w(x-t\rho+y\tau)}}\right)\right), \tag{15}$$

where $w=\lambda+2m\mu,\ \kappa=\left(1-\rho^2\right)\left(2d^2-w^2\right)$.

Case 2. When we consider another coefficient to the Equation (1) given as:

$$\begin{gathered}
a_{-1}=-m\sqrt{-1+\rho^2}(\lambda+m\mu),a_0=\tfrac{1}{2}\lambda\sqrt{-1+\rho^2},a_1=0,\\
b=\tfrac{1}{4}\left(-\left(-1+\rho^2\right)\left(2d^2-(\lambda+2m\mu)^2\right)-4d\rho\tau-2\tau^2\right),
\end{gathered} \tag{16}$$

it gives another singular complex wave solution to the governing model as:

$$h_2=\frac{\sqrt{\rho^2-1}}{2}\left(\lambda-\frac{2m\gamma}{m+\frac{\gamma}{-\mu+\varpi e^{-(\lambda+2m\mu)(x-t\rho+y\tau)}\gamma}}\right)e^{i(dt-x(\rho+\tau)+\frac{1}{4}y(v-4d\rho\tau-2\tau^2)+\theta_0)}, \tag{17}$$

in which $\gamma = \lambda + 2m\mu, v = \left(1-\rho^2\right)\left(2d^2-\gamma^2\right)$.

Case 3. Choosing as:

$$a_{-1} = \frac{(-1-i\sqrt{2})m}{2\sqrt{d^2+\lambda^2}}\sqrt{-2b\lambda^2+\frac{\lambda^2\tau\left(d^2\tau-\lambda^2\tau-2d\sqrt{-2b(d^2+\lambda^2)+(d^2+\lambda^2)^2-\lambda^2\tau^2}\right)}{d^2+\lambda^2}},$$

$$a_0 = \frac{1}{2\sqrt{d^2+\lambda^2}}\sqrt{-2b\lambda^2+\frac{\lambda^2\tau\left(d^2\tau-\lambda^2\tau-2d\sqrt{-2b(d^2+\lambda^2)+(d^2+\lambda^2)^2-\lambda^2\tau^2}\right)}{d^2+\lambda^2}}, \tag{18}$$

$$a_1 = 0,\ \rho = \frac{-d\tau+\sqrt{-2b(d^2+\lambda^2)+(d^2+\lambda^2)^2-\lambda^2\tau^2}}{d^2+\lambda^2},\ \mu = \frac{i(i+\sqrt{2})\lambda}{2m},$$

we extract the following periodic complex wave solution to the Equation (1):

$$h_3 = \frac{\left(2i+\sqrt{2}-4i\omega e^{-i\sqrt{2}\lambda\left(x+y\tau+\frac{t(d\tau-\sqrt{\beta})}{d^2+\lambda^2}\right)}m\right)e^{i\left(dt+by-x\tau+\frac{dx(d\tau-\sqrt{\beta})}{d^2+\lambda^2}+\theta_0\right)}}{2\left(-i+\sqrt{2}+2\sqrt{2}\omega e^{-i\sqrt{2}\lambda\left(x+y\tau+\frac{t(d\tau-\sqrt{\beta})}{d^2+\lambda^2}\right)}m\right)\sqrt{d^2+\lambda^2}}\sqrt{-2b\lambda^2+\frac{\lambda^2\tau\left(d^2\tau-\lambda^2\tau-2d\sqrt{\beta}\right)}{d^2+\lambda^2}}, \tag{19}$$

where $\beta = d^4+2d^2\lambda^2+\lambda^4-2b\left(d^2+\lambda^2\right)-\lambda^2\tau^2 > 0$, with strain condition.

Case 4. If it is taken as following form:

$$a_{-1} = 0,\ a_0 = -\frac{\sqrt{\frac{\lambda^2\left((d-\lambda)(d+\lambda)\tau^2-2b(d^2+\lambda^2)+2d\tau\sqrt{(d^2+\lambda^2)^2-2b(d^2+\lambda^2)-\lambda^2\tau^2}\right)}{d^2+\lambda^2}}}{2\sqrt{d^2+\lambda^2}},$$

$$a_1 = \frac{(1-i\sqrt{2})\sqrt{\frac{\lambda^2\left(-2b(d^2+\lambda^2)+(d-\lambda)(d+\lambda)\tau^2+2d\tau\sqrt{-2b(d^2+\lambda^2)+(d^2+\lambda^2)^2-\lambda^2\tau^2}\right)}{d^2+\lambda^2}}}{2m\sqrt{d^2+\lambda^2}}, \tag{20}$$

$$\rho = -\frac{d\tau+\sqrt{-2b(d^2+\lambda^2)+(d^2+\lambda^2)^2-\lambda^2\tau^2}}{d^2+\lambda^2},\ \mu = \frac{i(i+\sqrt{2})\lambda}{2m},$$

produces following new complex traveling wave solution given as

$$h_4 = -\frac{e^{i\left(dt+by-x\tau+\frac{dx(d\tau+\sqrt{\beta})}{d^2+\lambda^2}+\theta_0\right)}\left(\sqrt{2}-2i-4i\omega e^{-i\sqrt{2}\lambda\left(x+y\tau+\frac{t(d\tau+\sqrt{\beta})}{d^2+\lambda^2}\right)}m\right)\sqrt{-2b\lambda^2+\frac{\lambda^2\tau\left(d^2\tau-\lambda^2\tau+2d\sqrt{\beta}\right)}{d^2+\lambda^2}}}{2\left(i+\sqrt{2}-2\sqrt{2}\omega e^{-i\sqrt{2}\lambda\left(x+y\tau+\frac{t(d\tau+\sqrt{\beta})}{d^2+\lambda^2}\right)}m\right)\sqrt{d^2+\lambda^2}}, \tag{21}$$

where $-2b\lambda^2+\frac{\lambda^2\tau\left(d^2\tau-\lambda^2\tau+2d\sqrt{\beta}\right)}{d^2+\lambda^2} > 0$, with strain condition.

4. Results and Discussions

First, it may be observed that Figures 1 and 2 are singular complex wave solutions to the governing model, Figures 3 and 4 are periodic complex wave solutions for the Equation (1).Unlike many analytical methods, we offer different solutions from the $(1/G')$-expansion method [25–28] which produces hyperbolic type traveling wave solution. What is interesting here is the idea that at the beginning, if $m = 0$, the solutions produced by the $(1/G')$-expansion method are obtained. However, if $m = 0$ is taken in Equation (20), μ is undefined. Therefore, we offered different solutions from the solution produced by the classic $(1/G')$-expansion method. Such solutions include singular points. Solutions containing single points are important for the shock wave structure. Moreover, the solutions that provide the equation due to the structure of the Schrödinger equation are of the complex wave solution. These solutions are in hyperbolic form and are different from the solutions produced in other analytical solutions. Appropriate values are given so that the structure of the functions created by the parameters is not disrupted. The special values given to these constants have rendered to draw the shape of the wave at any given moment.

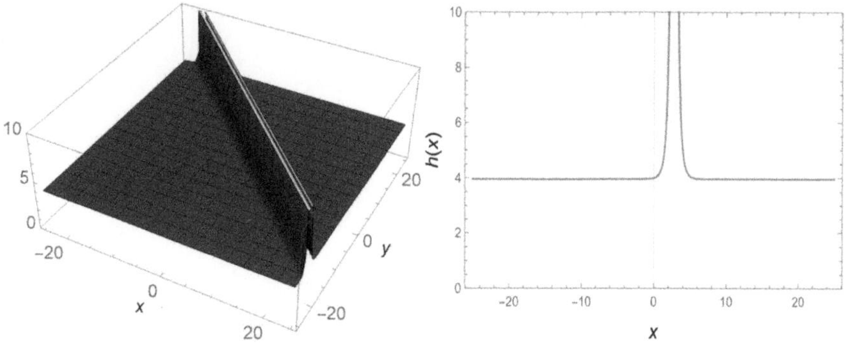

Figure 1. Three-dimensional and 2D graphs of Equation (15) for $t = 2, \theta_0 = 1, \lambda = 0.3, m = 2, \mu = 0.5, d = 2, \rho = 2, \tau = 1, b = 1, \varpi = 1$ values and $y = 2$ for 2D.

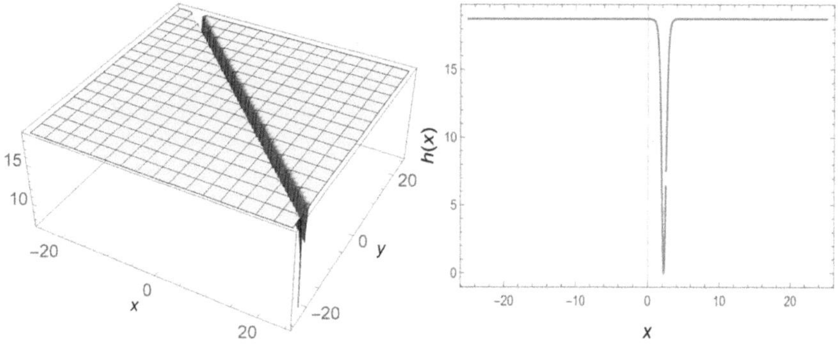

Figure 2. Three-dimensional and 2D graphs for values $t = 2, \theta_0 = 1, \lambda = 3, m = 2, \mu = 0.5, d = 0.4, \rho = 2, \tau = 1, \varpi = 1$ of Equation (17) and $y = 2$ for 2D.

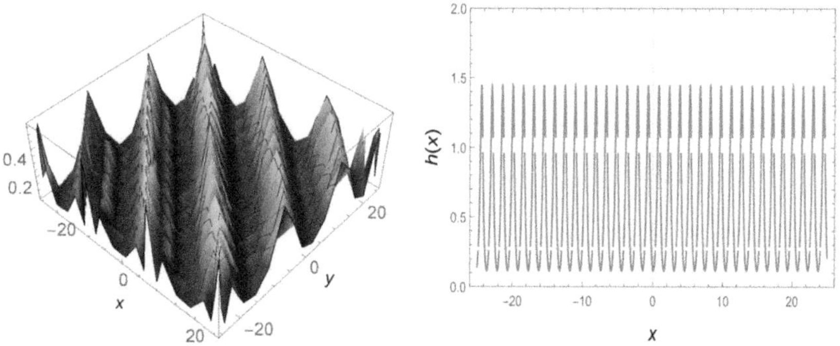

Figure 3. Three-dimensional and 2D graphs for values $t = 2, \theta_0 = 1, \lambda = 3, m = 2, d = 1, \tau = 1, b = -1, \varpi = 1$ of Equation (19) and $y = 2$ for 2D.

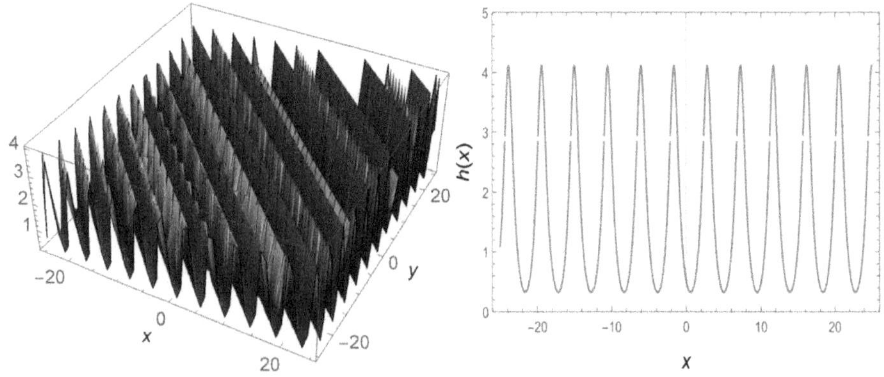

Figure 4. Three-dimensional and 2D graphs for values $t = 2, \theta_0 = 1, \lambda = 3, m = 2, \mu = 0.5, d = 1, \rho = 1, \tau = 1, b = -1, \varpi = 1$ of Equation (21) and $y = 2$ for 2D.

5. Conclusions

In this article, entirely new singular and periodic wave solutions to the governing model were successfully extracted via projected method. Strain conditions are also reported in this paper for validating the results. It may be also observed that these results satisfied the governing models. Figures of these solutions were plotted in 3D and 2D with the help of computational programs.

Comparing these results with the results obtained exp function solutions in [19], it may be seen that these results are entirely different solutions to the governing model. In this sense, these solutions may be also used to explain the nonlinear wave properties in defined intervals. Although it is quite difficult to obtain the solutions of NPDEs, the constructions of these solutions are facilitated with the help of some developed and modified methods. It can be also used that this method can be recommended in investigations of many other mathematical models with high nonlinearity. Considering these figures drawn in this paper and using symbolic calculation, the $(m + 1/G')$-expansion method was to be an effective, powerful and reliable mathematical tool for governing models.

Author Contributions: Conceptualization, H.D.; methodology, E.I.; formal analysis, and writing—review and editing, H.B. All authors have read and agreed to the published version of the manuscript.

Funding: This research received no external funding.

Acknowledgments: Authors extend their thanks to the Editors and anonymous reviewers.

Conflicts of Interest: The authors declare no conflict of interest.

References

1. Ismael, H.F.; Bulut, H.; Baskonus, H.M. Optical soliton solutions to the Fokas–Lenells equation via sine-Gordon expansion method and (m + (G′/G))-expansion method. *Pramana* **2020**, *94*, 35. [CrossRef]
2. Gao, W.; Ismael, H.F.; Husien, A.M.; Bulut, H.; Baskonus, H.M. Optical soliton solutions of the cubic-quartic nonlinear Schrödinger and resonant nonlinear Schrödinger equation with the parabolic law. *Appl. Sci.* **2020**, *10*, 219. [CrossRef]
3. Yokus, A.; Durur, H.; Ahmad, H. Hyperbolic Type solutions for the couple Boiti-Leon-Pempinelli system. *Facta Univ. Ser. Math. Inform.* **2020**, *35*, 523–531.
4. Ali, K.K.; Dutta, H.; Yilmazer, R.; Noeiaghdam, S. On the new wave behaviors of the Gilson-Pickering equation. *Front. Phys.* **2020**, *8*, 54. [CrossRef]
5. Durur, H.; Yokuş, A. Analytical solutions of Kolmogorov–Petrovskii–Piskunov equation. *J. Balikesir Univ. Inst. Sci. Technol.* **2020**, *22*, 628–636.
6. Darvishi, M.T.; Najafi, M.; Wazwaz, A.M. Construction of exact solutions in amagneto-electro-elastic circular rod. *Waves Random Complex Media* **2020**, *30*, 340–353. [CrossRef]

7. Gao, W.; Silambarasan, R.; Baskonus, H.M.; Anand, R.V.; Rezazadeh, H. Periodic waves of the nondissipative double dispersive micro strain wave in the micro structured solids. *Phys. A Stat. Mech. Appl.* **2020**, *545*, 123772. [CrossRef]
8. Su-Ping, Q.; Li-Xin, T. Modification of the Clarkson–Kruskal Direct method for a coupled system. *Chin. Phys. Lett.* **2007**, *24*, 2720. [CrossRef]
9. Durur, H. Different types analytic solutions of the (1+1)-dimensional resonant nonlinear Schrödinger's equation using (G′/G)-expansion method. *Mod. Phys. Lett. B* **2020**, *34*, 2050036. [CrossRef]
10. Rezazadeh, H.; Kumar, D.; Neirameh, A.; Eslami, M.; Mirzazadeh, M. Applications of three methods for obtaining optical soliton solutions for the Lakshmanan–Porsezian–Daniel model with Kerr law nonlinearity. *Pramana* **2020**, *94*, 39. [CrossRef]
11. Baskonus, H.M.; Bulut, H.; Atangana, A. On the complex and hyperbolic structures of the longitudinal wave equation in a magneto-electro-elastic circular rod. *Smart Mater. Struct.* **2016**, *25*, 035022. [CrossRef]
12. Liu, H.; Bai, C.L.; Xin, X. Painlevé analysis, group classification and exact solutions to the nonlinear wave equations. *Eur. Phys. J. B* **2020**, *93*, 26. [CrossRef]
13. Yokus, A.; Durur, H.; Ahmad, H.; Yao, S.W. Construction of different types analytic solutions for the Zhiber-Shabate quation. *Mathematics* **2020**, *8*, 908. [CrossRef]
14. Yavuz, M.; Sulaiman, T.A.; Usta, F.; Bulut, H. Analysis and numerical computations of the fractional regularized long-wave equation with damping term. *Math. Methods Appl. Sci.* **2020**. [CrossRef]
15. Guan, X.; Liu, W.; Zhou, Q.; Biswas, A. Some lump solutions for a generalized (3+1)-dimensional Kadomtsev–Petviashvili equation. *Appl. Math. Comput.* **2020**, *366*, 124757. [CrossRef]
16. El-Labany, S.K.; El-Taibany, W.F.; Behery, E.E.; Fouda, S.M. Collision of dustion acoustic multi solitons in a non-extensive plasma using Hirota bilinear method. *Phys. Plasmas* **2018**, *25*, 013701. [CrossRef]
17. Sharma, B.; Kumar, S.; Cattani, C.; Baleanu, D. Nonlinear dynamics of Cattaneo–Christov heat flux model for third-grade power-law fluid. *J. Comput. Nonlinear Dyn.* **2020**, *15*, 011009. [CrossRef]
18. Srivastava, H.M.; Baleanu, D.; Machado, J.A.T.; Osman, M.S.; Rezazadeh, H.; Arshed, S.; Günerhan, H. Traveling wave solutions to nonlinear directional couplers by modified Kudryashov method. *Phys. Scr.* **2020**. [CrossRef]
19. Ali, K.K.; Wazwaz, A.M.; Mehanna, M.S.; Osman, M.S. On short-range pulse propagation described by (2+1)-dimensional Schrödinger's hyperbolic equation in nonlinear optical. *Phys. Scr.* **2020**, *95*, 075203. [CrossRef]
20. Zayed, E.M.E.; Al-Nowehy, A.G. Exact solutions and optical soliton solutions for the (2 + 1)-dimensional hyperbolic nonlinear Schrödinger equation. *Optik* **2016**, *127*, 4970–4983. [CrossRef]
21. Seadawy, A.R.; Kumar, D.; Chakrabarty, A.K. Dispersive optical soliton solutions for the hyperbolic and cubic-quintic nonlinear Schrödinger equations via the extended sinh-Gordon equation expansion method. *Eur. Phys. J. Plus* **2018**, *133*, 182. [CrossRef]
22. Ahmed, I.; Chunlai, M.; Zheng, P. Exact solution of the (2+1)-dimensional hyperbolic nonlinear Schrödinger equation byAdomian decomposition method. *Malaya J. Mat.* **2014**, *2*, 160–164.
23. El-Ganaini, S.I.A. The first integral method to the nonlinear Schrodinger equations in higher dimensions. *Abst. Appl. Anal.* **2013**, *2013*, 1–10. [CrossRef]
24. Pelinovsky, D.E.; Rouvinskaya, E.A.; Kurkina, O.E.E.; Deconinck, B. Short-wave transverse instabilities of line solitons of the two-dimensional hyperbolic nonlinear Schrödinger equation. *Theor. Math. Phys.* **2014**, *179*, 452–461. [CrossRef]
25. Yokuş, A.; Durur, H. Complex hyperbolic traveling wave solutions of Kuramoto-Sivashinsky equation using (1/G′)expansion method for nonlinear dynamic theory. *J. Balikesir Univ. Inst. Sci. Technol.* **2019**, *21*, 590–599.
26. Durur, H.; Yokuş, A. Hyperbolic traveling wave solutions for Sawada–Kotera equation using (1/G′)-expansion method. *Afyon Kocatepe Univ. J. Sci. Eng. Sci.* **2019**, *19*, 615–619.
27. Yokuş, A. Comparison of Caputo and conformable derivatives for time-fractional Korteweg–deVries equation via the finite difference method. *Int. J. Mod. Phys. B* **2018**, *32*, 1850365. [CrossRef]
28. Yavuz, M.; Yokus, A. Analytical and numerical approaches to nerve impulse model of fractional-order. *Numer. Methods Part. Differ. Equ.* **2020**. [CrossRef]
29. Goufo, E.F.D.; Tenkam, H.M.; Khumalo, M. A behavioral analysis of KdVB equation under the law of Mittag–Leffler function. *Chaos Solitons Fractals* **2019**, *125*, 139–145. [CrossRef]
30. Khan, Z.H.; Hussain, S.T.; Hammouch, Z. Flow and heat transfer analysis of water and ethyleneglycol based Cunano particles between two parallel disks with suction/injection effects. *J. Mol. Liq.* **2016**, *221*, 298–304.

31. Guedda, M.; Hammouch, Z. On similarity and pseudo-similarity solutions of Falkner–Skan boundary layers. *Fluid Dyn. Res.* **2006**, *38*, 211–223. [CrossRef]
32. Goufo, E.F.D.; Atangana, A. Dynamics of traveling waves of variable order hyperbolic Liouville equation: Regulation and control. *Discret. Contin. Dyn. Syst. S* **2019**, *13*, 645–662. [CrossRef]
33. Seadawy, A.R. Stability analysis solutions for nonlinear three-dimensional modified Korteweg–de Vries–Zakharov–Kuznetsov equation in a magnetized electron–positron plasma. *Phys. A Stat. Mech. Appl.* **2016**, *455*, 44–51. [CrossRef]
34. Arshad, M.; Seadawy, A.; Lu, D.; Wang, J. Travelling wave solutions of generalized coupled Zakharov–Kuznetsov and dispersive long wave equations. *Results Phys.* **2016**, *6*, 1136–1145. [CrossRef]
35. Lu, D.; Seadawy, A.R.; Arshad, M.; Wang, J. New solitary wave solutions of (3+1)-dimensional nonlinear extended Zakharov-Kuznetsov and modified KdV-Zakharov-Kuznetsov equations and their applications. *Results Phys.* **2017**, *7*, 899–909. [CrossRef]
36. Özkan, Y.S.; Yaşar, E.; Seadawy, A.R. A third-order nonlinear Schrödinger equation: The exact solutions, group-invariant solutions and conservation laws. *J. Taibah Univ. Sci.* **2020**, *14*, 585–597. [CrossRef]
37. Ahmad, H.; Seadawy, A.R.; Khan, T.A.; Thounthong, P. Analytic approximate solutions for some nonlinear Parabolic dynamical wave equations. *J. Taibah Univ. Sci.* **2020**, *14*, 346–358. [CrossRef]
38. Arnous, A.H.; Seadawy, A.R.; Alqahtani, R.T.; Biswas, A. Optical solitons with complex Ginzburg–Landau equation by modified simple equation method. *Optik* **2017**, *144*, 475–480. [CrossRef]
39. Seadawy, A.R.; Jun, W. Mathematical methods and solitary wave solutions of three-dimensional Zakharov-Kuznetsov-Burgers equation in dusty plasma and its applications. *Results Phys.* **2017**, *7*, 4269–4277.
40. Durur, H.; Tasbozan, O.; Kurt, A. New analytical solutions of conformable time fractional bad and good modified Boussinesq equations. *Appl. Math. Nonlinear Sci.* **2020**, *5*, 447–454. [CrossRef]
41. Durur, H.; Kurt, A.; Tasbozan, O. New travelling wave solutions for KdV6 equation using sub equation method. *Appl. Math. Nonlinear Sci.* **2020**, *5*, 455–460. [CrossRef]
42. Kaya, D.; Yokuş, A.; Demiroğlu, U. Comparison of exact and numerical solutions for the Sharma–Tasso–Olver equation. In *Numerical Solutions of Realistic Nonlinear Phenomena*; Springer: Cham, Switzerland, 2020; pp. 53–65.
43. Apeanti, W.O.; Seadawy, A.R.; Lu, D. Complex optical solutions and modulation instability of hyperbolic Schrödinger dynamical equation. *Results Phys.* **2019**, *12*, 2091–2097. [CrossRef]
44. Arshad, M.; Seadawy, A.R.; Lu, D. Bright–dark solitary wave solutions of generalized higher-order nonlinear Schrödinger equation and its applications in optics. *J. Electromagn. Waves Appl.* **2017**, *31*, 1711–1721. [CrossRef]
45. Arshad, M.; Seadawy, A.R.; Lu, D. Exact bright–dark solitary wave solutions of the higher-order cubic–quintic nonlinear Schrödinger equation and its stability. *Optik* **2017**, *138*, 40–49. [CrossRef]
46. Arshad, M.; Seadawy, A.R.; Lu, D.; Jun, W. Modulation instability analysis of modify unstable nonlinear schrodinger dynamical equation and its optical soliton solutions. *Results Phys.* **2017**, *7*, 4153–4161. [CrossRef]
47. Baskonus, H.M.; Cattani, C.; Ciancio, A. Periodic, complex and kink-type solitons for the nonlinear model in microtubules. *J. Appl. Sci.* **2019**, *21*, 34–45.
48. Conte, R.; Musette, M. Elliptic general analytic solutions. *Stud. Appl. Math.* **2009**, *123*, 63–81. [CrossRef]
49. Conte, R.; Ng, T.W. Meromorphic solutions of a third order nonlinear differential equation. *J. Math. Phys.* **2010**, *51*, 033518. [CrossRef]

fractal and fractional

MDPI

Article

Fractional Kinetic Equations Associated with Incomplete *I*-Functions

Manish Kumar Bansal [1], Devendra Kumar [2,*], Priyanka Harjule [3] and Jagdev Singh [4]

1 Department of Applied Sciences, Government Engineering College, Banswara 327001, Rajasthan, India; bansalmanish443@gmail.com
2 Department of Mathematics, University of Rajasthan, Jaipur 302004, Rajasthan, India
3 Department of Mathematics, IIIT, Kota, MNIT Campus, Jaipur 302017, Rajasthan, India; priyanka.maths@iiitkota.ac.in
4 Department of Mathematics, JECRC University, Jaipur 303905, Rajasthan, India; jagdevsinghrathore@gmail.com
* Correspondence: devendra.maths@gmail.com

Received: 12 April 2020; Accepted: 30 April 2020; Published: 4 May 2020

Abstract: In this paper, we investigate the solution of fractional kinetic equation (FKE) associated with the incomplete *I*-function (IIF) by using the well-known integral transform (Laplace transform). The FKE plays a great role in solving astrophysical problems. The solutions are represented in terms of IIF. Next, we present some interesting corollaries by specializing the parameters of IIF in the form of simpler special functions and also mention a few known results, which are very useful in solving physical or real-life problems. Finally, some graphical results are presented to demonstrate the influence of the order of the fractional integral operator on the reaction rate.

Keywords: fractional kinetic equation; Riemann–Liouville fractional integral operator; incomplete *I*-functions; Laplace transform

1. Introduction

Arbitrary-order calculus (AOC) is a useful mathematical device that enables the study of arbitrary-order integrals and derivatives [1–4]. Its origin dates back to the 1695 letter from Leibniz to L'Hôpital. The noble developments in the field of fractional-order calculus (FOC) in relevant conceptual research and in solving real-time problems have been extensively studied comparatively recently. The pioneering contributions in fractional calculus were given by legendary mathematicians viz. Euler, Fourier, Abel, Liouville, or Riemann. For explicit knowledge of arbitrary-order derivatives and integrals, one can refer to [5] and the references therein. The intellect of fractional derivative equations (FDEs) along with their implications have had a significant impact on various science and engineering systems. In particular, the kinetic equations (KEs) characterize the relationship between concentrations of the materials and time. KE is applied in gas theory, plasma physics, aerodynamics, etc. The solution of KE gives the distribution function of the dynamical states of a single particle, which often depends on the coordinates, time, and velocity. The expansions and generic nature of arbitrary-order kinetic equations associated with the fractional-order operators was well established in [6–9]. Since the last few decades, fractional kinetic equations in several shapes and configurations have been widely and productively employed in describing various significant problems of physics and astrophysics (see the recent papers [10–17]).

The FDE describing the rates at which the reaction, destruction, and production change was determined by Haubold and Mathai [6], which is presented in the following equation:

$$\frac{d\Theta}{d\mathsf{w}} = -d(\Theta_{\mathsf{w}}) + \mathsf{p}(\Theta_{\mathsf{w}}), \tag{1}$$

where $\Theta = \Theta(\mathrm{w})$ gives the reaction rate, $d = d(\Theta)$ gives the destruction rate, $\mathrm{p} = \mathrm{p}(\Theta)$ is the production rate, and Θ_{w} represents the function defined by $\Theta_{\mathrm{w}}(\mathrm{w}^*) = \Theta(\mathrm{w} - \mathrm{w}^*), \mathrm{w}^* > 0$.

Now, if the spatial fluctuation and the inhomogeneities in the quantity $\Theta(\mathrm{w})$ are ignored, then (1) is converted into:

$$\frac{d\Theta_i}{d\mathrm{w}} = -\mathrm{c}_i\Theta_i(\mathrm{w}), \tag{2}$$

subject to the initial condition that $\Theta_i(\mathrm{w} = 0) = \Theta_0$ is the number density of species iat initial time $(\mathrm{w} = 0), \mathrm{c}_i > 0$.

Equation (2) can be written after integrating:

$$\Theta(\mathrm{w}) - \Theta_0 = -\mathrm{c}\, {}_0D_{\mathrm{w}}^{-1}\Theta(\mathrm{w}), \tag{3}$$

where D_{w}^{-1} is known as the integral operator.

Haubold and Mathai [6] gave the extension of Equation (3) (known as the fractional kinetic equation (FKE)) as follows:

$$\Theta(\mathrm{w}) - \Theta_0 = -\mathrm{c}^{\beta}\, {}_0D_{\mathrm{w}}^{-\beta}\Theta(\mathrm{w}), \tag{4}$$

where $D_{\mathrm{w}}^{-\beta}$ denotes the familiar Riemann–Liouville fractional integral operator.

The solution of FKE (4) is given below:

$$\Theta(\mathrm{w}) = \Theta_0 \sum_{\kappa=0}^{\infty} \frac{(-1)^{\kappa}}{\Gamma(\beta\kappa + 1)}(\mathrm{cw})^{\beta\kappa}. \tag{5}$$

From the perspective of the effectiveness and great significance of the KE in many physics and astrophysical problems, we established a solution of FKE involving the IIF.

The very familiar gamma function $\Gamma(s)$ is defined as follows:

$$\Gamma(\Im) = \begin{cases} \int_0^{\infty} e^{-u}u^{\Im-1}du, & (\Re(\Im) > 0) \\ \frac{\Gamma(\Im+\mathfrak{K})}{(\Im)_{\mathfrak{K}}}, & (\Im \in \mathbb{C} \setminus \mathbb{Z}_0^-;\ \mathfrak{K} \in \mathbb{N}_0), \end{cases} \tag{6}$$

where $(\Im)_{\mathfrak{K}}$ denotes the Pochhammer symbol defined (for $\Im \in \mathbb{C}$ and $\mathfrak{K} \in \mathbb{N}_0$) by:

$$(\Im)_{\mathfrak{K}} = \frac{\Gamma(\Im + \mathfrak{K})}{\Gamma(\Im)} = \begin{cases} 1, & (\mathfrak{K} = 0;\ \Im \in \mathbb{C} \setminus \{0\}) \\ \Im(\Im + 1) \cdots (\Im + s - 1), & (\mathfrak{K} = s \in \mathbb{N};\ \Im \in \mathbb{C}), \end{cases} \tag{7}$$

provided that the gamma quotient exists.

The incomplete gamma functions (IGFs) $\gamma(\Im, x)$ and $\Gamma(\Im, x)$ are presented in the following manner:

$$\gamma(\Im, x) = \int_0^x u^{\Im-1}e^{-u}du, \qquad (\Re(\Im) > 0;\ x \geqq 0), \tag{8}$$

and:

$$\Gamma(\Im, x) = \int_x^{\infty} u^{\Im-1}e^{-u}du, \qquad (x \geqq 0;\ \Re(\Im) > 0 \text{ when } x = 0), \tag{9}$$

respectively, which satisfy the subsequent decomposition formula:

$$\gamma(\Im, x) + \Gamma(\Im, x) = \Gamma(\Im), \qquad (\Re(\Im) > 0). \tag{10}$$

The gamma function $\Gamma(\Im)$ and IGFs $\gamma(\Im, x)$ and $\Gamma(\Im, x)$, which is defined in (6), (8), and (9), respectively, play the main role in the field of communication theory, probability theory, groundwater pumping modeling, quantum physics, mathematical physics, statistics, solid state physics, engineering, and science (see, for example, [18,19]; see also the recent papers [20–28]).

Recently, Bansal and Kumar ([29], p. 1248, Equations (1.6)–(1.9)) defined the incomplete I-functions ${}^{(\Gamma)}I^{m,n}_{p_i,q_i,r}(z)$ and ${}^{(\gamma)}I^{m,n}_{p_i,q_i,r}(z)$ associated with the IGFs $\gamma(\Im, x)$ and $\Gamma(\Im, x)$ as follows:

$$\begin{aligned} {}^{(\Gamma)}I^{m,n}_{p_\ell,q_\ell,r}(z) &= {}^{(\Gamma)}I^{m,n}_{p_\ell,q_\ell,r}\left[z \left| \begin{matrix} (e_1, E_1, x), (e_j, E_j)_{2,n}, (e_{j\ell}, E_{j\ell})_{n+1,p_\ell} \\ \\ (f_j, F_j)_{1,m}, (f_{j\ell}, F_{j\ell})_{m+1,q_\ell} \end{matrix} \right. \right] \\ &= \frac{1}{2\pi i} \int_{\mathfrak{L}} \mathbb{K}(\xi, x) z^{-\xi} d\xi, \end{aligned} \tag{11}$$

for all $z \neq 0$; here, $i = \sqrt{-1}$ and:

$$\mathbb{K}(\xi, x) = \frac{\Gamma(1 - e_1 - E_1\xi, x) \prod_{j=1}^{m} \Gamma(f_j + F_j\xi) \prod_{j=2}^{n} \Gamma(1 - e_j - E_j\xi)}{\sum_{\ell=1}^{r} \left[\prod_{j=m+1}^{q_\ell} \Gamma(1 - f_{j\ell} - F_{j\ell}\xi) \prod_{j=n+1}^{p_\ell} \Gamma(e_{j\ell} + E_{j\ell}\xi) \right]}, \tag{12}$$

and:

$$\begin{aligned} {}^{(\gamma)}I^{m,n}_{p_\ell,q_\ell,r}(z) &= {}^{(\gamma)}I^{m,n}_{p_\ell,q_\ell,r}\left[z \left| \begin{matrix} (e_1, E_1, x), (e_j, E_j)_{2,n}, (e_{j\ell}, E_{j\ell})_{n+1,p_\ell} \\ \\ (f_j, F_j)_{1,m}, (f_{j\ell}, F_{j\ell})_{m+1,q_\ell} \end{matrix} \right. \right] \\ &= \frac{1}{2\pi i} \int_{\mathfrak{L}} \mathbb{L}(\xi, x) z^{-\xi} d\xi, \end{aligned} \tag{13}$$

for all $z \neq 0$; here, $i = \sqrt{-1}$ and:

$$\mathbb{L}(\xi, x) = \frac{\gamma(1 - e_1 - E_1\xi, x) \prod_{j=1}^{m} \Gamma(f_j + F_j\xi) \prod_{j=2}^{n} \Gamma(1 - e_j - E_j\xi)}{\sum_{\ell=1}^{r} \left[\prod_{j=m+1}^{q_\ell} \Gamma(1 - f_{j\ell} - F_{j\ell}\xi) \prod_{j=n+1}^{p_\ell} \Gamma(e_{j\ell} + E_{j\ell}\xi) \right]}. \tag{14}$$

The incomplete I-functions ${}^{(\Gamma)}I^{m,n}_{p_\ell,q_\ell,r}(z)$ and ${}^{(\gamma)}I^{m,n}_{p_\ell,q_\ell,r}(z)$ in (11) and (13) exist for all $x \geq 0$ under the set of conditions as mentioned below.

The contour $\mathfrak{L}$ in the complex ξ-plane extends from $\gamma - i\infty$ to $\gamma + i\infty$, $\gamma \in \mathbb{R}$, and poles of the gamma functions $\Gamma(1 - e_j - E_j\xi)$, $j = \overline{1, n}$ do not exactly match with the poles of the gamma functions $\Gamma(f_j + F_j\xi)$, $j = \overline{1, m}$. The parameters m, n, p_ℓ, q_ℓ are non-negative integers satisfying $0 \leq n \leq p_\ell$, $0 \leq m \leq q_\ell$ for $i = \overline{1, r}$. The parameters $E_j, F_j, E_{j\ell}, F_{j\ell}$ are positive numbers, and $e_j, f_j, e_{j\ell}, f_{j\ell}$ are complex. All poles of $\mathbb{K}(\xi, x)$ and $\mathbb{L}(\xi, x)$ are supposed to be simple, and the empty product is treated as unity.

$$\mathfrak{H}_i > 0, \qquad |\arg(z)| < \frac{\pi}{2}\mathfrak{H}_i, \qquad i = \overline{1, r}, \tag{15}$$

$$\mathfrak{H}_i \geq 0, \qquad |\arg(z)| < \frac{\pi}{2}\mathfrak{H}_i \qquad \text{and} \qquad \Re(\zeta_i) + 1 < 0, \tag{16}$$

where:

$$\mathfrak{H}_i = \sum_{j=2}^{n} E_j + \sum_{j=2}^{m} F_j - \sum_{j=n+1}^{p_i} E_{ji} - \sum_{j=m+1}^{q_i} F_{ji}, \tag{17}$$

$$\zeta_i = \sum_{j=2}^{m} f_j - \sum_{j=2}^{n} e_j + \sum_{j=m+1}^{q_i} E_{ji} - \sum_{j=n+1}^{p_i} F_{ji} + \frac{1}{2}(p_i - q_i), \qquad i = \overline{1, r}. \tag{18}$$

The incomplete I-functions ${}^{(\Gamma)}I^{m,n}_{p_\ell,q_\ell,r}(z)$ and ${}^{(\gamma)}I^{m,n}_{p_\ell,q_\ell,r}(z)$ presented in (11) and (13) reduce to the many well-known special functions as follows:

1. On setting $x = 0$, (11) and (13) reduce to the I-function proposed by Saxena [30]:

$$ {}^{(\Gamma)}I^{m,n}_{p_\ell,q_\ell,r}\left[z \left| \begin{matrix} (e_1, E_1, 0), (e_j, E_j)_{2,n}, (e_{j\ell}, E_{j\ell})_{n+1,p_\ell} \\ \\ (f_j, F_j)_{1,m}, (f_{j\ell}, F_{j\ell})_{m+1,q_\ell} \end{matrix} \right. \right] = I^{m,n}_{p_\ell,q_\ell,r}\left[z \left| \begin{matrix} (e_j, E_j)_{1,n}, (e_{j\ell}, E_{j\ell})_{n+1,p_\ell} \\ \\ (f_j, F_j)_{1,m}, (f_{j\ell}, F_{j\ell})_{m+1,q_\ell} \end{matrix} \right. \right]. \tag{19}$$

2. Again, setting $r = 1$ in (11) and (13), then it reduces to the IHFs introduced by Srivastava [31] (see also [32]):

$$ {}^{(\Gamma)}I^{m,n}_{p_\ell,q_\ell,1}\left[z \left| \begin{matrix} (e_1, E_1, x), (e_j, E_j)_{2,n}, (e_{j\ell}, E_{j\ell})_{n+1,p_\ell} \\ \\ (f_j, F_j)_{1,m}, (f_{j\ell}, F_{j\ell})_{m+1,q_\ell} \end{matrix} \right. \right] = \Gamma^{m,n}_{p,q}\left[z \left| \begin{matrix} (e_1, E_1, x), (e_j, E_j)_{2,p} \\ \\ (f_j, F_j)_{1,q} \end{matrix} \right. \right], \tag{20}$$

and:

$$ {}^{(\gamma)}I^{m,n}_{p_\ell,q_\ell,1}\left[z \left| \begin{matrix} (e_1, E_1, x), (e_j, E_j)_{2,n}, (e_{j\ell}, E_{j\ell})_{n+1,p_\ell} \\ \\ (f_j, F_j)_{1,m}, (f_{j\ell}, F_{j\ell})_{m+1,q_\ell} \end{matrix} \right. \right] = \gamma^{m,n}_{p,q}\left[z \left| \begin{matrix} (e_1, E_1, x), (e_j, E_j)_{2,p} \\ \\ (f_j, F_j)_{1,q} \end{matrix} \right. \right]. \tag{21}$$

A complete description of IHFs can be found in the article [31].

3. Further, taking $m = 1, n = p_\ell$, q_ℓ is replaced by $q_\ell + 1$, and taking the suitable parameter, then the functions (20) and (21) reduce to the incomplete Fox–Wright Ψ-functions ${}_p\Psi_q^{(\Gamma)}$ and ${}_p\Psi_q^{(\gamma)}$, which were defined by Srivastava et al. [31].

$$ \Gamma^{1,p}_{p,q+1}\left[-z \left| \begin{matrix} (1 - e_1, E_1, x), (1 - e_j, E_j)_{2,p} \\ \\ (0, 1), (1 - f_j, F_j)_{1,q} \end{matrix} \right. \right] = {}_p\Psi_q^{(\Gamma)}\left[\begin{matrix} (e_1, E_1, x), (e_j, E_j)_{2,p}; \\ \\ (f_j, F_j)_{1,q}; \end{matrix} \; z \right], \tag{22}$$

and:

$$ \gamma^{1,p}_{p,q+1}\left[-z \left| \begin{matrix} (1 - e_1, E_1, x), (1 - e_j, E_j)_{2,p} \\ \\ (0, 1), (1 - f_j, F_j)_{1,q} \end{matrix} \right. \right] = {}_p\Psi_q^{(\gamma)}\left[\begin{matrix} (e_1, E_1, x), (e_j, E_j)_{2,p}; \\ \\ (f_j, F_j)_{1,q}; \end{matrix} \; z \right]. \tag{23}$$

4. Next, we take $x = 0$ and $r = 1$ in (11). The incomplete I-function reduces to the familiar Fox's H-function, which is defined and expressed in the following manner (see, for example, [33], p. 10):

$$ {}^{(\Gamma)}I^{m,n}_{p_\ell,q_\ell,1}\left[z \left| \begin{matrix} (e_1, E_1, 0), (e_j, E_j)_{2,n}, (e_{j\ell}, E_{j\ell})_{n+1,p_\ell} \\ \\ (f_j, F_j)_{1,m}, (f_{j\ell}, F_{j\ell})_{m+1,q_\ell} \end{matrix} \right. \right] = H^{m,n}_{p,q}\left[z \left| \begin{matrix} (e_1, E_1), \cdots, (e_p, E_p) \\ \\ (f_1, F_1), \cdots, (f_q, F_q) \end{matrix} \right. \right]. \tag{24}$$

Numerous special functions can be obtained from the incomplete I-functions for which some interesting functions are used in Section 3.

2. Arbitrary-Order Kinetic Equation

This part deals with the solution of FKE associated with the incomplete I-functions (11) and (13).

Theorem 1. *If* $x > 0, \alpha > 0, \beta > 0, c > 0, \wp > 0, E_\imath > 0 (\imath = 1, \cdots, p)$, *and* $F_\imath > 0 (\imath = 1, \cdots, q)$, *then the following arbitrary-order kinetic equation:*

$$\Theta(w) - \Theta_0 w^{\alpha-1} {}^{(\Gamma)}I^{m,n}_{p_\ell,q_\ell,r}\left[-\wp^\beta w^\beta \left| \begin{matrix} (e_1, E_1, x), (e_\imath, E_\imath)_{2,n}, (e_{\imath\ell}, E_{\imath\ell})_{n+1,p_\ell} \\ (f_\imath, F_\imath)_{1,m}, (f_{\imath\ell}, F_{\imath\ell})_{m+1,q_\ell} \end{matrix} \right.\right] = -c^\beta {}_0D_w^{-\beta}\Theta(w), \quad (25)$$

has a solution of the form:

$$\Theta(w) = \Theta_0 w^{\alpha-1} \sum_{\kappa=0}^{\infty} (-c^\beta w^\beta)^\kappa {}^{(\Gamma)}I^{m,n+1}_{p_\ell+1,q_\ell+1,r}\left[-\wp^\beta w^\beta \left| \begin{matrix} (e_1, E_1, x), (1-\alpha, \beta), (e_\imath, E_\imath)_{2,n}, (e_{\imath\ell}, E_{\imath\ell})_{n+1,p_\ell} \\ (f_\imath, F_\imath)_{1,m}, (1-\alpha-\beta\kappa, \beta), (f_{\imath\ell}, F_{\imath\ell})_{m+1,q_\ell} \end{matrix} \right.\right]. \quad (26)$$

Proof. Taking the Laplace transform [34] on both sides of FKE (25), we obtain:

$$\bar{\Theta}(\mathfrak{p}) - \Theta_0 \frac{1}{2\pi i} \int_{\mathfrak{L}} \mathbb{K}(\xi, x)(-\wp^\beta)^{-\xi} \frac{\Gamma(\alpha - \beta\xi)}{\mathfrak{p}^{\alpha-\beta\xi}} d\xi = -c^\beta \mathfrak{p}^{-\beta} \bar{\Theta}(\mathfrak{p}),$$

where $\mathbb{K}(\xi, x)$ is given in (12).

Upon simplifying the above equation, we get:

$$\bar{\Theta}(\mathfrak{p}) = \frac{\Theta_0}{(1 + c^\beta \mathfrak{p}^{-\beta})} \frac{1}{2\pi i} \int_{\mathfrak{L}} \mathbb{K}(\xi, x)(-\wp^\beta)^{-\xi} \frac{\Gamma(\alpha - \beta\xi)}{\mathfrak{p}^{\alpha-\beta\xi}} d\xi,$$

$$= \Theta_0 \sum_{\kappa=0}^{\infty} (-1)^\kappa (c^\beta \mathfrak{p}^{-\beta})^\kappa \frac{1}{2\pi i} \int_{\mathfrak{L}} \mathbb{K}(\xi, x)(-\wp^\beta)^{-\xi} \frac{\Gamma(\alpha - \beta\xi)}{\mathfrak{p}^{\alpha-\beta\xi}} d\xi.$$

Finally, taking the inverse Laplace transform on both sides of the trailing equation, we get the desired result (26). □

Theorem 2. *If* $x > 0, \alpha > 0, \beta > 0, c > 0, \wp > 0, E_\imath > 0 (\imath = 1, \cdots, p)$, *and* $F_\imath > 0 (\imath = 1, \cdots, q)$, *then the following arbitrary-order kinetic equation:*

$$\Theta(w) - \Theta_0 w^{\alpha-1} {}^{(\gamma)}I^{m,n}_{p_\ell,q_\ell,r}\left[-\wp^\beta w^\beta \left| \begin{matrix} (e_1, E_1, x), (e_\imath, E_\imath)_{2,n}, (e_{\imath\ell}, E_{\imath\ell})_{n+1,p_\ell} \\ (f_\imath, F_\imath)_{1,m}, (f_{\imath\ell}, F_{\imath\ell})_{m+1,q_\ell} \end{matrix} \right.\right] = -c^\beta {}_0D_w^{-\beta}\Theta(w), \quad (27)$$

has a solution of the form:

$$\Theta(w) = \Theta_0 w^{\alpha-1} \sum_{\kappa=0}^{\infty} (-c^\beta w^\beta)^\kappa {}^{(\gamma)}I^{m,n+1}_{p_\ell+1,q_\ell+1,r}\left[-\wp^\beta w^\beta \left| \begin{matrix} (e_1, E_1, x), (1-\alpha, \beta), (e_\imath, E_\imath)_{2,n}, (e_{\imath\ell}, E_{\imath\ell})_{n+1,p_\ell} \\ (f_\imath, F_\imath)_{1,m}, (1-\alpha-\beta\kappa, \beta), (f_{\imath\ell}, F_{\imath\ell})_{m+1,q_\ell} \end{matrix} \right.\right]. \quad (28)$$

Proof. The proof of Theorem 2 is given in a similar way as that of Theorem 1. □

3. Special Cases and Remarks

In this part, we record certain interesting corollaries of the main results (Theorems 1 and 2):

Corollary 1. *If $\alpha > 0, \beta > 0, c > 0, \wp > 0, E_\imath > 0(\imath = 1, \cdots, p)$, and $F_\imath > 0(\imath = 1, \cdots, q)$, then the following arbitrary-order kinetic equation:*

$$\Theta(w) - \Theta_0 w^{\alpha-1} I^{m,n}_{p_\ell,q_\ell,r}\left[-\wp^\beta w^\beta \,\middle|\, \begin{matrix} (e_\imath, E_\imath)_{1,n}, (e_{\imath\ell}, E_{\imath\ell})_{n+1,p_\ell} \\ (f_\imath, F_\imath)_{1,m}, (f_{\imath\ell}, F_{\imath\ell})_{m+1,q_\ell} \end{matrix}\right] = -c^\beta {}_0D_w^{-\beta}\Theta(w), \tag{29}$$

has a solution of the form:

$$\Theta(w) = \Theta_0 w^{\alpha-1} \sum_{\kappa=0}^{\infty} (-c^\beta w^\beta)^\kappa I^{m,n+1}_{p_\ell+1,q_\ell+1,r}\left[-\wp^\beta w^\beta \,\middle|\, \begin{matrix} (1-\alpha, \beta), (e_\imath, E_\imath)_{1,n}, (e_{\imath\ell}, E_{\imath\ell})_{n+1,p_\ell} \\ (f_\imath, F_\imath)_{1,m}, (1-\alpha-\beta\kappa, \beta), (f_{\imath\ell}, F_{\imath\ell})_{m+1,q_\ell} \end{matrix}\right]. \tag{30}$$

Proof. Taking $x = 0$ in the result (25), we get the desired result. □

Corollary 2. *If $x > 0, \alpha > 0, \beta > 0, c > 0, \wp > 0, E_\imath > 0(\imath = 1, \cdots, p)$, and $F_\imath > 0(\imath = 1, \cdots, q)$, then the following arbitrary-order kinetic equation:*

$$\Theta(w) - \Theta_0 w^{\alpha-1} \Gamma^{m,n}_{p,q}\left[-\wp^\beta w^\beta \,\middle|\, \begin{matrix} (e_1, E_1, x), (e_\imath, E_\imath)_{2,p} \\ (f_\imath, F_\imath)_{1,q} \end{matrix}\right] = -c^\beta {}_0D_w^{-\beta}\Theta(w), \tag{31}$$

has a solution of the form:

$$\Theta(w) = \Theta_0 w^{\alpha-1} \sum_{\kappa=0}^{\infty} (-c^\beta w^\beta)^\kappa \Gamma^{m,n+1}_{p+1,q+1}\left[-\wp^\beta w^\beta \,\middle|\, \begin{matrix} (e_1, E_1, x), (1-\alpha, \beta), (e_\imath, E_\imath)_{2,p} \\ (f_\imath, F_\imath)_{1,q}, (1-\alpha-\beta\kappa, \beta) \end{matrix}\right]. \tag{32}$$

Proof. Again, setting $r = 1$ in Theorem 1, we achieve the desired result (32). □

Corollary 3. *If $x > 0, \alpha > 0, \beta > 0, c > 0, \wp > 0, E_\imath > 0(\imath = 1, \cdots, p)$, and $F_\imath > 0(\imath = 1, \cdots, q)$, then the following arbitrary-order kinetic equation:*

$$\Theta(w) - \Theta_0 w^{\alpha-1} \gamma^{m,n}_{p,q}\left[-\wp^\beta w^\beta \,\middle|\, \begin{matrix} (e_1, E_1, x), (e_\imath, E_\imath)_{2,p} \\ (f_\imath, F_\imath)_{1,q} \end{matrix}\right] = -c^\beta {}_0D_w^{-\beta}\Theta(w), \tag{33}$$

has a solution of the form:

$$\Theta(w) = \Theta_0 w^{\alpha-1} \sum_{\kappa=0}^{\infty} (-c^\beta w^\beta)^\kappa \gamma^{m,n+1}_{p+1,q+1}\left[-\wp^\beta w^\beta \,\middle|\, \begin{matrix} (e_1, E_1, x), (1-\alpha, \beta), (e_\imath, E_\imath)_{2,p} \\ (f_\imath, F_\imath)_{1,q}, (1-\alpha-\beta\kappa, \beta) \end{matrix}\right]. \tag{34}$$

Proof. Setting $r = 1$ in Theorem 2, we arrive at the desired result (34). □

Corollary 4. *If $x > 0, \alpha > 0, \beta > 0, c > 0, \wp > 0, E_\imath > 0(\imath = 1, \cdots, p)$, and $F_\imath > 0(\imath = 1, \cdots, q)$, then the following arbitrary-order kinetic equation:*

$$\Theta(w) - \Theta_0 w^{\alpha-1} {}_p\Psi_q^{(\Gamma)}\left[\wp^\beta w^\beta \,\middle|\, \begin{matrix} (e_1, E_1, x), (e_\imath, E_\imath)_{2,p} \\ (f_\imath, F_\imath)_{1,q} \end{matrix}\right] = -c^\beta {}_0D_w^{-\beta}\Theta(w), \tag{35}$$

has a solution of the form:

$$\Theta(w)=\Theta_0 w^{\alpha-1}\sum_{\kappa=0}^{\infty}(-c^{\beta}w^{\beta})^{\kappa}\,{}_{p+1}\Psi_{q+1}^{(\Gamma)}\left[\wp^{\beta}w^{\beta}\,\middle|\,\begin{matrix}(e_1,E_1,x),(1-\alpha,\beta),(e_\iota,E_\iota)_{2,p}\\ (f_\iota,F_\iota)_{1,q},(1-\alpha-\beta\kappa,\beta)\end{matrix}\right]. \tag{36}$$

Proof. Taking the suitable parameter in Equation (31), we get the desired result. □

Corollary 5. *If $x>0,\alpha>0,\beta>0,c>0,\wp>0,E_\iota>0(\iota=1,\cdots,p)$, and $F_\iota>0(\iota=1,\cdots,q)$, then the following arbitrary-order kinetic equation:*

$$\Theta(w)-\Theta_0 w^{\alpha-1}\,{}_p\Psi_q^{(\gamma)}\left[\wp^{\beta}w^{\beta}\,\middle|\,\begin{matrix}(e_1,E_1,x),(e_\iota,E_\iota)_{2,p}\\ (f_\iota,F_\iota)_{1,q}\end{matrix}\right]=-c^{\beta}\,{}_0D_w^{-\beta}\Theta(w), \tag{37}$$

has a solution of the form:

$$\Theta(w)=\Theta_0 w^{\alpha-1}\sum_{\kappa=0}^{\infty}(-c^{\beta}w^{\beta})^{\kappa}\,{}_{p+1}\Psi_{q+1}^{(\gamma)}\left[\wp^{\beta}w^{\beta}\,\middle|\,\begin{matrix}(e_1,E_1,x),(1-\alpha,\beta),(e_\iota,E_\iota)_{2,p}\\ (f_\iota,F_\iota)_{1,q},(1-\alpha-\beta\kappa,\beta)\end{matrix}\right]. \tag{38}$$

Proof. Taking the suitable parameter in Equation (33), we get the desired result. □

Corollary 6. *If $\alpha>0,\beta>0,c>0,\wp>0,E_\iota>0(\iota=1,\cdots,p)$, and $F_\iota>0(\iota=1,\cdots,q)$, then the following arbitrary-order kinetic equation:*

$$\Theta(w)-\Theta_0 w^{\alpha-1}H_{p,q}^{m,n}\left[-\wp^{\beta}w^{\beta}\,\middle|\,\begin{matrix}(e_\iota,E_\iota)_{1,p}\\ (f_\iota,F_\iota)_{1,q}\end{matrix}\right]=-c^{\beta}\,{}_0D_w^{-\beta}\Theta(w), \tag{39}$$

has a solution of the form:

$$\Theta(w)=\Theta_0 w^{\alpha-1}\sum_{\kappa=0}^{\infty}(-c^{\beta}w^{\beta})^{\kappa}H_{p+1,q+1}^{m,n+1}\left[-\wp^{\beta}w^{\beta}\,\middle|\,\begin{matrix}(1-\alpha,\beta),(e_\iota,E_\iota)_{1,p}\\ (f_\iota,F_\iota)_{1,q},(1-\alpha-\beta\kappa,\beta)\end{matrix}\right]. \tag{40}$$

Proof. Again, taking $x=0$ in (31), we achieve the required result. □

Corollary 7. *If $\alpha>0,\beta>0,c>0,\wp>0,E_\iota>0(\iota=1,\cdots,p)$, and $F_\iota>0(\iota=1,\cdots,q)$, then the following fractional kinetic equation:*

$$\Theta(w)-\Theta_0 w^{\alpha-1}\,{}_p\Psi_q\left[\wp^{\beta}w^{\beta}\,\middle|\,\begin{matrix}(e_\iota,E_\iota)_{1,p}\\ (f_\iota,F_\iota)_{1,q}\end{matrix}\right]=-c^{\beta}\,{}_0D_w^{-\beta}\Theta(w), \tag{41}$$

has a solution of the form:

$$\Theta(w)=\Theta_0 w^{\alpha-1}\sum_{\kappa=0}^{\infty}(-c^{\beta}w^{\beta})^{\kappa}\,{}_{p+1}\Psi_{q+1}\left[\wp^{\beta}w^{\beta}\,\middle|\,\begin{matrix}(1-\alpha,\beta),(e_\iota,E_\iota)_{1,p}\\ (f_\iota,F_\iota)_{1,q},(1-\alpha-\beta\kappa,\beta)\end{matrix}\right]. \tag{42}$$

Proof. Again, taking $x=0$ in (35) and (37), we arrive at the required result. □

Corollary 8. *If $x > 0, \alpha > 0, \beta > 0, c > 0, \wp > 0$, then the following arbitrary-order kinetic equation:*

$$\Theta(w) - \Theta_0 w^{\alpha-1}{}_p\Gamma_q\left[\wp^\beta w^\beta \left| \begin{matrix} (e_1,x), e_2, \cdots, e_p \\ \\ f_1, \cdots, f_q \end{matrix} \right.\right] = -c^\beta{}_0D_w^{-\beta}\Theta(w), \tag{43}$$

has a solution of the form:

$$\Theta(w) = \Theta_0 w^{\alpha-1}\sum_{\kappa=0}^{\infty}(-c^\beta w^\beta)^\kappa \Gamma^{1,p+1}_{p+1,q+2}\left[\wp^\beta w^\beta \left| \begin{matrix} (1-e_1,1,x), (\alpha,\beta), (1-e_\iota,1)_{2,p} \\ \\ (0,1), (1-f_\iota,1)_{1,q}, (\alpha+\beta\kappa,\beta) \end{matrix} \right.\right]. \tag{44}$$

Proof. Again, setting $E_\iota = F_k = 1 (\iota = 1, \cdots, p; k = 1, \cdots, q)$ in Equation (31), we arrive at the desired result (44). □

Corollary 9. *If $x > 0, \alpha > 0, \beta > 0, c > 0, \wp > 0$, then the following arbitrary-order kinetic expression:*

$$\Theta(w) - \Theta_0 w^{\alpha-1}{}_p\gamma_q\left[\wp^\beta w^\beta \left| \begin{matrix} (e_1,x), e_2, \cdots, e_p \\ \\ f_1, \cdots, f_q \end{matrix} \right.\right] = -c^\beta{}_0D_w^{-\beta}\Theta(w), \tag{45}$$

has a solution of the form:

$$\Theta(w) = \Theta_0 w^{\alpha-1}\sum_{\kappa=0}^{\infty}(-c^\beta w^\beta)^\kappa \gamma^{1,p+1}_{p+1,q+2}\left[\wp^\beta w^\beta \left| \begin{matrix} (1-e_1,1,x), (\alpha,\beta), (1-e_\iota,1)_{2,p} \\ \\ (0,1), (1-f_\iota,1)_{1,q}, (\alpha+\beta\kappa,\beta) \end{matrix} \right.\right]. \tag{46}$$

Proof. Again, setting $E_\iota = F_k = 1 (\iota = 1, \cdots, p; k = 1, \cdots, q)$ in Equation (33), we arrive at the desired result (46). □

Corollary 10. *If $\alpha > 0, \beta > 0, c > 0, \wp > 0$, then the following arbitrary-order kinetic expression:*

$$\Theta(w) - \Theta_0 w^{\alpha-1}{}_pF_q\left[\wp^\beta w^\beta \left| \begin{matrix} e_1, \cdots, e_p \\ \\ f_1, \cdots, f_q \end{matrix} \right.\right] = -c^\beta{}_0D_w^{-\beta}\Theta(w), \tag{47}$$

has a solution of the form:

$$\Theta(w) = \Theta_0 w^{\alpha-1}\sum_{\kappa=0}^{\infty}(-c^\beta w^\beta)^\kappa H^{1,p+1}_{p+1,q+2}\left[\wp^\beta w^\beta \left| \begin{matrix} (1-e_1,1), (\alpha,\beta), (1-e_\iota,1)_{2,p} \\ \\ (0,1), (1-f_\iota,1)_{1,q}, (\alpha+\beta\kappa,\beta) \end{matrix} \right.\right]. \tag{48}$$

Proof. Again, setting $x = 0$ in Equation (43), we arrive at the desired result (48). □

Remark 1. *If Fox's H-function reduces to generalized M-series ${}_p\overset{\alpha,\beta}{M}_q(a_1, \cdots, a_p; b_1, \cdots, b_q; z)$ in Equation (39), then the result is that recorded by Chaurasia and Kumar ([35], p. 777, Equation (14)).*

Remark 2. *If the Fox–Wright function ${}_p\Psi_q(z)$ reduces to the Mittag–Leffler function $E_{\alpha,\beta}(z)$ in Equation (41), then the result is that recorded by Saxena et al. ([15], Equation (21)).*

Remark 3. *If the incomplete H-function reduces to the Bessel function of the first kind $J_\nu(z)$ in (31), then the result is that recorded by Habenom et al. [12].*

4. Numerical Results and Discussion

In this section, we simulate the numerical results for FKE (25) at different values of various parameters presented in the form of Figures 1 and 2 by using Maple. We can see from Figures 1 and 2 that the value of Θ decreases with time w. It is also noticed from Figures 1 and 2 that as the value of β increases, the corresponding value of Θ initially enhances, but after some time, it depicts the opposite nature.

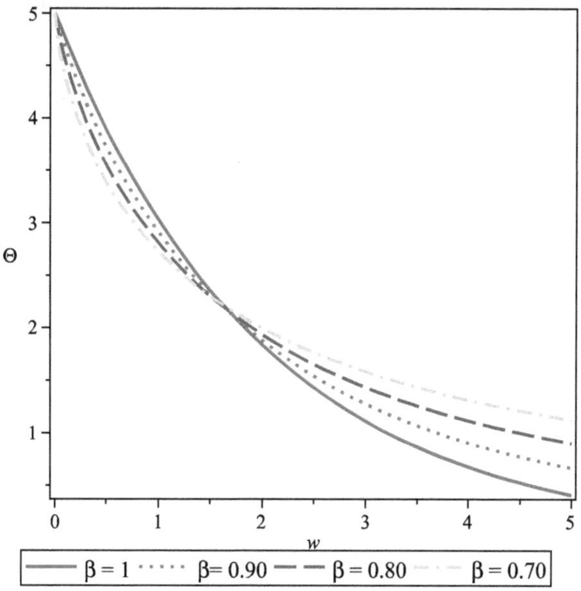

Figure 1. Plots of solution Θ for the fractional kinetic equation (FKE) (25) when $\Theta_0 = 5, \wp = 0$, and $c = 0.5$.

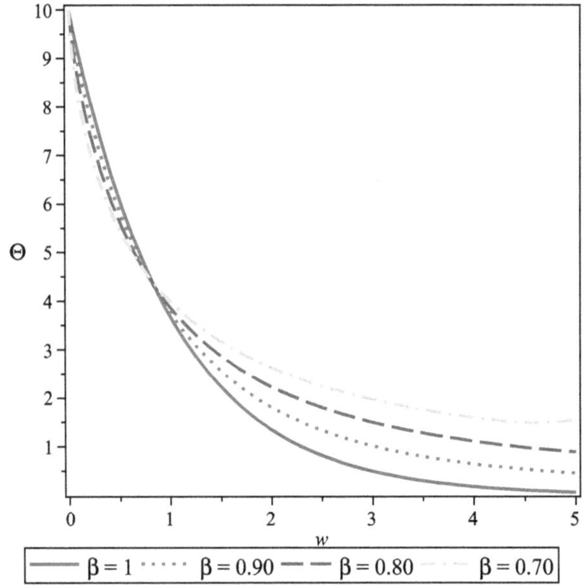

Figure 2. Plots of solution Θ for FKE (25) when $\Theta_0 = 10$, $\wp = 0$, and $c = 1$.

5. Conclusions

In this work, we introduced generalized FKEs of the FKE associated with the incomplete I-functions and found their solutions in terms of incomplete I-functions. The novelty and importance of the present work were that we suggested a novel computable extension of FKEs in terms of incomplete I-functions and presented some numerical results in graphical form, which were very useful to study reaction rate. The FKEs could be employed to determine the particle reaction rate and interpret the statistical mechanics pertaining to the particle distribution function. We also derived some special cases by assigning particular values to the parameters of incomplete I-functions and also provided some known and important results. The outcomes of the present study are very useful in astrophysics and space science.

Author Contributions: Conceptualization, M.K.B. and D.K.; methodology, M.K.B. and J.S.; software, M.K.B. and D.K.; validation, D.K., P.H., and J.S.; formal analysis, P.H. and J.S.; investigation, M.K.B. and D.K.; resources, M.K.B.; data curation, D.K.; writing, original draft preparation, M.K.B. and J.S.; writing, review and editing, P.H. and J.S.; visualization, D.K.; supervision, D.K. and J.S.; project administration, M.K.B.; funding acquisition, M.K.B. All authors read and agreed to the published version of the manuscript.

Funding: The present investigation was supported, in part, by the TEQIP-III under CRS Grant 1-5730065311.

Acknowledgments: The authors would like to express their deep-felt thanks for the reviewers' valuable comments to improve this paper as it stands.

Conflicts of Interest: The authors declare no conflict of interest.

References

1. Miller, K. S.; Ross, B. *An Introduction to the Fractional Calculus and Fractional Differential Equations*; John Wiley & Sons, INC.: New York, NY, USA, 1993.
2. Oldham, K.; Spanier, J. *Fractional Calculus: Theory and Applications of Differentiation and Integration of Arbitrary Order*; Academic Press: New York, NY, USA, 1974.

3. Kilbas, A.A.; Srivastava, H.M.; Trujillo, J.J. *Theory and Applications of Fractional Differential Equations*; North-Holland Mathematical Studies; Elsevier (North-Holland) Science Publishers: Amsterdam, The Netherlands; London, UK; New York, NY, USA, 2006; Volume 204.
4. Podlubny, I. *Fractional Differential Equations*; Academic Press: San Diego, CA, USA, 1999.
5. Srivastava, H.M.; Saxena, R.K. Operators of Fractional Integration and Their Applications. *Appl. Math. Comput.* **2001**, *118*, 1–52. [CrossRef]
6. Haubold, H.J.; Mathai, A.M. The fractional kinetic equation and thermonuclear functions. *Astrophys. Space Sci.* **2000**, *273*, 53–63. [CrossRef]
7. Saichev, A.I.; Zaslavsky, G.M. Fractional kinetic equations: Solutions and applications. *Chaos* **1997**, *7*, 753–764. [CrossRef] [PubMed]
8. Saxena, R.K.; Mathai, A.M.; Haubold, H.J. On generalized fractional kinetic equations. *Physics A* **2004**, *344*, 657–664. [CrossRef]
9. Saxena, R.K.; Kalla, S.L. On the solutions of certain fractional kinetic equations. *Appl. Math. Comput.* **2008**, *199*, 504–511. [CrossRef]
10. Chaurasia, V.B.L.; Pandey, S.C. On the new computable solution of the generalized fractional kinetic equations involving the generalized function for the fractional calculus and related functions. *Astrophys. Space Sci.* **2008**, *317*, 213–219. [CrossRef]
11. Goswami, A.; Singh, J.; Kumar, D.; Sushila. An efficient analytical approach for fractional equal width equations describing hydro-magnetic waves in cold plasma. *Physics A* **2019**, *524*, 563–575. [CrossRef]
12. Habenom, H.; Suthar, D.L.; Gebeyehu, M. Application of Laplace Transform on Fractional Kinetic Equation Pertaining to the Generalized Galué Type Struve Function. *Adv. Math. Phys.* **2019**, *2019*, 1–8. [CrossRef]
13. Kumar, D.; Singh, J.; Tanwar, K.; Baleanu, D. A new fractional exothermic reactions model having constant heat source in porous media with power, exponential and Mittag-Leffler Laws. *Int. J. Heat Mass Transf.* **2019**, *138*, 1222–1227. [CrossRef]
14. Kumar, D.; Singh, J.; Qurashi, M.A.; Baleanu, D. A new fractional SIRS-SI malaria disease model with application of vaccines, anti-malarial drugs, and spraying. *Adv. Differ. Equ.* **2019**, *2019*, 278. [CrossRef]
15. Saxena, R.K.; Mathai, A.M.; Haubold, H.J. On Fractional Kinetic Equations. *Astrophys. Space Sci.* **2002**, *282*, 281–287. [CrossRef]
16. Yavuz, M.; Özdemir, N. Numerical inverse Laplace homotopy technique for fractional heat equations. *Therm. Sci.* **2018**, *22*, 185–194. [CrossRef]
17. Yavuz, M.; Özdemir, N. European vanilla option pricing model of fractional order without singular kernel. *Fractal Fract.* **2018**, *2*, 3. [CrossRef]
18. Abramowitz, M.; Stegun, I.A. *Handbook of Mathematical Functions with Formulas*; Graphs; and Mathematical Tables, Applied Mathematics Series; National Bureau of Standards: Washington, DC, USA, 1964; Dover Publications: New York, NY, USA, 1965; Volume 55.
19. Andrews, L.C. *Special Functions for Engineers and Applied Mathematicians*; Macmillan Company: New York, NY, USA, 1985.
20. Bansal, M.K.; Kumar, D.; Jain, R. Interrelationships Between Marichev–Saigo–Maeda Fractional Integral Operators, the Laplace Transform and the $\bar{H}$-Function. *Int. J. Appl. Comput. Math* **2019**, *5*, 103. [CrossRef]
21. Bansal, M.K.; Jolly, N.; Jain, R.; Kumar, D. An integral operator involving generalized Mittag-Leffler function and associated fractional calculus results. *J. Anal.* **2019**, *27*, 727–740. [CrossRef]
22. Bansal, M.K.; Kumar, D.; Jain, R. A Study of Marichev-Saigo-Maeda Fractional Integral Operators Associated with S-Generalized Gauss Hypergeometric Function. *Kyungpook Math. J.* **2019**, *59*, 433–443.
23. Goswami, A.; Singh, J.; Kumar, D.; Gupta, S.; Sushila. An efficient analytical technique for fractional partial differential equations occurring in ion acoustic waves in plasma. *J. Ocean Eng. Sci.* **2019**, *4*, 85–99. [CrossRef]
24. Kumar, D.; Singh, J.; Baleanu, D. On the analysis of vibration equation involving a fractional derivative with Mittag-Leffler law. *Math. Methods Appl. Sci.* **2020**, *43*, 443–457. [CrossRef]
25. Kumar, D.; Singh, J.; Purohit, S.D.; Swroop, R. A hybrid analytical algorithm for nonlinear fractional wave-like equations. *Math. Model. Nat. Phenom.* **2019**, *14*, 304. [CrossRef]
26. Singh, J.; Kumar, D.; Baleanu, D. New aspects of fractional Biswas-Milovic model with Mittag-Leffler law. *Math. Model. Nat. Phenom.* **2019**, *14*, 303. [CrossRef]

27. Srivastava, H.M.; Chaudhry, M.A.; Agarwal, R.P. The incomplete Pochhammer symbols and their applications to hypergeometric and related functions. *Integral Transform. Spec. Funct.* **2012**, *23*, 659–683. [CrossRef]
28. Srivastava, H.M.; Bansal, M.K.; Harjule, P. A study of fractional integral operators involving a certain generalized multi-index Mittag-Leffler function. *Math. Methods Appl. Sci.* **2018**, *41*, 6108–6121. [CrossRef]
29. Bansal, M.K.; Kumar, D. On the integral operators pertaining to a family of incomplete I-functions. *AIMS Math.* **2020**, *5*, 1247–1259. [CrossRef]
30. Saxena, V.P. Formal solution of certain new pair of dual integral equations involving H-functions. *Proc. Natl. Acad. Sci. India Sect. A* **1982**, *52*, 366–375.
31. Srivastava, H.M.; Saxena, R.K.; Parmar, R.K. Some Families of the Incomplete H-Functions and the Incomplete $\bar{H}$-Functions and Associated Integral Transforms and Operators of Fractional Calculus with Applications. *Russ. J. Math. Phys.* **2018**, *25*, 116–138. [CrossRef]
32. Bansal, M.K.; Choi, J. A Note on Pathway Fractional Integral Formulas Associated with the Incomplete $H-$Functions. *Int. J. Appl. Comput. Math.* **2019**, *5*, 133. [CrossRef]
33. Srivastava, H.M.; Gupta, K.C.; Goyal, S.P. *The H-Functions of One and Two Variables with Applications*; South Asian Publishers: New Delhi, India, 1982.
34. Sneddon, I.N. *The Use of Integral Transforms*; Tata McGrawHill: New Delhi, India, 1979.
35. Chaurasia, V.B.L.; Kumar, D. On the solutions of generalized fractional kinetic equations. *Adv. Stud. Theor. Phys.* **2010**, *4*, 773–780.

fractal and fractional

MDPI

Article

Exact Solution of Two-Dimensional Fractional Partial Differential Equations

Dumitru Baleanu [1,2] and Hassan Kamil Jassim [3,*]

1 Department of Mathematics and Computer Sciences, Faculty of Art and Sciences, Çankaya University, Ankara 06530, Turkey; dumitru@cankaya.edu.tr
2 Institute of Space Sciences, Magurele-Bucharest P.O. Box MG-23, Ro 077125 Bucharest-Magurele, Romania
3 Department of Mathematics, Faculty of Education for Pure Sciences, University of Thi-Qar, Nasiriyah 64001, Iraq
* Correspondence: hassankamil@utq.edu.iq

Received: 30 March 2020; Accepted: 6 May 2020; Published: 12 May 2020

Abstract: In this study, we examine adapting and using the Sumudu decomposition method (SDM) as a way to find approximate solutions to two-dimensional fractional partial differential equations and propose a numerical algorithm for solving fractional Riccati equation. This method is a combination of the Sumudu transform method and decomposition method. The fractional derivative is described in the Caputo sense. The results obtained show that the approach is easy to implement and accurate when applied to various fractional differential equations.

Keywords: fractional differential equations; fractional generalized biologic population; Sumudu transform; Adomian decomposition method; Caputo fractional derivative

1. Introduction

Fractional calculus has been utilized as an excellent instrument to discover the hidden aspects of various material and physical processes that deal with derivatives and integrals of arbitrary orders [1–4]. The theory of fractional differential equations translates the reality of nature excellently in a useful and systematic manner [5]. Fractional differential equations are viewed as option models to nonlinear differential equations. Varieties of them play important roles and tools, not only in mathematics, but also in physics, dynamical systems, control systems and engineering, to create the mathematical modeling of many physical phenomena. Furthermore, they are employed in social science such as food supplement, climate and economics [6]. The mathematical physics governing by nonlinear partial deferential dynamical equations have applications in physical science. The analytical solutions for these dynamical equations play an important role in many phenomena in optics; fluid mechanics; plasma physics and hydrodynamics [7–10]. In recent years, many authors have investigated partial differential equations of fractional order by various techniques such as homotopy analysis technique [11,12], variational iteration method [13–15], homotopy perturbation method [16], homotopy perturbation transform method [17], Laplace variational iteration method [18–20], reduce differential transform method [21], Laplace decomposition method [22] and other methods [23–27].

There are numerous integral transforms such as the Laplace, Sumudu, Fourier, Mellin and Elzaki to solve PDEs. Of these, the Laplace transformation and Sumudu transformation are the most widely used. The Sumudu transformation method is one of the most important transform methods introduced in the early 1990 [28]. It is a powerful tool for solving many kinds of PDEs in various fields of science and engineering. In addition, various methods are combined with the Sumudu transformation method such as the homotopy perturbation transform method [29] which is a combination of the homotopy perturbation method and the Sumudu transformation method. Another example is the homotopy analysis Sumudu transform method [30], which is a combination of the Sumudu transform method and the homotopy analysis method.

Fractional operators are non-local operators; thus, they are used successfully for describing the phenomena with memory effect. We stress on the fact than by replacing the classical derivative with respect with time by a given fractional operator we change the nature of the partial differential equation from local to a nonlocal one. In this way we can describe better processes with faster of lower velocities, depending on the value of alpha, which in the classical class we cannot do. The domain of the utilized fractional operator and the type, namely local or nonlocal, are other key factors in modeling with high accuracy some real-world phenomena which cannot be described properly by using the classical calculus models. Successful examples of changing the differential operator into the fractional ones can be fined in modeling accurately the fluid mechanics models as well as the mathematical biology models, including the top-level epidemiological models. This article considers the efficiency of fractional Sumudu decomposition method (FSDM) to solve two-dimensional differential equations. The FSDM is a graceful coupling of two powerful techniques, namely ADM and Sumudu transform algorithms and gives more refined convergent series solution.

2. Preliminaries

Some fractional calculus definitions and notation needed [2,16,29] in the course of this work are discussed in this section.

Definition 1. *A real function $\varphi(\mu)$, $\mu > 0$, is said to be in the space C_ϑ, $\vartheta \in R$ if there exists a real number q, $(q > \vartheta)$, such that $\varphi(\mu) = \mu^q \varphi_1(\mu)$, where $\varphi_1(\mu) \in C[0,\infty)$, and it is said to be in the space C_ϑ^m if $\varphi^{(m)} \in C_\vartheta$, $m \in N$.*

Definition 2. *The Riemann Liouville fractional integral operator of order $\varepsilon \geq 0$, of a function $\varphi(\mu) \in C_\vartheta$, $\vartheta \geq -1$ is defined as*

$$I^\varepsilon \varphi(\mu) = \begin{cases} \frac{1}{\Gamma(\varepsilon)} \int_0^\mu (\mu-\tau)^{\varepsilon-1} \varphi(\tau) d\tau, & \varepsilon > 0,\ \mu > 0, \\ I^0 \varphi(\mu) = \varphi(\mu), & \varepsilon = 0, \end{cases} \tag{2.1}$$

where $\Gamma(\cdot)$ is the well-known Gamma function.

Properties of the operator $I\alpha$, which we will use here, are as follows:

For $\varphi \in C_\vartheta$, $\vartheta \geq -1$, ε, $\epsilon \geq 0$,

1. $I^\varepsilon I^\epsilon \varphi(\mu) = I^{\varepsilon+\epsilon} \varphi(\mu)$.
2. $I^\varepsilon I^\epsilon \varphi(\mu) = I^\epsilon I^\varepsilon \varphi(\mu)$
3. $I^\varepsilon \mu^m = \frac{\Gamma(m+1)}{\Gamma(\varepsilon+m+1)} \mu^{\varepsilon+m}$.

Definition 3. *The fractional derivative of $\varphi(\mu)$ in the Caputo sense is defined as*

$$D^\varepsilon \varphi(\mu) = I^{m-\varepsilon} D^m \varphi(\mu) = \frac{1}{\Gamma(m-\varepsilon)} \int_0^\mu (\mu-\tau)^{m-\varepsilon-1} \varphi^{(m)}(\tau) d\tau, \tag{2.2}$$

for $m-1 < \varepsilon \leq m$, $m \in N$, $\mu > 0$, $\varphi \in C_{-1}^m$.

The following are the basic properties of the operator D^ε:

1. $D^\varepsilon D^\epsilon \varphi(\mu) = D^{\varepsilon+\epsilon} \varphi(\mu)$.
2. $D^\varepsilon \mu^m = \frac{\Gamma(1+m)}{\Gamma(1+m-\varepsilon)} \mu^{m-\varepsilon}$.
3. $D^\varepsilon I^\varepsilon \varphi(\mu) = \varphi(\mu)$.
4. $I^\varepsilon D^\varepsilon \varphi(\mu) = \varphi(\mu) - \sum_{k=0}^{m-1} \varphi^{(k)}(0) \frac{\mu^k}{k!}$.

Definition 4. *The Mittag–Leffler function* E_δ *with* $\varepsilon > 0$ *is defined as*

$$E_\varepsilon\left(z\right) = \sum_{m=0}^{\infty} \frac{z^\varepsilon}{\Gamma(m\varepsilon + 1)} \tag{2.3}$$

Definition 5. *The Sumudu transform is defined over the set of function*

$$A = \left\{\varphi(\tau) / \ \exists M,\ \omega_1, \omega_2 > 0,\ \left|\varphi(\tau)\right| < Me^{|\tau|/\omega_j},\ if\ \tau \in (-1)^j \times [0, \infty)\right\}$$

by the following formula [30,31]:

$$S[\varphi(\tau)] = \int_0^\infty e^{-\tau}\varphi(\omega\tau)d\tau,\ \omega \in (-\omega_1, \omega_2). \tag{2.4}$$

Definition 6. *The Sumudu transform of the Caputo fractional derivative is defined as* [30,31]:

$$S[D_\tau^{m\varepsilon}\varphi(\mu,\gamma,\tau)] = \omega^{-m\varepsilon}S[\varphi(\mu,\gamma,\tau] - \sum_{k=0}^{m-1} \omega^{(-m\varepsilon+k)}\varphi^{(k)}(\mu,\gamma,0),\ m-1 < m\varepsilon < m. \tag{2.5}$$

3. Fractional Sumudu Decomposition Method (FSDM)

Let us consider a general fractional nonlinear partial differential equation of the form:

$$D_\tau^\varepsilon\varphi(\mu,\gamma,\tau) + L[\varphi(\mu,\gamma,\tau)] + N[\varphi(\mu,\gamma,\tau)] = g(\mu,\gamma,\tau), \tag{3.1}$$

with $n-1 < \varepsilon \leq n$ and subject to the initial condition

$$\frac{\partial^s}{\partial\tau^s}\varphi(\mu,\gamma,0) = \varphi^{(s)}(\mu,\gamma,0) = \varphi_s(\mu,\gamma),\ s = 0,1,\ldots,\ n-1, \tag{3.2}$$

where $\varphi(\mu,\gamma,\tau)$ is an unknown function, $D_\tau^\varepsilon\varphi(\mu,\gamma,\tau)$ is the Caputo fractional derivative of the function $\varphi(\mu,\gamma,\tau)$, L is the linear differential operator, N represents the general nonlinear differential operator and $g(\mu,\gamma,\tau)$ is the source term.

Taking the ST on both sides of (3.1), we have

$$S[D_\tau^\varepsilon\varphi(\mu,\gamma,\tau)] + S[L[\varphi(\mu,\gamma,\tau)]] + S[N[\varphi(\mu,\gamma,\tau)]] = S[g(\mu,\gamma,\tau)]. \tag{3.3}$$

Using the property of the ST, we obtain

$$S[\varphi(\mu,\gamma,\tau)] = \sum_{k=0}^{n-1} \omega^\varepsilon\varphi_k(\mu,\gamma) + \omega^\varepsilon S[g(\mu,\gamma,\tau)] - \omega^\varepsilon S[L[\varphi(\mu,\gamma,\tau)] + N[\varphi(\mu,\gamma,\tau)]]. \tag{3.4}$$

Operating with the ST on both sides of (3.4) gives

$$\begin{aligned} \varphi(\mu,\gamma,\tau) = \ & S^{-1}\left(\sum_{k=0}^{n-1} \omega^\varepsilon\varphi_k(\mu,\gamma)\right) + S^{-1}(\omega^\varepsilon S[g(\mu,\gamma,\tau)]) \\ & -S^{-1}(\ \omega^\varepsilon S[L[\varphi(\mu,\gamma,\tau)] + N[\varphi(\mu,\gamma,\tau)]]). \end{aligned} \tag{3.5}$$

Now, we represent solution as an infinite series given below

$$\varphi(\mu,\gamma,\tau)=\sum_{m=0}^{\infty}\varphi_m(\mu,\gamma,\tau), \tag{3.6}$$

and the nonlinear term can be decomposed as

$$N[\varphi(\mu,\gamma,\tau)]=\sum_{m=0}^{\infty}A_m(\varphi_0,\varphi_1,\dots,\varphi_m), \tag{3.7}$$

where

$$A_m(\varphi_0,\varphi_1,\dots,\varphi_m)=\frac{1}{m!}\frac{\partial^m}{\partial\lambda^m}\left[N\left(\sum_{i=0}^{\infty}\lambda^i\varphi_i\right)\right]_{\lambda=0}.$$

Substituting (3.6) and (3.7) in (3.5), we get

$$\begin{aligned}\sum_{m=0}^{\infty}\varphi_m(\mu,\gamma,\tau)= \quad & S^{-1}\left(\sum_{k=0}^{n-1}\omega^{\varepsilon}\varphi_k(\mu,\gamma)\right)+S^{-1}(\omega^{\varepsilon}S[g(\mu,\gamma,\tau)])\\ & -S^{-1}\left(\omega^{\varepsilon}S\left[L\left[\sum_{m=0}^{\infty}\varphi_m(\mu,\gamma,\tau)\right]+\sum_{m=0}^{\infty}A_m\right]\right)\end{aligned} \tag{3.8}$$

On comparing both sides of the Equation (3.8), we get

$$\begin{aligned}\varphi_0(\mu,\gamma,\tau)&=S^{-1}\left(\sum_{k=0}^{n-1}\omega^{\varepsilon}\varphi_k(\mu,\gamma)\right)+S^{-1}(\omega^{\varepsilon}S[g(\mu,\gamma,\tau)]),\\ \varphi_1(\mu,\gamma,\tau)&=-S^{-1}(\omega^{\varepsilon}S[L[\varphi_0(\mu,\gamma,\tau)]+A_0]),\\ \varphi_2(\mu,\gamma,\tau)&=-S^{-1}(\omega^{\varepsilon}S[L[\varphi_1(\mu,\gamma,\tau)]+A_1]),\\ &\vdots\\ \varphi_m(\mu,\gamma,\tau)&=-S^{-1}(\omega^{\varepsilon}S[L[\varphi_{m-1}(\mu,\gamma,\tau)]+A_{m-1}]),\ m\geq 1.\end{aligned} \tag{3.9}$$

Finally, we approximate the analytical solution $\varphi(\mu,\gamma,\tau)$ by truncated series:

$$\varphi(\mu,\gamma,\tau)=\sum_{m=0}^{\infty}\varphi_n(\mu,\gamma,\tau). \tag{3.10}$$

4. Applications

In this section, we will implement the fractional Sumudu decomposition method for solving two dimensional fractional partial differential equations.

Example 1. *First, we consider the two-dimensional fractional partial differential equations of the form:*

$$D_{\tau}^{\varepsilon}\varphi(\mu,\gamma,\tau)=2\left(\frac{\partial^2\varphi(\mu,\gamma,\tau)}{\partial\mu^2}+\frac{\partial^2\varphi(\mu,\gamma,\tau)}{\partial\gamma^2}\right), \tag{4.1}$$

with $1<\varepsilon\leq 2$, *subject to initial condition*

$$\varphi(\mu,\gamma,0)=\sin(\mu)\sin(\gamma). \tag{4.2}$$

From (3.9) and (4.1), the successive approximations are

$$\begin{aligned}\varphi_0(\mu,\gamma,\tau)&=\varphi(\mu,\gamma,0),\\ \varphi_m(\mu,\gamma,\tau)&=S^{-1}\left(\omega^{\delta}S\left[2\left(\frac{\partial^2\varphi_{m-1}(\mu,\gamma,\tau)}{\partial\mu^2}+\frac{\partial^2\varphi_{m-1}(\mu,\gamma,\tau)}{\partial\gamma^2}\right)\right]\right).\end{aligned} \tag{4.3}$$

Then, we have

$$\begin{aligned}
\varphi_0(\mu,\gamma,\tau) &= \sin(\mu)\sin(\gamma),\\
\varphi_1(\mu,\gamma,\tau) &= \mathbf{S}^{-1}\Big(\omega^{\delta}\mathbf{S}\Big[2\Big(\tfrac{\partial^2\varphi_0(\mu,\gamma,\tau)}{\partial\mu^2}+\tfrac{\partial^2\varphi_0(\mu,\gamma,\tau)}{\partial\gamma^2}\Big)\Big]\Big)\\
&= \mathbf{S}^{-1}\big(\omega^{\delta}\mathbf{S}[-4\sin(\mu)\sin(\gamma)]\big)\\
&= -4\sin(\mu)\sin(\gamma)\mathbf{S}^{-1}(\omega^{\varepsilon})\\
&= \tfrac{-4\tau^{\varepsilon}}{\Gamma(\varepsilon+1)}\sin(\mu)\sin(\gamma).\\
\varphi_2(\mu,\gamma,\tau) &= \mathbf{S}^{-1}\Big(\omega^{\delta}\mathbf{S}\Big[2\Big(\tfrac{\partial^2\varphi_1(\mu,\gamma,\tau)}{\partial\mu^2}+\tfrac{\partial^2\varphi_1(\mu,\gamma,\tau)}{\partial\gamma^2}\Big)\Big]\Big)\\
&= \mathbf{S}^{-1}\Big(\omega^{\delta}\mathbf{S}\Big[\tfrac{16\tau^{\varepsilon}}{\Gamma(\varepsilon+1)}\sin(\mu)\sin(\gamma)\Big]\Big)\\
&= 16\sin(\mu)\sin(\gamma)\mathbf{S}^{-1}\big(\omega^{2\varepsilon}\big)\\
&= \tfrac{16\tau^{2\varepsilon}}{\Gamma(2\varepsilon+1)}\sin(\mu)\sin(\gamma).\\
\varphi_3(\mu,\gamma,\tau) &= \mathbf{S}^{-1}\Big(\omega^{\delta}\mathbf{S}\Big[2\Big(\tfrac{\partial^2\varphi_2(\mu,\gamma,\tau)}{\partial\mu^2}+\tfrac{\partial^2\varphi_2(\mu,\gamma,\tau)}{\partial\gamma^2}\Big)\Big]\Big)\\
&= \mathbf{S}^{-1}\Big(\omega^{\delta}\mathbf{S}\Big[-\tfrac{64\tau^{2\varepsilon}}{\Gamma(2\varepsilon+1)}\sin(\mu)\sin(\gamma)\Big]\Big)\\
&= -64\sin(\mu)\sin(\gamma)\mathbf{S}^{-1}\big(\omega^{3\varepsilon}\big)\\
&= \tfrac{-64\tau^{3\varepsilon}}{\Gamma(3\varepsilon+1)}\sin(\mu)\sin(\gamma).\\
&\ \ \vdots\\
\varphi_m(\mu,\gamma,\tau) &= \tfrac{(-4)^m\tau^{m\varepsilon}}{\Gamma(m\varepsilon+1)}\sin(\mu)\sin(\gamma).
\end{aligned}$$

Hence, the solution of (4.1) is given by:

$$\begin{aligned}
\varphi(\mu,\gamma,\tau) &= \sum_{m=0}^{\infty}\varphi_n(\mu,\gamma,\tau).\\
= \sum_{m=0}^{\infty}\tfrac{(-4)^m\tau^{m\varepsilon}}{\Gamma(m\varepsilon+1)}\sin(\mu)\sin(\gamma) &= \sin(\mu)\sin(\gamma)\Big(1-\tfrac{4\tau^{\varepsilon}}{\Gamma(\varepsilon+1)}+\tfrac{4^2\tau^{2\varepsilon}}{\Gamma(2\varepsilon+1)}-\tfrac{4^3\tau^{3\varepsilon}}{\Gamma(3\varepsilon+1)}+\cdots\Big)\\
&= \sin(\mu)\sin(\gamma)E_{\varepsilon}(-4\tau^{\varepsilon}).
\end{aligned} \tag{4.4}$$

If we put $\varepsilon \to 2$ *in Equation (4.4), we get the exact solution:*

$$\begin{aligned}
\varphi(\mu,\gamma,\tau) &= \sum_{m=0}^{\infty}\tfrac{(-1)^m(2\tau)^{2m}}{\Gamma(2m+1)}\sin(\mu)\sin(\gamma)\\
&= \sin(\mu)\sin(\gamma)\cos(2\tau).
\end{aligned}$$

Example 2. *we consider the fractional generalized biologic population model of the form:*

$$D_{\tau}^{\varepsilon}\varphi(\mu,\gamma,\tau) = \left(\frac{\partial^2\varphi^2(\mu,\gamma,\tau)}{\partial\mu^2}+\frac{\partial^2\varphi^2(\mu,\gamma,\tau)}{\partial\gamma^2}\right)+\varphi(\mu,\gamma,\tau)-r\varphi^2(\mu,\gamma,\tau), \tag{4.5}$$

with $0<\varepsilon\leq 1$, *subject to initial condition*

$$\varphi(\mu,\gamma,0) = e^{\frac{1}{2}\sqrt{\frac{r}{2}}(\mu+\gamma)}. \tag{4.6}$$

From (3.9) and (4.6), the successive approximations are

$$\begin{aligned}
\varphi_0(\mu,\gamma,\tau) &= \varphi(\mu,\gamma,0),\\
\varphi_m(\mu,\gamma,\tau) &= \mathbf{S}^{-1}\Big(\omega^{\delta}\mathbf{S}\Big[\Big(\tfrac{\partial^2A_{m-1}}{\partial\mu^2}+\tfrac{\partial^2A_{m-1}}{\partial\gamma^2}\Big)+\varphi_{m-1}(\mu,\gamma,\tau)-rA_{m-1}\Big]\Big),
\end{aligned} \tag{4.7}$$

where

$$\begin{aligned} A_0 &= \varphi_0^2 \\ A_1 &= 2\varphi_0\varphi_1 \\ A_2 &= 2\varphi_0\varphi_2 + \varphi_1^2 \\ A_3 &= 2\varphi_0\varphi_3 + 2\varphi_1\varphi_2 \\ &\vdots \end{aligned}$$

Then, we have

$$\begin{aligned}
\varphi_0(\mu,\gamma,\tau) &= e^{\frac{1}{2}\sqrt{\frac{r}{2}}(\mu+\gamma)}, \\
\varphi_1(\mu,\gamma,\tau) &= S^{-1}\Big(\omega^{\delta} S\Big[\Big(\frac{\partial^2 A_0}{\partial\mu^2}+\frac{\partial^2 A_0}{\partial\gamma^2}\Big)+\varphi_0(\mu,\gamma,\tau)-rA_0\Big]\Big) \\
&= S^{-1}\Big(\omega^{\delta} S\Big[e^{\frac{1}{2}\sqrt{\frac{r}{2}}(\mu+\gamma)}\Big]\Big) \\
&= e^{\frac{1}{2}\sqrt{\frac{r}{2}}(\mu+\gamma)} S^{-1}(\omega^{\varepsilon}) \\
&= \frac{\tau^{\varepsilon}}{\Gamma(\varepsilon+1)} e^{\frac{1}{2}\sqrt{\frac{r}{2}}(\mu+\gamma)}. \\
\varphi_2(\mu,\gamma,\tau) &= S^{-1}\Big(\omega^{\delta} S\Big[\Big(\frac{\partial^2 A_1}{\partial\mu^2}+\frac{\partial^2 A_1}{\partial\gamma^2}\Big)+\varphi_1(\mu,\gamma,\tau)-rA_1\Big]\Big) \\
&= S^{-1}\Big(\omega^{\delta} S\Big[\frac{\tau^{\varepsilon}}{\Gamma(\varepsilon+1)} e^{\frac{1}{2}\sqrt{\frac{r}{2}}(\mu+\gamma)}\Big]\Big) \\
&= e^{\frac{1}{2}\sqrt{\frac{r}{2}}(\mu+\gamma)} S^{-1}\Big(\omega^{2\varepsilon}\Big) \\
&= \frac{\tau^{2\varepsilon}}{\Gamma(2\varepsilon+1)} e^{\frac{1}{2}\sqrt{\frac{r}{2}}(\mu+\gamma)}. \\
\varphi_3(\mu,\gamma,\tau) &= S^{-1}\Big(\omega^{\delta} S\Big[\Big(\frac{\partial^2 A_2}{\partial\mu^2}+\frac{\partial^2 A_2}{\partial\gamma^2}\Big)+\varphi_2(\mu,\gamma,\tau)-rA_2\Big]\Big) \\
&= S^{-1}\Big(\omega^{\delta} S\Big[\frac{\tau^{2\varepsilon}}{\Gamma(2\varepsilon+1)} e^{\frac{1}{2}\sqrt{\frac{r}{2}}(\mu+\gamma)}\Big]\Big) \\
&= e^{\frac{1}{2}\sqrt{\frac{r}{2}}(\mu+\gamma)} S^{-1}\Big(\omega^{3\varepsilon}\Big) \\
&= \frac{\tau^{3\varepsilon}}{\Gamma(3\varepsilon+1)} e^{\frac{1}{2}\sqrt{\frac{r}{2}}(\mu+\gamma)}. \\
&\vdots \\
\varphi_m(\mu,\gamma,\tau) &= \frac{\tau^{m\varepsilon}}{\Gamma(m\varepsilon+1)} e^{\frac{1}{2}\sqrt{\frac{r}{2}}(\mu+\gamma)}.
\end{aligned}$$

Hence, the fractional series form of (4.5) is given by

$$\begin{aligned}
\varphi(\mu,\gamma,\tau) &= \sum_{m=0}^{\infty} \frac{\tau^{m\varepsilon}}{\Gamma(m\varepsilon+1)} e^{\frac{1}{2}\sqrt{\frac{r}{2}}(\mu+\gamma)} \\
&= e^{\frac{1}{2}\sqrt{\frac{r}{2}}(\mu+\gamma)}\Big(1+\frac{\tau^{\varepsilon}}{\Gamma(\varepsilon+1)}+\frac{\tau^{2\varepsilon}}{\Gamma(2\varepsilon+1)}+\frac{\tau^{3\varepsilon}}{\Gamma(3\varepsilon+1)}+\cdots\Big) \\
&= e^{\frac{1}{2}\sqrt{\frac{r}{2}}(\mu+\gamma)} E_{\varepsilon}(\tau^{\varepsilon}).
\end{aligned} \tag{4.8}$$

If we put $\varepsilon \to 1$ *in Equation (4.8), we get the exact solution*

$$\begin{aligned}
\varphi(\mu,\gamma,\tau) &= \sum_{m=0}^{\infty} \frac{\tau^{m}}{\Gamma(m+1)} e^{\frac{1}{2}\sqrt{\frac{r}{2}}(\mu+\gamma)} \\
&= e^{\frac{1}{2}\sqrt{\frac{r}{2}}(\mu+\gamma)+t}.
\end{aligned}$$

Example 3. *Consider the nonlinear time-fractional differential equation of the form:*

$$D_{\tau}^{\varepsilon}\varphi(\mu,\gamma,\tau) = \left(\frac{\partial^2\varphi^2(\mu,\gamma,\tau)}{\partial\mu^2}+\frac{\partial^2\varphi^2(\mu,\gamma,\tau)}{\partial\gamma^2}\right)+\varphi(\mu,\gamma,\tau), \tag{4.9}$$

with $0 < \varepsilon \leq 1$, *subject to initial condition*

$$\varphi(\mu,\gamma,0) = \sqrt{\sin(\mu)\sin h(\gamma)}. \tag{4.10}$$

From (3.9) and (4.10), the successive approximations are:

$$\begin{aligned} \varphi_0(\mu,\gamma,\tau) &= \varphi(\mu,\gamma,0), \\ \varphi_m(\mu,\gamma,\tau) &= S^{-1}\Big(\omega^\delta S\Big[\Big(\frac{\partial^2 A_{m-1}}{\partial\mu^2} + \frac{\partial^2 A_{m-1}}{\partial\gamma^2}\Big) + \varphi_{m-1}(\mu,\gamma,\tau)\Big]\Big), \end{aligned} \tag{4.11}$$

Then, we have

$$\begin{aligned} \varphi_0(\mu,\gamma,\tau) &= \sqrt{\sin(\mu)\sin h(\gamma)}, \\ \varphi_1(\mu,\gamma,\tau) &= S^{-1}\Big(\omega^\delta S\Big[\Big(\frac{\partial^2 A_0}{\partial\mu^2} + \frac{\partial^2 A_0}{\partial\gamma^2}\Big) + \varphi_0(\mu,\gamma,\tau)\Big]\Big) \\ &= S^{-1}\Big(\omega^\delta S\Big[\sqrt{\sin(\mu)\sin h(\gamma)}\Big]\Big) \\ &= \sqrt{\sin(\mu)\sin h(\gamma)}S^{-1}(\omega^\varepsilon) \\ &= \frac{\tau^\varepsilon}{\Gamma(\varepsilon+1)}\sqrt{\sin(\mu)\sin h(\gamma)}. \\ \varphi_2(\mu,\gamma,\tau) &= S^{-1}\Big(\omega^\delta S\Big[\Big(\frac{\partial^2 A_1}{\partial\mu^2} + \frac{\partial^2 A_1}{\partial\gamma^2}\Big) + \varphi_1(\mu,\gamma,\tau)\Big]\Big) \\ &= S^{-1}\Big(\omega^\delta S\Big[\frac{\tau^\varepsilon}{\Gamma(\varepsilon+1)}\sqrt{\sin(\mu)\sin h(\gamma)}\Big]\Big) \\ &= \sqrt{\sin(\mu)\sin h(\gamma)}S^{-1}(\omega^{2\varepsilon}) \\ &= \frac{\tau^{2\varepsilon}}{\Gamma(2\varepsilon+1)}\sqrt{\sin(\mu)\sin h(\gamma)}. \\ \varphi_3(\mu,\gamma,\tau) &= S^{-1}\Big(\omega^\delta S\Big[\Big(\frac{\partial^2 A_2}{\partial\mu^2} + \frac{\partial^2 A_2}{\partial\gamma^2}\Big) + \varphi_2(\mu,\gamma,\tau)\Big]\Big) \\ &= S^{-1}\Big(\omega^\delta S\Big[\frac{\tau^{2\varepsilon}}{\Gamma(2\varepsilon+1)}\sqrt{\sin(\mu)\sin h(\gamma)}\Big]\Big) \\ &= \sqrt{\sin(\mu)\sin h(\gamma)}S^{-1}(\omega^{3\varepsilon}) \\ &= \frac{\tau^{3\varepsilon}}{\Gamma(3\varepsilon+1)}\sqrt{\sin(\mu)\sin h(\gamma)}. \\ &\vdots \\ \varphi_m(\mu,\gamma,\tau) &= \frac{\tau^{m\varepsilon}}{\Gamma(m\varepsilon+1)}\sqrt{\sin(\mu)\sin h(\gamma)}. \end{aligned}$$

Hence, the fractional series form of (4.5) is given by

$$\begin{aligned} \varphi(\mu,\gamma,\tau) &= \sum_{m=0}^{\infty}\frac{\tau^{m\varepsilon}}{\Gamma(m\varepsilon+1)}\sqrt{\sin(\mu)\sin h(\gamma)} \\ &= \sqrt{\sin(\mu)\sin h(\gamma)}\Big(1 + \frac{\tau^\varepsilon}{\Gamma(\varepsilon+1)} + \frac{\tau^{2\varepsilon}}{\Gamma(2\varepsilon+1)} + \frac{\tau^{3\varepsilon}}{\Gamma(3\varepsilon+1)} + \cdots\Big) \\ &= \sqrt{\sin(\mu)\sin h(\gamma)}E_\varepsilon(\tau^\varepsilon). \end{aligned} \tag{4.12}$$

If we put $\varepsilon \to 1$ *in Equation (4.12), we get the exact solution*

$$\begin{aligned} \varphi(\mu,\gamma,\tau) &= \sum_{m=0}^{\infty}\frac{\tau^{m}}{\Gamma(m+1)}\sqrt{\sin(\mu)\sin h(\gamma)} \\ &= \sqrt{\sin(\mu)\sin h(\gamma)}\, e^t. \end{aligned}$$

5. Conclusions

The coupling of the Adomian decomposition method (ADM) and the Sumudu transform method in the sense of Caputo fractional derivatives proved very effective for solving two-dimensional fractional partial differential equations. The proposed algorithm provides a solution in a series form that converges rapidly to an exact solution if it exists. From the obtained results, it is clear that the FSDM yields very accurate solutions using only a few iterates. As a result, the conclusion that comes through this work is that FSDM can be applied to other fractional partial differential equations of higher order, due to the efficiency and flexibility in the application as can be seen in the proposed examples.

Author Contributions: H.K.J. wrote some sections of the paper; D.B. prepared some other sections of the paper and analyzed. All authors have read and agreed to the published version of the manuscript.

Funding: This research received no external funding.

Acknowledgments: The authors are very grateful to the referees and the Editor for useful comments and suggestions towards the improvement of this paper.

Conflicts of Interest: The authors declare no conflict of interest.

References

1. Baleanu, D.; Jassim, H.K. A Modification Fractional Homotopy Perturbation Method for Solving Helmholtz and Coupled Helmholtz Equations on Cantor Sets. *Fractal Fract.* **2019**, *3*, 30. [CrossRef]
2. Al-Mazmumy, M. The Modified Adomian Decomposition Method for Solving Nonlinear Coupled Burger's Equations. *Nonlinear Anal. Differ. Equ.* **2015**, *3*, 111–122. [CrossRef]
3. Podlubny, I. *Fractional Differential Equations*; Academic Press: San Diego, CA, USA, 1999.
4. Baleanu, D.; Jassim, H.K.; Qurashi, M.A. Solving Helmholtz Equation with Local Fractional Operators. *Fractal Fract.* **2019**, *3*, 43. [CrossRef]
5. Baleanu, D.; Jassim, H.K.; Khan, H. A Modification Fractional Variational Iteration Method for solving Nonlinear Gas Dynamic and Coupled KdV Equations Involving Local Fractional Operators. *Therm. Sci.* **2018**, *22*, S165–S175. [CrossRef]
6. Ibrahim, R.W.; Darus, M. On a New Solution of Fractional Differential Equation Using Complex Transform in the Unit Disk. *Math. Comput. Appl.* **2014**, *19*, 152–160. [CrossRef]
7. Seadawy, A.R.; Manafian, J. New soliton solution to the longitudinal wave equation in a magneto-electro-elastic circular rod. *Results Phys.* **2018**, *8*, 1158–1167. [CrossRef]
8. Selima, E.; Seadawy, A.R.; Yao, X. The nonlinear dispersive Davey-Stewartson system for surface waves propagation in shallow water and its stability. *Eur. Phys. J. Plus* **2016**, *131*, 1–14. [CrossRef]
9. Seadawy, A.R.; El-Rashidy, K. Dispersive solitary wave solutions of Kadomtsev Petviashvili andmodified Kadomtsev-Petviashvili dynamical equations in unmagnetizeddust plasma. *Results Phys.* **2018**, *8*, 1216–1222. [CrossRef]
10. Seadawy, A.R.; Alamri, S.Z. Mathematical methods via the nonlinear two-dimensional water waves of Olver dynamical equation and its exact solitary wave solutions. *Results Phys.* **2018**, *8*, 286–291. [CrossRef]
11. Dehghan, M.; Shakeri, F. A semi-numerical technique for solving the multi-point boundary value problems and engineering applications. *Int. J. Numer. Methods Heat Fluid Flow* **2011**, *21*, 794–809. [CrossRef]
12. Singh, J.; Kumar, D.; Swroop, R. Numerical solution of time- and space-fractional coupled Burger's equations via homotopy algorithm. *Alex. Eng. J.* **2016**, *55*, 1753–1763. [CrossRef]
13. Jassim, H.K.; Shahab, W.A. Fractional variational iteration method to solve one dimensional second order hyperbolic telegraph equations. *J. Phys. Conf. Ser.* **2018**, *1032*, 012015. [CrossRef]
14. Xu, S.; Ling, X.; Zhao, Y.; Jassim, H.K. A Novel Schedule for Solving the Two-Dimensional Diffusion in Fractal Heat Transfer. *Therm. Sci.* **2015**, *19*, S99–S103. [CrossRef]
15. Jafari, H.; Jassim, H.K.; Tchier, F.; Baleanu, D. On the Approximate Solutions of Local Fractional Differential Equations with Local Fractional Operator. *Entropy* **2016**, *18*, 150. [CrossRef]
16. Yildirim, A.; Kelleci, A. Homotopy perturbation method for numerical solutions of coupled Burgers equations with time-space fractional derivatives. *Int. J. Numer. Methods Heat Fluid Flow* **2010**, *20*, 897–909. [CrossRef]
17. Jassim, H.K. Homotopy Perturbation Algorithm Using Laplace Transform for Newell-Whitehead-Segel Equation. *Int. J. Adv. Appl. Math. Mech.* **2015**, *2*, 8–12.
18. Jassim, H.K. New Approaches for Solving Fokker Planck Equation on Cantor Sets within Local Fractional Operators. *J. Math.* **2015**, *2015*, 1–8. [CrossRef]
19. Jafari, H.; Jassim, H.K.; Al-Qurashi, M.; Baleanu, D. On the Existence and Uniqueness of Solutions for Local differential equations. *Entropy* **2016**, *18*, 420. [CrossRef]
20. Jassim, H.K. The Approximate Solutions of Three-Dimensional Diffusion and Wave Equations within Local Fractional Derivative Operator. *Abstr. Appl. Anal.* **2016**, *2016*, 1–5. [CrossRef]

21. Jassim, H.K.; Baleanu, D. A novel approach for Korteweg-de Vries equation of fractional order. *J. Appl. Comput. Mech.* **2019**, *5*, 192–198.
22. Baleanu, D.; Jassim, H.K. Approximate Solutions of the Damped Wave Equation and Dissipative Wave Equation in Fractal Strings. *Fractal Fract.* **2019**, *3*, 26. [CrossRef]
23. Abd-Elhameed, W.M.; Youssri, Y.H. A Novel Operational Matrix of Caputo Fractional Derivatives of Fibonacci Polynomials: Spectral Solutions of Fractional Differential Equations. *Entropy* **2016**, *18*, 345. [CrossRef]
24. Doha, E.H.; Abd-Elhameed, W.M.; Elkot, N.A.; Youssri, Y.H. Integral spectral Tchebyshev approach for solving space Riemann-Liouville and Riesz fractional advection-dispersion problems. *Adv. Differ. Equ.* **2017**, *284*. [CrossRef]
25. Youssri, Y.H.; Abd-Elhameed, W.M. Numerical spectral Legendre-Galerkin algorithm For Solving Time Fractional Telegraph Equation. *Rom. J. Phys.* **2018**, *63*, 1–16.
26. Hafez, R.M.; Youssri, Y.H. Jacobi collocation scheme for variable-order fractional reaction-sub diffusion equation. *Comput. Appl. Math.* **2018**, *37*, 5315–5333. [CrossRef]
27. Youssri, Y.H.; Hafez, R.M. Exponential Jacobi spectral method for hyperbolic partial differential equations. *Math. Sci.* **2019**, *13*, 347–354. [CrossRef]
28. Karbalaie, A.; Montazeri, M.M.; Muhammed, H.H. Exact Solution of Time-Fractional Partial Differential Equations Using Sumudu Transform. *WSEAS Trans. Math.* **2014**, *13*, 142–151.
29. Kumar, D.; Singh, J.; Baskonus, H.M.; Bulut, H. An effective computational approach to local fractional telegraph equations. *Nonlinear Sci. Lett. A* **2017**, *8*, 200–206.
30. Rathore, S.; Kumar, D.; Singh, J.; Gupta, S. Homotopy Analysis Sumudu Transform Method for Nonlinear Equations. *Int. J. Ind. Math.* **2018**, *4*, 1–8.
31. Jassim, H.K.; Mohammed, M.G.; Khafif, S.A. The Approximate solutions of time-fractional Burger's and coupled time-fractional Burger's equations. *Int. J. Adv. Appl. Math. Mech.* **2019**, *6*, 64–70.

fractal and fractional

MDPI

Article

Analysis of Fractional Order Chaotic Financial Model with Minimum Interest Rate Impact

Muhammad Farman [1], Ali Akgül [2,*], Dumitru Baleanu [3,4,5], Sumaiyah Imtiaz [1] and Aqeel Ahmad [1]

1 Department of Mathematics and Statistics, University of Lahore, Lahore 54590, Pakistan; farmanlink@gmail.com (M.F.); sumaiyah.imtiaz88@gmail.com (S.I.); aqeelahmad.740@gmail.com (A.A.)
2 Art and Science Faculty, Department of Mathematics, Siirt University, Siirt 56100, Turkey
3 Department of Mathematics, Cankaya University, Ankara 06530, Turkey; dumitru.baleanu@gmail.com
4 Institute of Space Sciences, R76900 Magurele-Bucharest, Romania
5 Department of Medical Research, China Medical University, Taichung 40402, Taiwan
* Correspondence: aliakgul00727@gmail.com

Received: 19 July 2020; Accepted: 14 August 2020; Published: 21 August 2020

Abstract: The main objective of this paper is to construct and test fractional order derivatives for the management and simulation of a fractional order disorderly finance system. In the developed system, we add the critical minimum interest rate d parameter in order to develop a new stable financial model. The new emerging paradigm increases the demand for innovation, which is the gateway to the knowledge economy. The derivatives are characterized in the Caputo fractional order derivative and Atangana-Baleanu derivative. We prove the existence and uniqueness of the solutions with fixed point theorem and an iterative scheme. The interest rate begins to rise according to initial conditions as investment demand and price exponent begin to fall, which shows the financial system's actual macroeconomic behavior. Specifically component of its application to the large scale and smaller scale forms, just as the utilization of specific strategies and instruments such fractal stochastic procedures and expectation.

Keywords: chaotic finance; fractional calculus; Atangana-Baleanu derivative; uniqueness of the solution; fixed point theory

1. Introduction

Different parts of the financial sector are investigated through mathematical models, this article is helpful in discussing advantages and drawbacks of mathematical models in the financial associations. Different solutions for improving mathematical models and obstructions in the application zone is also discussed. Mathematical modeling is the technique in which sensible and similar numerical expressions from vertical frameworks are made which is used in translating different issues including drawing systematic ideas. These systematic ideas are used in formulating strategy by choosing information and understanding problem [1]. Mathematical models help in different fields of science such as sociology and engineering. Mathematics have an important place in the field of finance. In the field of finance, account related theory on assessment of exercises on the money related administrators [2]. Different parts of financial market types and different scientific and numerical systems are drawn by using mathematical models [3].

Different types of genuine certified systems are derived through the device of fractional calculus [4]. We establish some writing with the help of the research work and construct the hypothesis of fractional calculus and exhibiting several utilizations. The recently presented Caputo Fabrizio fractional derivative is used to examine the partial model of an adjusted Kawahara condition by Kumar et al. [5]. The Atangana-Baleanu partial administrator is used to formulate fragmentary augmentation of a regularized long wave condition [6]. Arrangement of the fragmentary control issues including a Mittag–Leffler non-specific piece is proposed by Baleanu et al. [7]. In another work, the development of fractional analysis has been given in [8]. Fractional calculus is used by the scientist named Jajarmi for separating a hyperchaotic financial system [9]. The fractional calculus operatives including different functions have been derived effectively for mathematical modeling of various complex issues in changed areas of science and engineering, for example, liquid elements, plasma material science, astronomy, picture handling, stochastic dynamical framework, and controlled atomic combination [1,10–12]. Recently, Caputo and Fabrizio [13] derived another fractional derivative for some engineering and thermo dynamical systems, and this new derivation is better than the old style of Caputo derivative. Another fractional derivative for observing the possibility of Fisher's response dispersion condition is derived by Atangana [14]. In this article [15], by using these two approaches, we have defined a new contraction in one of the most extended abstract spaces known. In [16], we have demonstrated a novel approximate-analytical solution method, which is called the Laplace homotopy analysis method (LHAM) using the Caputo–Fabrizio fractional derivative operator. We investigated in [17] existence and uniqueness conditions of solutions of a nonlinear differential equation containing the Caputo–Fabrizio operator in Banach spaces. A solution method is coupled with a kind of integral transformation, namely the Elzaki transform, and apply it to two different nonlinear regularized long wave equations in [18]. In [19], time-fractional partial differential equations (FPDEs) involving singular and non-singular kernel are considered. For more details, see [20–22].

In this paper, we need to use fractional parameters using the Caputo and ABC derivatives method with fractional derivatives to build the model of complex nonlinear differential equations. Complex financial system models of complex actions provide a new perspective as a result of patterns and actual behavior of the financial system's internal structure.

2. Preliminaries

The fractional derivative of Liouville Caputo [13,23] is presented as

$$ {}_{t_0}^{C}D_t^{\kappa}\{g(t)\} = \frac{1}{\Gamma(1-\kappa)}\int_{t_0}^{t}\frac{d}{dt}g(\psi)(t-\psi)^{-\kappa}d\psi, \tag{1} $$

where $\Gamma(.)$ refers to the function of Gamma. Laplace transform of the above derivative is obtained as [23,24]:

$$ \mathcal{L}\{{}_0^{C}D_t^{\kappa}\{g(t)\}\}(s) = S^{\kappa}G(S) - \sum_{k=0}^{m-1} S^{\kappa-k-1}g^{(k)}(0). \tag{2} $$

Recently, Atangana and Baleanu proposed a fractional derivative with the Mittag–Leffler function as the kernel of differentiation. This kernel is non-singular and nonlocal and preserves the benefits of the above Liouville–Caputo derivative. The Atangana–Baleanu derivative has been defined as [25]:

$$ {}_{t_0}^{ABC}D_t^{\kappa}\{g(t)\} = \frac{Z(\kappa)}{1-\kappa}\int_{t_0}^{t}\frac{d}{dt}g(\psi)E_{\kappa}[-\kappa\frac{(t-\psi)^{\kappa}}{1-\kappa}]d\psi, n-1 < \kappa(t) \leq n, \tag{3} $$

where $\kappa\epsilon\Re, Z(\kappa)$ refers to the $Z(0) = Z(1) = 1$ and $E\kappa(.)$ refers to the equation Mittag–Leffler. Equation (3) Laplace is defined as follows:

$$ \mathcal{L}\{{}_0^{ABC}D_t^{\kappa}\{g(t)\}\}(s) = \frac{Z(\kappa)}{1-\kappa}\mathcal{L}[\int_{\kappa}^{t}\frac{d}{dt}g(\psi)E_{\kappa}[-\kappa\frac{(t-\psi)^{\kappa}}{1-\kappa}]d\psi](s) = \frac{Z(\kappa)}{1-\kappa}\frac{s^{\kappa}\mathcal{L}[g(t)](s) - s^{\kappa-1}g(0)}{s^{\kappa}+\frac{\kappa}{1-\kappa}} \tag{4} $$

The fractional integral associated with the Atangana–Baleanu derivative with non-local kernel is defined as

$$ {}^{AB}_{t_0}D^{\kappa}_{t}\{g(t)\} = \frac{1-\kappa}{Z(\kappa)}g(t) + \frac{\kappa}{Z(\kappa)\Gamma(\kappa)}\int_{t_0}^{t} g(\psi)(t-\psi)^{\kappa-1}d\psi, \tag{5} $$

When κ is equivalent to zero, the initial function will be retrieved. $\kappa = 1$ will be retrieved from the classical ordinary integral.

3. Liouville–Caputo Sense

The strategy is an experimental system dependent on the blend of homotopy analysis technique and Laplace's transformation with polynomial homotopy [23,26]. The primary steps of this strategy are characterized as follows:

Step 1. We should take a look at the following condition:

$$ D^{\kappa}_{t}\{g(h,\, t)\} + \Xi[h]g(h,\, t) + \wedge[h]g(h,\, t) = \eta(h,\, t), \quad t > 0, \quad h\epsilon\Re, \quad 0 < \kappa \leq 1, \tag{6} $$

where $\Xi[h]$ is a bounded linear operator in h. While the nonlinear operator $\wedge[h]$ in h is Lipschitz continuous and satisfying $| \wedge (g) - \wedge(\phi)| \leq \theta|g-\phi|$, where $\theta > 0$ and $\eta(h,t)$ is a continuous function. The boundary and initial conditions can be treated in a similar way.

Step 2. Applying the methodology proposed in [23,27], we get the following m-th order deformation equation:

$$ g_m(h,\, t) = (X_m + \hbar)g_{m-1} - \hbar(1-X_m)\sum_{i=0}^{j-1} t^i g^{(i-1)}(0) $$
$$ +\hbar\mathcal{L}^{-1}(\frac{1}{s^{\kappa}}\mathcal{L}(\Xi_{m-1}[h]g_{m-1}(h) + \sum_{k=0}^{m-1} P_k(g_0, g_1, ..., g_m) - \Psi(h,\, t))), \tag{7} $$

where the Laplace transform is implemented in Caputo sense (1) and P_k is the homotopy polynomial described by Odibat in [28].

Step 3. Regarding homotopy polynomials, the nonlinear term $\wedge[h]g(h,t)$ is extended as

$$ \wedge[g(h,\, t)] = \wedge(\sum_{k=0}^{m-1} g_m(h,\, t)) = \sum_{m=0}^{\infty} P_m g^m \tag{8} $$

Step 4. Expanding the nonlinear term in (6) as a progression of polynomials for homotopy, we can compute the diverse $g_m(h,t)$ for $m > 1$ and Equation solutions (5) can be written as

$$ g(h,\, t) = \sum_{\infty}^{m=0} g_m(h,\, t). \tag{9} $$

The classical form of the model first studied in [29] and we modify the model by adding d as critical minimum interest rate. By using this methodology, a Liouville–Caputo fractional order derivative was utilized to solve the using time-fractional funding model:

$$ {}^{C}_{0}D^{\kappa}_{t}x(t) = z(t) + x(t)y(t) - ax(t), \tag{10} $$

$$ {}^{C}_{0}D^{\kappa}_{t}y(t) = 1 - by(t) - x(t)x(t), \tag{11} $$

$$ {}^{C}_{0}D^{\kappa}_{t}z(t) = d - x(t) - cz(t), \tag{12} $$

where x, y, and z are the state variables representing interest rate, investment demand, and price index, respectively, and we add the critical minimum interest rate d parameter in [30]. The parameter a is for savings, b is to cost per investment and c is the elasticity of market demand, although the parameters are non-negative constants i.e., $a = 3$, $b = 0.1$ and $c = 1$.

From the above model (10)–(12) , we use the parameter d to modify the model, where d represents critical minimum interest rate with initial conditions $x(0) = n_1 = 0.1, y(0) = n_2 = 4, z(0) = n_3 = 0.5$.

Solution. We also implemented the Laplace transform (2) to the system's first formula on (10):

$$s^{\kappa}\overline{x}(s) - s^{\kappa-1}x(0) = \mathcal{L}\{z(t) + x(t)y(t) - ax(t)\} \tag{13}$$

The initial conditions are taken and the above equation is simplified

$$\overline{x}(s) = \frac{x(0)}{s} + \mathcal{L}\{z(t) + x(t)y(t) - ax(t)\} \tag{14}$$

With inverse Laplace transform to Equation (14), getting

$$x(t) = n_1 + \mathcal{L}^{-1}[\frac{1}{s^{\kappa}}\mathcal{L}\{z(t) + x(t)y(t) - ax(t)\}], \tag{15}$$

For the other equations shown in Equations (11) and (12), we get

$$y(t) = n_2 + \frac{t^{\kappa}}{\Gamma(\kappa+1)} - \mathcal{L}^{-1}\frac{1}{s^{\kappa}}\mathcal{L}\{by(t) + x(t)x(t)\}, \tag{16}$$

$$z(t) = n_3 + \frac{dt^{\kappa}}{\Gamma(\kappa+1)} - \mathcal{L}^{-1}\frac{1}{s^{\kappa}}\mathcal{L}\{x(t) + cz(t)\}, \tag{17}$$

$$[_{\mathfrak{j}}(\mathfrak{t};\mathfrak{p})] = \mathcal{L}[\phi_j(t;p)],\ j = 1,\ 2,\ 3 \tag{18}$$

with feature $(\mathfrak{e}) = 0$ where e is constant. Let's describe the following system as:

$$N[\phi_1(t;p)] = \mathcal{L}[\phi_1(t;p)] - n_1 + \frac{1}{s^{\kappa}}\mathcal{L}\{\phi_3 + \phi_1\phi_2 - a\phi_1\} \tag{19}$$

$$N[\phi_2(t;p)] = \mathcal{L}[\phi_2(t;p)] - n_2 - \frac{1}{s^{\kappa}}\mathcal{L}\{b\phi_2 + \phi_1\phi_1\} \tag{20}$$

$$N[\phi_3(t;p)] = \mathcal{L}[\phi_3(t;p)] - n_3 - \frac{1}{s^{\kappa}}\mathcal{L}\{\phi_1 + c\phi_3\} \tag{21}$$

The equation of so-called zero-order deformation is given by

$$(1-p)[_{\mathfrak{j}}(\mathfrak{t};\mathfrak{p}) - \mathfrak{u}_{\mathfrak{o}}(\mathfrak{t})] = p\hbar[\phi_j(t;p)], j = 1,\ 2,\ 3 \tag{22}$$

when $p = 0$ and $p = 1$, we have

$$\phi_j(t;0) = u_0(t),\ \phi_j(t;1) = u(t),\ j = 1,\ 2,\ 3 \tag{23}$$

The deformation equations of the mth-order are given

$$\mathcal{L}\{x_m(t) - P_m x_{m-1}(t)\} = \hbar S_m(\overrightarrow{x_{m-1}},\ t) \tag{24}$$

$$\mathcal{L}\{y_m(t) - P_m y_{m-1}(t)\} = \hbar S_m(\overrightarrow{y_{m-1}}, t) \tag{25}$$

$$\mathcal{L}\{z_m(t) - P_m z_{m-1}(t)\} = \hbar S_m(\overrightarrow{z_{m-1}}, t) \tag{26}$$

Transforming the inverse Laplace into Equations (24)–(26). We've got this

$$x_m(t) = P_m x_{m-1}(t) + \hbar S_m(\overrightarrow{x_{m-1}}, t) \tag{27}$$

$$y_m(t) = P_m y_{m-1}(t) + \hbar S_m(\overrightarrow{y_{m-1}}, t) \tag{28}$$

$$z_m(t) = P_m z_{m-1}(t) + \hbar S_m(\overrightarrow{z_{m-1}}, t) \tag{29}$$

where

$$S_m(\overrightarrow{x_{m-1}}, t) = \mathcal{L}[x_{m-1}(t)] - (1 - P_m)(n_1 + \frac{1}{s^{\kappa}}\mathcal{L}\{z_{m-1} + H_m - a.x_{m-1}\}) \tag{30}$$

$$S_m(\overrightarrow{y_{m-1}}, t) = \mathcal{L}[y_{m-1}(t)] - (1 - P_m)(n_2 + \frac{t^{\kappa}}{\Gamma(\kappa+1)} - \frac{1}{s^{\kappa}}\mathcal{L}\{b.y_{m-1} + K_m\}) \tag{31}$$

$$S_m(\overrightarrow{z_{m-1}}, t) = \mathcal{L}[z_{m-1}(t)] - (1 - P_m)(n_3 + \frac{dt^{\kappa}}{\Gamma(\kappa+1)} - \frac{1}{s^{\kappa}}\mathcal{L}\{x_{m-1} + c.z_{m-1}\}) \tag{32}$$

The mth-order deformation equation solution (24)–(26) is presented as:

$$x_m(t) = (P_m + \hbar)x_{m-1} - \hbar(1 - P_m)(n_1) + \hbar\mathcal{L}^{-1}\{\frac{1}{s^{\kappa}}\mathcal{L}\{z_{m-1} + H_m - a.x_{m-1}\}\} \tag{33}$$

$$y_m(t) = (P_m + \hbar)y_{m-1} - \hbar(1 - P_m)(n_2 + \frac{t^{\kappa}}{\Gamma(\kappa+1)}) - \hbar\mathcal{L}^{-1}\{\frac{1}{s^{\kappa}}\mathcal{L}\{b.y_{m-1} + K_m\}\} \tag{34}$$

$$z_m(t) = (P_m + \hbar)z_{m-1} - \hbar(1 - P_m)(n_3 + \frac{dt^{\kappa}}{\Gamma(\kappa+1)}) - \hbar\mathcal{L}^{-1}\{\frac{1}{s^{\kappa}}\mathcal{L}\{x_{m-1} + c.z_{m-1}\}\} \tag{35}$$

where

$$H_m = \frac{1}{\Gamma m + 1}[\frac{d^m}{dp^m}N[(p\phi_1(t;p))(p\phi_2(t;p))]]_{p=0'} \tag{36}$$

$$K_m = \frac{1}{\Gamma m + 1}[\frac{d^m}{dp^m}N[(p\phi_1(t;p))(p\phi_1(t;p))]]_{p=0'} \tag{37}$$

Finally, the solutions of the Equations (10)–(12) are

$$x(t) = x_0(t) + x_1(t) + x_2(t) + ... = \sum_{m=0}^{\infty} x_m(t) \tag{38}$$

$$y(t) = y_0(t) + y_1(t) + y_2(t) + ... = \sum_{m=0}^{\infty} y_m(t) \tag{39}$$

$$z(t) = z_0(t) + z_1(t) + z_2(t) + ... = \sum_{m=0}^{\infty} z_m(t) \tag{40}$$

Through combining the Laplace transform (2) and its inverse, another model (10)–(12) solution can be obtained. The iterative scheme is given through

$$x_n(t) = n_1 + \mathcal{L}^{-1}\{\frac{1}{s^{\kappa}}\mathcal{L}\{z_{n-1}(t) + x_{n-1}(t).y_{n-1}(t) - a.x_{n-1}(t)\}(s)\}(t) \tag{41}$$

$$y_n(t) = n_2 + \mathcal{L}^{-1}\{\frac{1}{s^{\kappa}}\mathcal{L}\{1 - b.y_{n-1}(t) - x_{n-1}(t).x_{n-1}(t)\}(s)\}(t) \tag{42}$$

$$z_n(t) = n_3 + \mathcal{L}^{-1}\{\frac{1}{s^{\kappa}}\mathcal{L}\{d - x_{n-1}(t) - c.z_{n-1}(t)\}(s)\}(t) \tag{43}$$

where n_1, n_2, and n_3 are the initial conditions. If n tends to infinity, it is assumed that the solution is a limit

$$x(t) = \lim_{n\to\infty} x_n(t), y(t) = \lim_{n\to\infty} y_n(t), z(t) = \lim_{n\to\infty} z_n(t)$$

Theorem 1. *Equations recursive forms (41)–(43) are stable.*

Proof. We are going to assume the following. There are five positive constants D, E, and F can be found such that for all $0 \leq t \leq T \leq \infty$,

$$\| x(t) \| < D; \ \ \| y(t) \| < E; \| z(t) \| < F. \tag{44}$$

Now, we consider a subset of $L_2((e, f)(0, T))$ defined as follows:

$$\Xi = \{\beta : (e,\ f)(0,\ T) \to \Xi, \frac{1}{\Gamma(\kappa)} \int (t-\beta)^{(\kappa-1)} v(\beta) u(\beta) d\beta < \infty\} \tag{45}$$

We have

$$\begin{aligned} \vartheta(x,\ y,\ z) &= z(t) + x(t)y(t) - ax(t) \\ &= 1 - by(t) + x(t)x(t) \\ &= d - x(t) - cz(t) \end{aligned} \tag{46}$$

Then,

$$\begin{aligned} &=< \vartheta(x,\ y,\ z) - \vartheta(x_1,\ y_1,\ z_1), (x - x_1,\ y - y_1,\ z - z_1) >, \\ < (z(t) - z_1(t)) + (x(t) - x_1(t))(y(t) - y_1(t)) - a(x(t) - x_1(t)), &(x(t) - x_1(t)) >, \\ < 1 - b(y(t) - y_1(t)) + (x(t) - x_1(t))(x(t) - x_1(t)), &(y(t) - y_1(t)) >, \\ < d - (x(t) - x_1(t)) - c(z(t) - z_1(t)), &(z(t) - z_1(t)) >, \end{aligned} \tag{47}$$

where

$$x(t) \neq x_1(t); y(t) \neq y_1(t); z(t) \neq z_1(t) \tag{48}$$

We obtain

$$< \vartheta(x,y,z) - \vartheta(x_1,y_1,z_1),(x-x_1,y-y_1,z-z_1)>,$$
$$< \{\frac{\| z(t)-z_1(t) \|}{\| x(t)-x_1(t) \|} + \| y(t)-y_1(t) \| - a\} \| x(t)-x_1(t) \|^2,$$
$$< \{\frac{1}{\| y(t)-y_1(t) \|} - b - \frac{\| x(t)-x_1(t) \|^2}{\| y(t)-y_1(t) \|}\} \| y(t)-y_1(t) \|^2,$$
$$< \{\frac{d}{\| z(t)-z_1(t) \|} + \frac{\| x(t)-x_1(t) \|}{\| z(t)-z_1(t) \|} - c\} \| z(t)-z_1(t) \|^2, \tag{49}$$

where

$$< \vartheta(x,y,z) - \vartheta(x_1,y_1,z_1),(x-x_1,y-y_1,z-z_1)>,$$
$$< A \| x(t)-x_1(t) \|^2,$$
$$< B \| y(t)-y_1(t) \|^2,$$
$$< C \| z(t)-z_1(t) \|^2, \tag{50}$$

with

$$A = \frac{\| z(t)-z_1(t) \|}{\| x(t)-x_1(t) \|} + \| y(t)-y_1(t) \| - a$$
$$B = \frac{1}{\| y(t)-y_1(t) \|} - b - \frac{\| x(t)-x_1(t) \|^2}{\| y(t)-y_1(t) \|}$$
$$C = \frac{d}{\| z(t)-z_1(t) \|} + \frac{\| x(t)-x_1(t) \|}{\| z(t)-z_1(t) \|} - c \tag{51}$$

Additionally, if we find a non-null vector (x_1, y_1, z_1) using a certain routine as above, we get

$$< A \| x(t)-x_1(t) \| \| x(t) \|$$
$$< B \| y(t)-y_1(t) \| \| y(t) \|$$
$$< C \| z(t)-z_1(t) \| \| z(t) \| \tag{52}$$

We conclude from the results of Equations (50) and (52) that the iterative method used is stable. Then, we obtain the same in [31]:

$$x(t) = \sum_{u=0}^{n-1} \delta_1^u \frac{t^u}{u!} + \frac{1}{\Gamma(\kappa)} \int_0^t (t-\psi)^{\kappa-1}[z(\psi) + x(\psi)y(\psi) - ax(\psi)]du, \tag{53}$$

$$y(t) = \sum_{u=0}^{n-1} \delta_2^u \frac{t^u}{u!} + \frac{1}{\Gamma(\kappa)} \int_0^t (t-\psi)^{\kappa-1}[1 - by(\psi) + x(\psi)x(\psi)]du, \tag{54}$$

$$z(t) = \sum_{u=0}^{n-1} \delta_3^u \frac{t^u}{u!} + \frac{1}{\Gamma(\kappa)} \int_0^t (t-\psi)^{\kappa-1}[d - x(\psi) - cz(\psi)]du, \tag{55}$$

□

4. Atangana–Baleanu–Caputo Sense

Considering the system with an ABC fractional order derivative according to the methodology mentioned in [23,26]:

$$ {}_{0}^{ABC}D_t^{\kappa} x(t) = z + xy - ax \tag{56}$$

$$ {}_{0}^{ABC}D_t^{\kappa} y(t) = 1 - by - xx \tag{57}$$

$$ {}_{0}^{ABC}D_t^{\kappa} z(t) = d - x - cz \tag{58}$$

with initial conditions $x(0) = n_1 \geq 0, y(0) = n_2 \geq 0, z(0) = n_3 \geq 0$

Solution: We apply the Laplace transformation (4) to Equation (56), we have

$$\frac{R(\kappa)}{1-\kappa} \frac{s^{\kappa}\tilde{x}(s) - s^{\kappa-1}x(0)}{s^{\kappa} + \frac{\kappa}{1-\kappa}} = \mathcal{L}\{z(t) + x(t)y(t) - ax(t)\}$$

Simplifying the above equation with taking initial conditions

$$\tilde{x}(s) = \frac{x(0)}{s} + \frac{(1-\kappa)s^{\kappa} + \kappa}{R(\kappa)s^{\kappa}} \mathcal{L}\{z(t) + x(t)y(t) + ax(t)\}, \tag{59}$$

Then, we have

$$x(t) = n_1 + \mathcal{L}^{-1}\{\frac{(1-\kappa)s^{\kappa} + \kappa}{R(\kappa)s^{\kappa}} \mathcal{L}\{z(t) + x(t)y(t) + ax(t)\}\}, \tag{60}$$

Similarly to Equations (57) and (58), we have

$$y(t) = n_2 + \frac{(1-\kappa)}{R(\kappa)s} + \frac{\kappa}{R(\kappa)s^{(\kappa)}} - \mathcal{L}^{-1}\{\frac{(1-\kappa)s^{\kappa} + \kappa}{R(\kappa)s^{\kappa}} \mathcal{L}\{by(t) + x(t)x(t)\}\}, \tag{61}$$

$$z(t) = n_3 + \frac{(1-\kappa)}{R(\kappa)s} + \frac{\kappa}{R(\kappa)s^{(\kappa)}} - \mathcal{L}^{-1}\{\frac{(1-\kappa)s^{\kappa} + \kappa}{R(\kappa)s^{\kappa}} \mathcal{L}\{x(t) + cz(t)\}\}, \tag{62}$$

Here, we select a operator that is of linear type as

$$[_{j}(t;\mathfrak{p})] = \mathcal{L}[\phi_j(t;p)],\ j = 1,\ 2,\ 3. \tag{63}$$

Next, we describe the model below:

$$N[\phi_1(t;p)] = \mathcal{L}[\phi_1(t;p)] - n_1 - \frac{(1-\kappa)s^{\kappa} + \kappa}{R(\kappa)s^{\kappa}} \mathcal{L}\{\phi_3 - \phi_1\phi_2 + a\phi_1\} \tag{64}$$

$$N[\phi_2(t;p)] = \mathcal{L}[\phi_2(t;p)] - n_2 - \frac{(1-\kappa)s^{\kappa} + \kappa}{R(\kappa)s^{\kappa}} \mathcal{L}\{b\phi_2 + \phi_1^2\} \tag{65}$$

$$N[\phi_3(t;p)] = \mathcal{L}[\phi_3(t;p)] - n_3 - \frac{(1-\kappa)s^{\kappa} + \kappa}{R(\kappa)s^{\kappa}} \frac{1}{s^{\kappa}} \mathcal{L}\{\phi_1 + c\phi_3\} \tag{66}$$

This is the so-called zeroth-order deformation is presented by:

$$(1-p)[_{j}(t;\mathfrak{p}) - u_o(t)] = p\hbar N[\phi_j(t;p)], j = 1,\ 2,\ 3 \tag{67}$$

$$\phi_j(t;0) = u_0(t),\ \phi_j(t;1) = u(t),\ j = 1,\ 2,\ 3 \tag{68}$$

The equations of the mth-order deformation are presented by

$$\mathcal{L}\{x_m(t) - P_m x_{m-1}(t)\} = \hbar S_m(x_{m-1}^{\rightarrow},\ t) \tag{69}$$

$$\mathcal{L}\{y_m(t) - P_m y_{m-1}(t)\} = \hbar S_m(y_{m-1}^{\rightarrow},\ t) \tag{70}$$

$$\mathcal{L}\{z_m(t) - P_m z_{m-1}(t)\} = \hbar S_m(z_{m-1}^{\rightarrow},\ t) \tag{71}$$

Use the inverse Laplace to transform the Equations (69)–(71), and we obtain

$$x_m(t) = P_m x_{m-1}(t) + \hbar S_m(x_{m-1}^{\rightarrow},\ t) \tag{72}$$

$$y_m(t) = P_m y_{m-1}(t) + \hbar S_m(y_{m-1}^{\rightarrow},\ t) \tag{73}$$

$$z_m(t) = P_m z_{m-1}(t) + \hbar S_m(z_{m-1}^{\rightarrow},\ t) \tag{74}$$

where

$$S_m(x_{m-1}^{\rightarrow},\ t) = \mathcal{L}[x_{m-1}(t)] - (1 - P_m)n_1 + \frac{(1-\kappa)s^\kappa + \kappa}{R(\kappa)s^\kappa}\mathcal{L}\{z_{m-1} + H_{m-1} - a x_{m-1}\} \tag{75}$$

$$S_m(y_{m-1}^{\rightarrow},\ t) = \mathcal{L}[y_{m-1}(t)] - (1 - P_m)(n_2 + \tfrac{(1-\kappa)}{R(\kappa)} + \tfrac{\kappa t^\kappa}{\Gamma(\kappa+1)}) - \tfrac{(1-\kappa)s^\kappa+\kappa}{R(\kappa)s^\kappa}\mathcal{L}\{b y_{m-1} + K_{m-1}\} \tag{76}$$

$$S_m(z_{m-1}^{\rightarrow},\ t) = \mathcal{L}[z_{m-1}(t)] - (1 - P_m)(n_3 + \tfrac{d(1-\kappa)}{R(\kappa)} + \tfrac{d\kappa t^\kappa}{\Gamma(\kappa+1)}) - \tfrac{(1-\kappa)s^\kappa+\kappa}{R(\kappa)s^\kappa}\mathcal{L}\{x_{m-1} + c z_{m-1}\} \tag{77}$$

The mth-order deformation of the system is specified as

$$x_m(t) = (P_m + \hbar)x_{m-1} - \hbar(1 - P_m)n_1 + \hbar\mathcal{L}^{-1}\{\frac{(1-\kappa)s^\kappa + \kappa}{R(\kappa)s^\kappa}\mathcal{L}[z_{m-1} + H_m - a x_{m-1}]\} \tag{78}$$

$$\begin{aligned} y_m(t) = (P_m + \hbar)y_{m-1} - \hbar(1 - P_m)(n_2 + \frac{(1-\kappa)}{R(\kappa)} + \frac{t^\kappa}{R(\kappa)\Gamma\kappa + 1}) - \\ \hbar\mathcal{L}^{-1}\{\frac{(1-\kappa)s^\kappa + \kappa}{R(\kappa)s^\kappa}\mathcal{L}[b y_{m-1} + K_m]\} \end{aligned} \tag{79}$$

$$\begin{aligned} z_m(t) = (P_m + \hbar)z_{m-1} - \hbar(1 - P_m)(n_3 + \frac{d(1-\kappa)}{R(\kappa)} + \frac{d\kappa t^\kappa}{\Gamma\kappa + 1}) \\ -\hbar\mathcal{L}^{-1}\{\frac{(1-\kappa)s^\kappa + \kappa}{R(\kappa)s^\kappa}\mathcal{L}[x_{m-1} + c z_{m-1}]\} \end{aligned} \tag{80}$$

where

$$H_m = \frac{1}{\Gamma(m+1)}[\frac{d^m}{dp^m}N[(p\phi_1(t;p))(p\phi_2(t;p))]]_{p=0'} \tag{81}$$

$$K_m = \frac{1}{\Gamma(m+1)}[\frac{d^m}{dp^m}N[(p\phi_1(t;p))(p\phi_1(t;p))]]_{p=0'} \tag{82}$$

Finally, the solutions of Equations (56)–(58) are given as

$$x(t) = \sum_{m=0}^{\infty} x_m(t),\ y(t) = \sum_{m=0}^{\infty} y_m(t), z(t) = \sum_{m=0}^{\infty} z_m(t) \tag{83}$$

Models (56)–(58) solution can be obtained with Equation (4). Systems (56)–(58) are similar to the Volterra form in the Atangana–Baleanu sense. With the iterative scheme, we get

$$x_{n+1}(t) = \frac{1-\kappa}{R(\kappa)}\{z_n(t) + x_n(t)y_n(t) - ax_n(t)\} + \\ \frac{\kappa}{R(\kappa)\Gamma(\kappa)}\int_0^t (t-\psi)^{\kappa-1}\{z_n(\psi) + x_n(\psi)y_n(\psi) - ax_n(\psi)\}d\psi, \tag{84}$$

$$y_{n+1}(t) = \frac{1-\kappa}{R(\kappa)}\{1 - by_n(t) - x_n(t)x_n(t)\} + \\ \frac{\kappa}{R(\kappa)\Gamma(\kappa)}\int_0^t (t-\psi)^{\kappa-1}\{1 - by_n(\psi) - x_n(\psi)x_n(\psi)\}d\psi, \tag{85}$$

$$z_{n+1}(t) = \frac{1-\kappa}{R(\kappa)}\{d - x_n(t) - cz_n(t)\} + \\ \frac{\kappa}{R(\kappa)\Gamma(\kappa)}\int_0^t (t-\psi)^{\kappa-1}\{d - x_n(\psi) - cz_n(\psi)\}d\psi, \tag{86}$$

Theorem 2. *We prove the existence and uniqueness of the solution using a Picard–Lindelof approach.*

Proof. The following operator is considered:

$$\begin{aligned} \Xi_1(t,\ \varsigma) &= z(t) + x(t)y(t) - ax(t) \\ \Xi_2(t,\ \varsigma) &= 1 - by(t) - x(t)x(t) \\ \Xi_3(t,\ \varsigma) &= d - x(t) - cz(t) \end{aligned} \tag{87}$$

Let

$$\Omega_1 = sup \parallel \gamma_{\epsilon,k_1}\Xi_1(t,\varsigma) \parallel; \tag{88}$$
$$\Omega_2 = sup \parallel \gamma_{\epsilon,k_2}\Xi_2(t,\varsigma) \parallel; \tag{89}$$
$$\Omega_3 = sup \parallel \gamma_{\epsilon,k_3}\Xi_3(t,\varsigma) \parallel; \tag{90}$$

where

$$\gamma_{\epsilon,k_1} = |t-a, t+a| \times [\vartheta - k_1, \vartheta + k_1] = \epsilon_1 \times k_1 \tag{91}$$

$$\gamma_{\epsilon,k_2} = |t-a, t+a| \times [\vartheta - k_2, \vartheta + k_2] = \epsilon_1 \times k_2 \tag{92}$$

$$\gamma_{\epsilon,k_3} = |t-a, t+a| \times [\vartheta - k_3, \vartheta + k_3] = \epsilon_1 \times k_3 \tag{93}$$

Considering the Picards operator, we have

$$\vartheta : \gamma(\epsilon_1, k_1, k_2, k_3) \rightarrow \gamma(\epsilon_1, k_1, k_2, k_3) \tag{94}$$

defined as follows:

$$\vartheta\Omega(t) = \Omega_0(t)_\Delta(t, \Omega(t))\frac{1-\kappa}{R(\kappa)} + \frac{\kappa}{R(\kappa)\Gamma(\kappa)}\int_0^t (t-\psi)^{\kappa-1}\Delta(\psi, \Omega(\psi))d\psi, \tag{95}$$

where

$$\Omega(t) = \{G(t),\ X(t),\ I(t)\} = \{g_1,\ g_2,\ g_3\},\ and\Delta(t,\ \Omega(t)) = \{\Xi_1(t,\ \vartheta(t)),\ \Xi_2(t,\ \vartheta(t)),\ \Xi_1(t,\ \vartheta(t))\}. \tag{96}$$

Now, we presume that all solutions are bound in a certain amount of time

$$\| \Omega(t) \|_\infty \leq max\{k_1, k_2, k_3\},$$

$$\| \Omega(t) - \Omega_0(t) \| = \| \Delta(t,\ \Omega(t))\frac{1-\kappa}{R(\kappa)} + \frac{\kappa}{R(\kappa)\Gamma(\kappa)}\int_0^t (t-\psi)^{\kappa-1}\Delta(\psi, \Omega(\psi)d\psi \| \tag{97}$$

$$\leq \frac{1-\kappa}{R(\kappa)} \| \Delta(t,\ \Omega(t)) \| + \frac{\kappa}{R(\kappa)\Gamma(\kappa)}\int_0^t (t-\psi)^{\kappa-1} \| \Delta(\psi, \Omega(\psi) \| d\psi \tag{98}$$

$$\leq \frac{1-\kappa}{R(\kappa)}X = max\{k_1, k_2, k_3\} + \frac{\kappa}{R(\kappa)}\xi\vartheta^\kappa \leq \vartheta\xi \leq k = max\{k_1, k_2, k_3\} \tag{99}$$

Here, we request that $\vartheta < \frac{k}{\xi}$ Then, we obtain

$$\| \vartheta\Omega_1 - \vartheta\Omega_2 \|_\infty = sup \|_{t\epsilon\varepsilon} |\Omega_1 - \Omega_2|, \tag{100}$$

$$\| \vartheta\Omega_1 - \vartheta\Omega_2 \| = \| \{\Delta(t,\ \Omega_1(t)) - \Delta(t,\ \Omega_2(t))\}\frac{1-\kappa}{R(\kappa)} \tag{101}$$

$$+\frac{\kappa}{R(\kappa)\Gamma(\kappa)}\int_0^t (t-\psi)^{\kappa-1}\{\Delta(\psi, \Omega_1(t)) - \Delta(\psi, \Omega_2(t))\}d\psi \|, \tag{102}$$

$$\leq \frac{1-\kappa}{R(\kappa)} \| \Delta(\psi, \Omega_1(t)) - \Delta(\psi, \Omega_2(t)) \| + \frac{\kappa}{R(\kappa)\Gamma(\kappa)}\int_0^t (t-\psi)^{\kappa-1}\{\Delta(\psi, \Omega_1(t)) - \| \Delta(\psi, \Omega_2(t))\} \| d\psi, \tag{103}$$

$$\leq \frac{1-\kappa}{R(\kappa)}\omega \| \Omega_1(t) - \Omega_2(t) \| + \frac{\kappa\omega}{R(\kappa)\Gamma(\kappa)}\int_0^t (t-\psi)^{\kappa-1} \| \Omega_1(t) - \Omega_2(t))) \| d\psi, \tag{104}$$

$$\leq \{\frac{1-\kappa}{R(\kappa)}\omega + \frac{\kappa\omega\vartheta^\kappa}{R(\kappa)\Gamma(\kappa)}\} \| \Omega_1(t) - \Omega_2(t) \| d\psi, \tag{105}$$

$$\leq \vartheta\omega \| \Omega_1(t) - \Omega_2(t) \|, \tag{106}$$

with ω less than 1. Since Ω is a contraction, we obtain $\theta\omega < 1$, so the specified ϑ operator is also a contraction. The Atangana–Baleanu fractional integral numerical approximation [27] using the Adams–Moulton rule is given by

$$\psi_t^\kappa[g(t_{n+1})] = \frac{1-\kappa}{R(\kappa)}\frac{g(t_{n+1} - g(t_n))}{2} + \frac{\kappa}{\Gamma(\kappa)}\sum_{k=0}^{\infty}[\frac{g(t_{k+1} - g(t_k))}{2}]b_k^\kappa, \tag{107}$$

where $b_k^\kappa = (k+1)^{1-\kappa} - (k)^{1-\kappa}$. Hence, it shows that existence and uniqueness of the solution for the dynamical finance system. We have the following generalized solution with the iterative method:

$$x_{(n+1)}(t) - x_{(n)}(t) = x_0^n(t) + \{\tfrac{1-\kappa}{R(\kappa)}[(\tfrac{z_{(n+1)}(t)-z_{(n)}(t)}{2}) + (\tfrac{x_{(n+1)}(t)-x_{(n)}(t)}{2}) (\tfrac{y_{(n+1)}(t)-y_{(n)}(t)}{2}) - a(\tfrac{x_{(n+1)}(t)-x_{(n)}(t)}{2})]\} + \tfrac{\kappa}{R(\kappa)}\Sigma_{k=0}^{\infty}(k+1)^d 1 - \kappa[(\tfrac{z_{(k+1)}(t)-z_{(k)}(t)}{2}) + (\tfrac{x_{(k+1)}(t)-x_{(k)}(t)}{2})(\tfrac{y_{(k+1)}(t)-y_{(k)}(t)}{2}) - a(\tfrac{x_{(k+1)}(t)-x_{(k)}(t)}{2})]$$

$$y_{(n+1)}(t) - y_{(n)}(t) = y_0^n(t) + \{\tfrac{1-\kappa}{R(\kappa)}[1 - b(\tfrac{y_{(n+1)}(t)-y_{(n)}(t)}{2}) - (\tfrac{x_{(n+1)}(t)-x_{(n)}(t)}{2}) (\tfrac{x_{(n+1)}(t)-x_{(n)}(t)}{2})]\} + \tfrac{\kappa}{R(\kappa)}\Sigma_{k=0}^{\infty}(k+1)^{1-\kappa}[1 - b(\tfrac{y_{(k+1)}(t)-y_{(k)}(t)}{2}) - (\tfrac{x_{(k+1)}(t)-x_{(k)}(t)}{2}) (\tfrac{x_{(k+1)}(t)-x_{(k)}(t)}{2})]$$

$$z_{(n+1)}(t) - z_{(n)}(t) = z_0^n(t) + \{\frac{1-\kappa}{R(\kappa)}[d - (\frac{x_{(n+1)}(t)-x_{(n)}(t)}{2}) - c(\frac{z_{(n+1)}(t)-z_{(n)}(t)}{2})]\} + \frac{\kappa}{R(\kappa)}\sum_{k=0}^{\infty}(k+1)^{1-\kappa}[d - (\frac{x_{(k+1)}(t)-x_{(k)}(t)}{2}) - c(\frac{z_{(k+1)}(t)-z_{(k)}(t)}{2})] \quad (108)$$

□

5. Numerical Results and Discussion

The ABC derivative has been used to present the theoretical solution of the fractional-order model consisting of a nonlinear system of the fractional differential equation. In this model, we represent $x(t), y(t)$ and $z(t)$ are interest rate, investment demand, and price exponent with initial conditions $x(0) = 0.1, y(0) = 4$ and $z(0) = 0.5$, while the parameter a is for savings, b is to cost per investment, and c is the commercial markets demand elasticity with $a = 3$, $b = 0.1$, and $c = 1$ are given in [30,32]. By utilizing Caputo and ABC fractional derivative, the numerical results of interest rate, investment demand, and price exponent for various fractional estimations of η are acquired. Figures 1–3 refer to the graphical solution of the finance system with the Caputo derivative of the finance system. Within this figure, we noticed that interest rate, investment demand, and the price exponent have more degree of freedom as contrasted with ordinary derivatives. From Figures 4–6, we use ABC fractional-order derivative of the financial system, we effectively have seen that interest rate, investment demand, and price exponent rates are the better estimations compared with ordinary derivatives. Figures 7–10 present the comparison of Caputo derivative and ABC derivative for the finance system. It should be observed that the behavior of the finance system is almost the same but ABC derivative presents more convenient and comfortable behavior in a system for closed-loop design. Caputo and ABC fractional derivatives are increasing or decreasing in the relationship between these variables. From Figures 1–10, remarkable responses are obtained from the developed model for compartments by taking non-integer fractional parameter values. Numerical results show that the system keeps the η chaotic motion. The interest rate begins to rise according to initial conditions as investment demand and price exponent begin to fall, which shows the financial system's actual macroeconomic behavior. It is observed here that a complex chaotic fractional system provides more appropriate and reliable results compared to time integer parameters for non-integer time-fractional parameters. In this system, we add parameter d to develop the new financial stable model which is the critical minimum interest rate. In order to observe the impact of factors on the mechanics of the fractional-order model, different numerical ways can be observed in Figures 11–13. These simulations reveal a change in the value of a critical minimum interest rate of the model. We see that decreasing the critical minimum interest rate decreases the price of the exponent and the investment demand becomes high. Due to increasing the investment demand, our economy will become stronger.

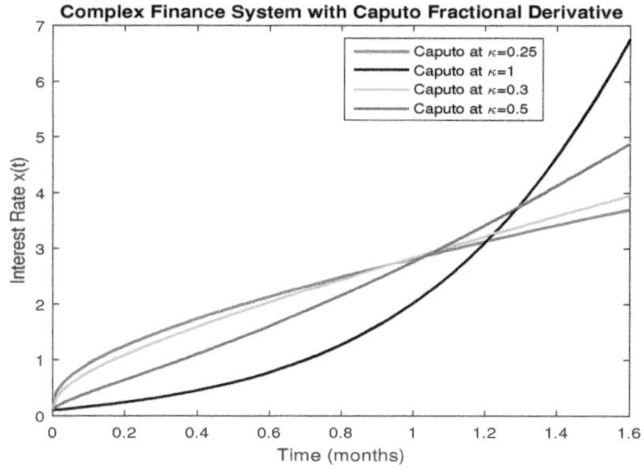

Figure 1. $x(t)$ interest rate with Caputo fractional derivative.

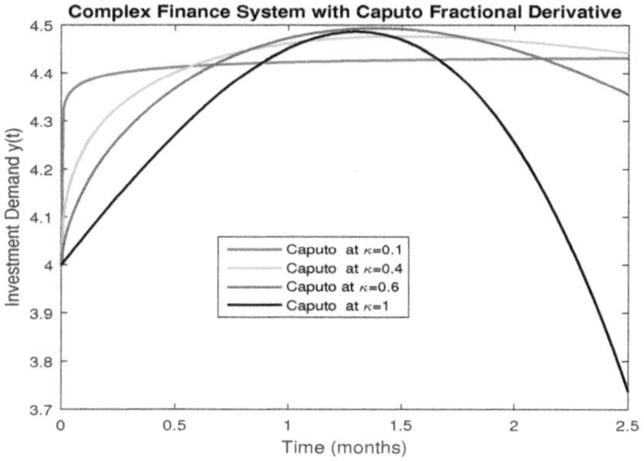

Figure 2. $y(t)$ investment demand with Caputo fractional derivative.

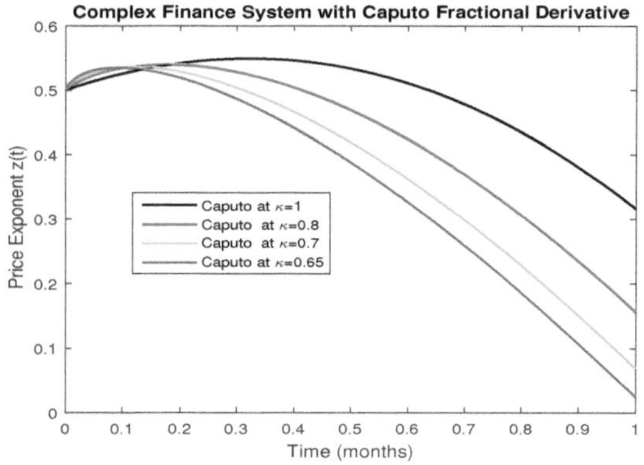

Figure 3. $z(t)$ price exponent with Caputo fractional derivative.

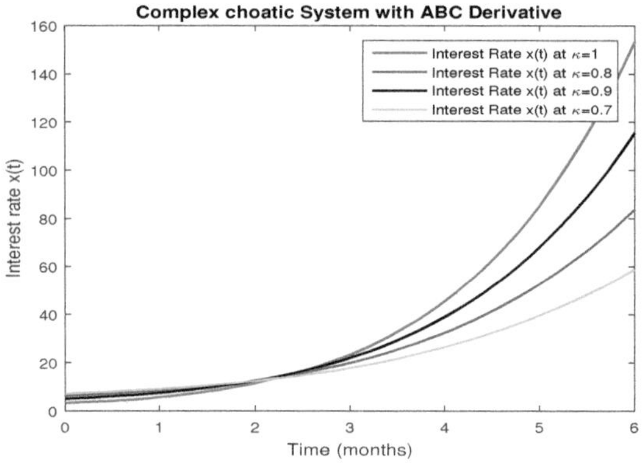

Figure 4. $x(t)$ interest rate with ABC derivative.

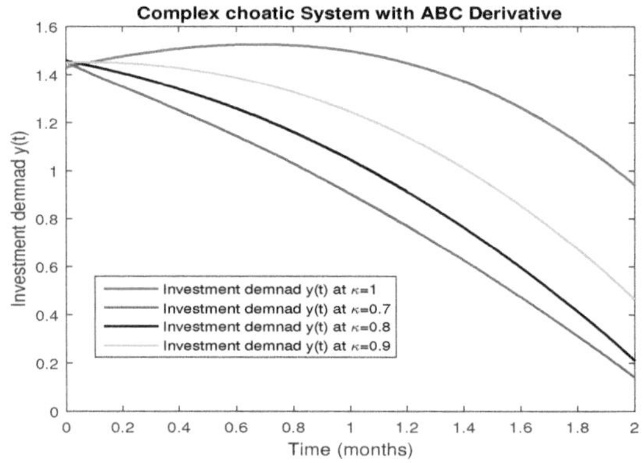

Figure 5. $y(t)$ investment demand with ABC derivative.

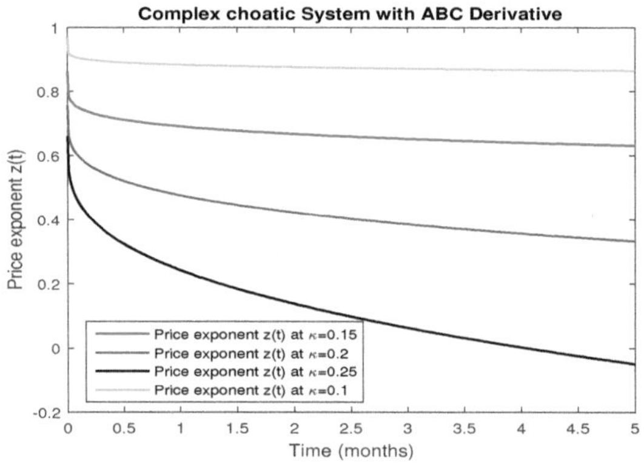

Figure 6. $z(t)$ price exponent with ABC derivative.

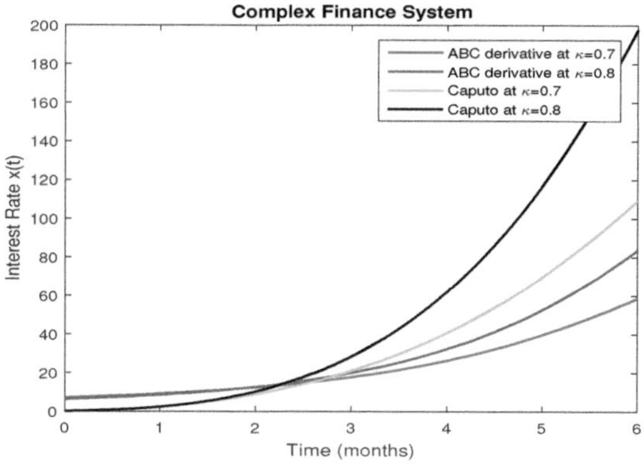

Figure 7. $x(t)$ interest rate with Caputo and ABC derivative.

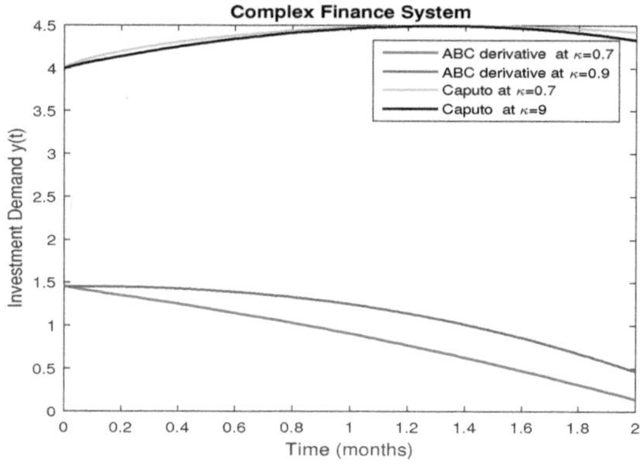

Figure 8. $y(t)$ investment demand with Caputo and ABC derivative.

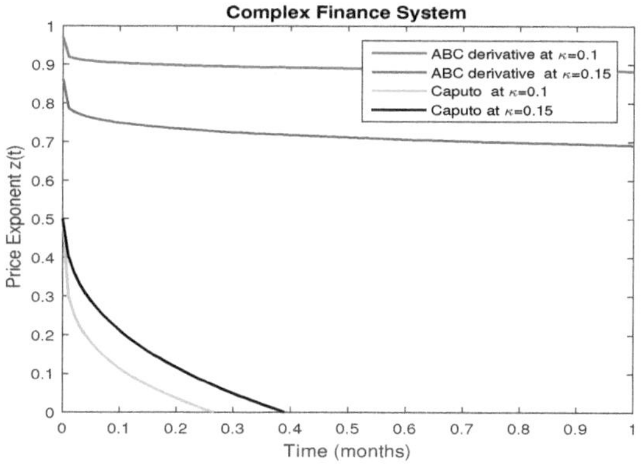

Figure 9. $z(t)$ price exponent with Caputo and ABC derivative.

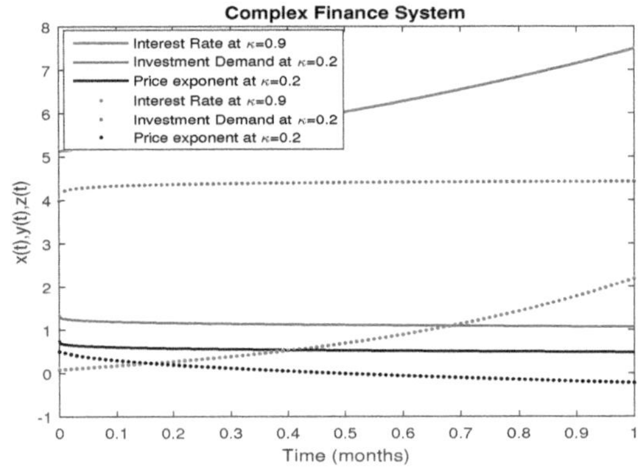

Figure 10. $z(t)$ price exponent with Caputo and ABC derivative.

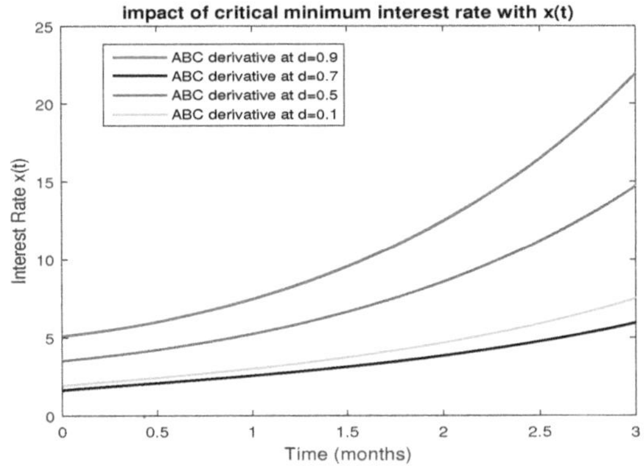

Figure 11. Impact of critical minimum interest rate with $x(t)$.

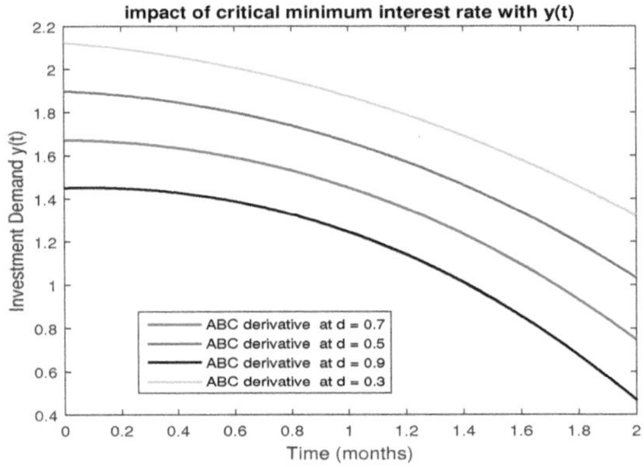

Figure 12. Impact of critical minimum interest rate with $y(t)$.

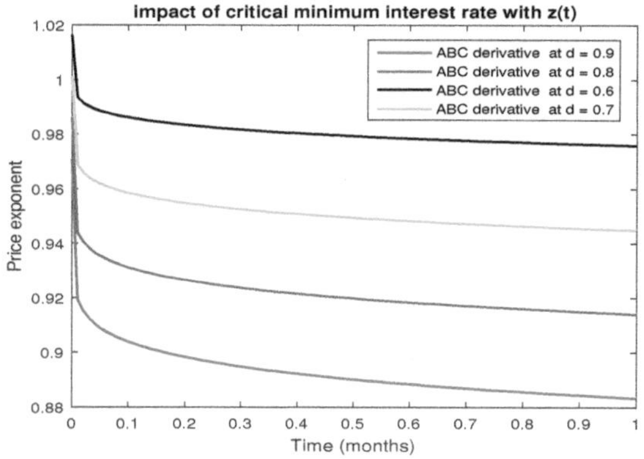

Figure 13. Impact of critical minimum interest rate with $z(t)$.

6. Conclusions

This paper uses a dynamic chaotic fractional order model with an ABC derivative to conduct the economic system. The basis of this fractional model consists of exponentially decreasing non-singular kernels that appear in the derivation of the ABC. The financial model is presented with theoretical and numerical investigation. This demonstrates the regulation of the economic system's critical minimum interest rate. In order to control the economic system, we are discussing a fractional order financing model. The modified model with ABC derivative shows a good financial system control agreement. The model offers the effect of evaluating numerical results on a critical minimum interest rate. Graphical representation shows the impact on the amount of critical minimum interest rate for variables with time. We can observe $\kappa = 1$ revealing more absorbing characteristics by numerical simulation using ABC non-integer order derivative. For interest rate, investment demand and price exponent, the concept of this research provides important results. Therefore, we conclude that the ABC derivative is useful to control and maintain the finance system to overcome the risk factors. The interest rate begins to rise according to initial conditions as investment demand and price exponent begin to fall, which shows the actual macroeconomic behavior of the financial system. It is observed here that the complex chaotic fractional system provides more appropriate and reliable results as compared to time integer parameters for non-integer time-fractional parameters.

Author Contributions: Conceptualization, M.F. and A.A. (Ali Akgül); Methodology, A.A. (Ali Akgül); Software, S.I.; Validation, A.H., A.A. (Aqeel Ahmad) and D.B.; Formal Analysis, D.B.; Investigation, A.A. (Aqeel Ahmad); Resources, A.A. (Aqeel Ahmad); Data Curation, M.F.; Writing-Original Draft Preparation, M.F.; Writing-Review & Editing, M.F.; All authors have read and agreed to the published version of the manuscript.

Funding: This research received no external funding .

Conflicts of Interest: The authors declare no conflict of interest.

References

1. Neumaier, A. Mathematical Modelling. Available online: http://www.mat.univie.ac.at/~neum/ms/model.pdf (accessed on 18 January 2011).
2. Merton, R.C.; Simons, R.V.; Wilkie, A.D. Influence of mathematical models in finance on practice: Past, present and future. *Philos. Trans. Phys. Sci. Eng.* **1994**, *347*, 451–463.
3. Karatzas, I. *Lectures on the Mathematics of Finance 8*; American Mathematical Society: Providence, RI, USA, 1997.
4. Hilfer, R. *Applications of Fractional Calculus in Physics*; World Scientific: Singapore, 2000; pp. 87–130.
5. Kumar, D.; Singh, J.; Baleanu, D. Modified Kawahara equation within a fractional derivative with non-singular kernel. *Therm. Sci.* **2017**, *22*, 789–796.

6. Kumar, D.; Singh, J.; Baleanu, D.; Sushila. Analysis of regularized long-wave equation associated with a new fractional operator with Mittag–Leffler type kernel. *Physica A* **2018**, *492*, 155–167. [CrossRef]
7. Baleanu, D.; Jajarmi, A.; Hajipour, M.; A new formulation of the fractional optimal control problems involving Mittag–Leffler nonsingular kernel. *J. Optim. Theory Appl.* **2017**, *175*, 718–737. [CrossRef]
8. Baleanu, D.; Jajarmi, A.; Asad, J.H.; Blaszczyk, T. The motion of a bead sliding on a wire in fractional sense. *Acta Phys. Pol. A* **2017**, *131*, 1561–1564. [CrossRef]
9. Jajarmi, A.; Hajipour, M.; Baleanu, D. New aspects of the adaptive synchronization and hyperchaos suppression of a financial model. *Chaos Solitons Fractals* **2017**, *99*, 285–296. [CrossRef]
10. Kilbas, A.A.; Srivastava, H.M.; Trujillo, J.J. *Theory and Applications of Fractional Differential Equations*; Elsevier: Amsterdam, The Netherlands, 2006. [CrossRef]
11. Baleanu, D.; Guvenc, Z.B.; Machado, J.A.T. *New Trends in Nanotechnology and Fractional Calculus Applications*; Springer: Dordrecht, The Netherlands, 2000. [CrossRef]
12. Yang, X.J.; Srivastava, H.M.; Machado, J.A.T. A new fractional derivative without singular kernel: Application to the modelling of the steady heat flow. *Therm. Sci.* **2016**, *20*, 753–756. [CrossRef]
13. Caputo, M.; Fabrizio, M. A new definition of fractional derivative without singular kernel. *Prog. Fract. Differ. Appl.* **2015**, *1*, 73–85.
14. Atangana, A. On the new fractional derivative and application to nonlinear Fisher's reaction diffusion equation. *Appl. Math. Comput.* **2016**, *273*, 948–956.
15. Panda, S.K.; Karapınar, E.; Atangana A. A numerical schemes and comparisons for fixed point results with applications to the solutions of Volterra integral equations in dislocated extended b a metric space. *Alex. Eng. J.* **2020**, *59*, 815–827. [CrossRef]
16. Yavuz, M.; Özdemir, N. European vanilla option pricing model of fractional order without singular kernel. *Fractal Fract.* **2018**, *2*, 3. [CrossRef]
17. Keten, A.; Yavuz, M.; Baleanu, D. Nonlocal Cauchy problem via a fractional operator involving power kernel in Banach Spaces. *Fractal Fract.* **2019**, *3*, 27. [CrossRef]
18. Yavuz, M.; Abdeljawad, T. Nonlinear regularized long-wave models with a new integral transformation applied to the fractional derivative with power and Mittag–Leffler kernel. *Adv. Differ. Equ.* **2020**, *2020*, 367. [CrossRef]
19. Yavuz, M.; Ozdemir, N.; Baskonus, H.M. Solutions of partial differential equations using the fractional operator involving Mittag–Leffler kernel. *Eur. Phys. J. Plus* **2018**, *133*, 215. [CrossRef]
20. Gao, W.; Baskonus, H.M.; Shi, L. New investigation of Bats-Hosts Reservoir-People coronavirus model and apply to 2019-nCoV system. *Adv. Differ. Equ.* **2020**, *2020*, 1–11.
21. Gao, W.; Veeresha, P.; Prakasha, D.G.; Baskonus, H.M. Novel dynamical structures of 2019-nCoV with nonlocal operator via powerful computational technique. *Biology* **2020**, *9*, 107. [CrossRef]
22. Gao, W.; Veeresha, P.; Baskonus, H.M.; Prakasha, D.G.; Kumar, P. A new study of unreported cases of 2019-nCOV epidemic outbreaks. *Chaos Solitons Fractals* **2020**, *138*, 109929. [CrossRef]
23. MoralesDelgadoa, V.F.; Aguilarb, J.F.; Taneco, M.A.; Escobar, R.F. Mathematical modeling of the smoking dynamics using fractional differential equations with local and nonlocal kernel. *J. Nonlinear Sci. Appl.* **2018**, *11*, 994–1014. [CrossRef]
24. Atangana A.; Baleanu D. New fractional derivatives with nonlocal and non Singular Kernel: Theory and Application to Heat Transfer Model. *Therm. Sci.* **2016**, *20*, 763–769. [CrossRef]
25. Kumar, S.; Kumar, A.; Argyros, I. K. A new analysis for the Keller-Segel model of fractional order. *Numer. Algorithms* **2017**, *75*, 213–228. [CrossRef]
26. Kumar, S.; Rashidi, M.M. New analytical method for gas dynamic equation arising in shock fronts. *Comput. Phys. Commun.* **2014**, *185*, 1947–1954. [CrossRef]
27. Odibat, Z.; Bataineh, A.S. An adaptation of homotopy analysis method for reliable treatment of strongly nonlinear problems: Construction of homotopy polynomials. *Math. Methods Appl. Sci.* **2015**, *38*, 991–1000.
28. Ma, J.H.; Chen, Y.S. Study for the bifurcation topological structure and the global complicated character of a kind of nonlinear finance system, I. *Appl. Math. Mech.* **2011**, *22*, 1240–1251. [CrossRef]
29. Singh, J.; Kumar, D.; Al Qurashi, M.; Baleanu, D. A new fractional model for giving up smoking dynamics. *Adv. Differ. Equ.* **2017**, *2017*, 88. [CrossRef]
30. Li, C.P.; Tao, C.X. On the fractional Adams method. *Comput. Math. Appl.* **2009**, *58*, 1573–1588. [CrossRef]

31. Alkahtani, B.S.T. Chua's circuit model with Atangana Baleanu derivative with fractional order. *Chaos Solitons Fractals* **2016**, *89*, 547–551. [CrossRef]
32. Zhen, W.; Huang, X.; Shi, G. Analysis of nonlinear dynamics and chaos in a fractional-order financial system with time delay. *Comput. Math. Appl.* **2011**, *62*, 1531–1539. [CrossRef]

fractal and fractional

Article

A New Approach for the Fractional Integral Operator in Time Scales with Variable Exponent Lebesgue Spaces

Lütfi Akın

Department of Business Administration, Mardin Artuklu University, 47200 Mardin, Turkey; lutfiakin@artuklu.edu.tr

Abstract: Integral equations and inequalities have an important place in time scales and harmonic analysis. The norm of integral operators is one of the important study topics in harmonic analysis. Using the norms in different variable exponent spaces, the boundedness or compactness of the integral operators are examined. However, the norm of integral operators on time scales has been a matter of curiosity to us. In this study, we prove the equivalence of the norm of the restricted centered fractional maximal diamond-α integral operator $M^c_{a,\delta}$ to the norm of the centered fractional maximal diamond-α integral operator M^c_a on time scales with variable exponent Lebesgue spaces. This study will lead to the study of problems such as the boundedness and compactness of integral operators on time scales.

Keywords: time scales; variable exponent; fractional integral; maximal operator

1. Introduction

The founder of the time scale theory is Stefan Hilger [1]. At the time, this theory caught the attention of many mathematicians who have demonstrated various aspects of integral inequalities, dynamic equations and integral operators on time scales [2–13]. For example, Li [4] demonstrated non-linear integral inequalities in two independent variables on time scales. Anastassiou [5] demonstrated some properties of fractional calculus on time scales. Uçar et al. [9] demonstrated fractional integral inequalities on time scales.

Dynamic equations and integral inequalities have many applications in different areas of science. Some areas are electrical engineering, fluid dynamics, quantum mechanics, physical problems, wave equations, heat transfer and economics [14–24]. Tisdell and Zaidi [15] demonstrated basic qualitative and quantitative results for solutions to non-linear dynamic equations on time scales with an application to economic modelling. Seadawy et al. [18] demonstrated non-linear wave solutions of the Kudryashov–Sinelshchikov dynamical equation in mixtures of liquid–gas bubbles under the consideration of heat transfer and viscosity. Akin [25] demonstrated fractional integral type inequalities on time scales. Higgins [26] demonstrated asymptotic behavior of second-order nonlinear dynamic equations on time scales. Ozturk and Higgins [27] demonstrated limit behaviors of non-oscillatory solutions of three-dimensional time scale systems.

The variable exponent, Lebesgue space $L^{p(\cdot)}$, is one of the cornerstones of harmonic analysis. Mathematicians working in this field have comprehensively analyzed the operators and inequalities in the variable exponent, Lebesgue space $L^{p(\cdot)}$ [28–37]. Akin and Dusunceli [38] demonstrated a new approach for weighted Hardy's operator in "variable exponent Lebesgue spaces" (VELS). This work also has been stimulated by problems of elasticity, fluid dynamics, electrorheological liquids and calculus of variations.

In variable exponential spaces, problems such as the boundedness and compactness of integral operators, take an important place. The concept of norms has the most important place in solving these problems. If we can obtain the norms of integral operators by the method we apply, then we can see the boundedness and compactness of these

Citation: Akın, L. A New Approach for the Fractional Integral Operator in Time Scales with Variable Exponent Lebesgue Spaces. *Fractal Fract.* **2021**, *5*, 7. https://doi.org/10.3390/fractalfract5010007

Received: 5 November 2020
Accepted: 5 January 2021
Published: 8 January 2021

operators. However, there are almost no studies on the problems of time scales. Our main purpose in this study is to examine the equivalence of the norms of fractional integral operators. Thanks to these results, we will be able to establish the constraint and compactness conditions of integral operators on time scales.

The organization of this article is as follows. In Section 2, we give necessary definitions, lemmas and theorems. In Section 3, we prove the equivalence of the norm variable exponent $L^{p(.)}$ of the restricted centered fractional maximal diamond-α integral $M^c_{a,\delta}$ to the norm variable exponent $L^{p(.)}$ of the centered fractional maximal diamond-α integral M^c_a for all $0 < \delta < \infty$ and $1 \leq p(x) < \infty$ on time scales. In Section 4, we give the conclusion.

2. Materials and Methods

In this section, we provide necessary concepts and statements related to time scale and variable exponent Lebesgue space. The reader can refer to the monographs [1–43] for details.

Definition 1. *[39] Let $\Omega \subset \mathbb{R}^n$ be an open set. The fractional maximal operator $M_a f$ is defined as follows*

$$M_a f(t) = \sup_{B \ni t} \frac{1}{|B|^{1-\frac{a}{n}}} \int_{B\cap\Omega} |f(y)|dy, \tag{1}$$

for $0 < a < n$. In the limiting case $a = 0$, the fractional maximal operator reduces to the Hardy–Littlewood maximal operator.

Let $L^{p(.)}(\Omega)$ denote the space of the measurable and integrable functions on Ω, such that for $\lambda > 0$, with norm

$$\|f\|_{p(.),\Omega} = \inf\left\{ \lambda > 0 : \int_{\Omega} \left(\frac{|f(t)|}{\lambda} \right)^{p(t)} dt \leq 1 \right\},$$

where $p(.) : \Omega \to [1, \infty)$ is a measurable function (for details, see [25,40]). These spaces are also the variable exponent Lebesgue spaces $L^{p(.)}$.

Now let us define some properties of the centered fractional maximal operator which will help us prove our results. We know that the centered fractional maximal operator is defined by

$$M^c_a f(t) = \sup_{r>0} \frac{1}{|B(t,r)|^{1-\frac{a}{n}}} \int_{B(t,r)\cap\Omega} |f(\tau)|d\tau, \tag{2}$$

and the uncentered fractional maximal operator is defined by

$$M_a f(t) = \sup_{B \ni t} \frac{1}{|B|^{1-\frac{a}{n}}} \int_{B\cap\Omega} |f(\tau)|d\tau \tag{3}$$

for $0 < a < n$ and $t \in \mathbb{R}^n$, where the supremum is again taken over all balls B, which contain t (for details, see [25,29,37]). We well know that the fractional maximal operator plays an important role in harmonic analysis. The restricted operators have important properties (for details, see [28,41]).

$$M^c_a f(t) \leq M_a f(t) \leq 2^m M^c_a f(t), \qquad \forall t \in \mathbb{R}^m. \tag{4}$$

Let us define the restricted centered fractional maximal operator and the restricted uncentered fractional maximal operator, respectively,

$$M^c_{a,\delta} f(t) = \sup_{\delta>r>0} \frac{1}{|B(t,r)|^{1-\frac{a}{n}}} \int_{B(t,r)\cap\Omega} |f(\tau)|d\tau, \tag{5}$$

and

$$M_{a,\delta}f(t) = \sup_{\delta>r>0,|x-t|<r} \frac{1}{|B|^{1-\frac{a}{n}}} \int_{B(x,r)\cap\Omega} |f(\tau)|d\tau, \tag{6}$$

for $t \in \mathbb{R}^m$, $0 < a < n$ and $\delta \in \mathbb{R}_+$ (for details, see [28,29,41]). It is clear that using (5) and (6), we can write the following inequalities

$$M^c_{a,\delta}f(t) \le M^c_{a,\theta}f(t) \le M^c_a f(t)$$

and

$$M_{a,\delta}f(t) \le M_{a,\theta}f(t) \le M_a f(t),$$

for $\delta \le \theta$, $\forall t \in \mathbb{R}^m$. As a result, again if we use (5)–(6) and $\delta \le \theta$, then we can write the following inequalities and

$$\begin{aligned}\|M_{a,\delta}f(t)\|_{L^{p(.)}(\mathbb{R}^m)\to L^{p(.)}(\mathbb{R}^m)} &\le \|M_{a,\theta}f(t)\|_{L^{p(.)}(\mathbb{R}^m)\to L^{p(.)}(\mathbb{R}^m)} \\ &\le \|M_a f(t)\|_{L^{p(.)}(\mathbb{R}^m)\to L^{p(.)}(\mathbb{R}^m)}\end{aligned}$$

for $1 < p(.) \le \infty$, $t \in \mathbb{R}^m$ and some real positive numbers δ, θ. We have seen here that the norm of the restricted operator is less than the norm of the unrestricted operator. The normed inequalities obtained above will help us prove our results.

To prove our main results, we first provide some definitions and lemmas which will be used as follows.

Definition 2. *[29] If f is a measurable function on $\mathbb{R}^m$, then distribution function d_f on $[0, +\infty]$ is defined by*

$$d_f(\beta) = |\{x \in \mathbb{R}^m : |f(x)| > \beta\}|, \tag{7}$$

where $|\{x \in \mathbb{R}^m : |f(x)| > \beta\}|$ is the Lebesgue measurable of the measurable of $\{x \in \mathbb{R}^m : |f(x)| > \beta\}$.

Lemma 1. *[30] If $f \in L^p(\mathbb{R}^m)$ with $0 < p < \infty$, then we have*

$$\|f\|^p_{L^p(\mathbb{R}^m)} = p\int_0^\infty \beta^{p-1} d_f(\beta)d\beta. \tag{8}$$

Lemma 2. *[31] Let π be a positive measure on $\mathcal{M}$ such that $\mathcal{M}$ is a σ-algebra. If $B_1 \subset B_2 \subset B_3, \ldots, B_m \in \mathcal{M}$, and $B = \cup_{m=1}^{\infty} B_m$, then $\lim_{m\to\infty} \pi(B_m) = \pi(B)$.*

Using Lemma 2, we can formulate the following conclusions.

Lemma 3. *(Lemma 2.3, [29]) If operators M^c_a and $M^c_{a,\delta}$ are defined as in (2) and (5), then the equality*

$$d_{M^c_a f}(\beta) = \lim_{\delta\to\infty} d_{M^c_{a,\delta}f}(\beta), \tag{9}$$

holds $\forall f \in L^p(\mathbb{R}^m)$ and $\beta > 0$.

Lemma 4. *(Lemma 2.4, [29]) If operators M_a and $M_{a,\delta}$ are defined as in (3) and (6), then the equality*

$$d_{M_a f}(\beta) = \lim_{\delta\to\infty} d_{M_{a,\delta}f}(\beta), \tag{10}$$

holds $\forall f \in L^p(\mathbb{R}^m)$ and $\beta > 0$.

Lemma 5. [29] *For $p > 1$ and $0 < \epsilon$, there exists a function $h \in C\_c^{\infty}$ $(R\grave{m})$ such that*

$$\|M_a^c\|_{L^p(\mathbb{R}^m)\to L^p(\mathbb{R}^m)} - \epsilon \le \frac{\|M_a^c h\|_{L^p(\mathbb{R}^m)}}{\|h\|_{L^p(\mathbb{R}^m)}}, \tag{11}$$

where $\|M_a^c\|_{L^p(\mathbb{R}^m)\to L^p(\mathbb{R}^m)} = \sup\limits_{\|h\|_{L^p(\mathbb{R}^m)}\neq 0} \frac{\|M_a^c h\|_{L^p(\mathbb{R}^m)}}{\|h\|_{L^p(\mathbb{R}^m)}}$.

Let us give information about the time scales that will help us in our work.

A time scale $\mathbb{T}$ is a nonempty closed subset of $\mathbb{R}$ (for details, see [19,20]). Let $[a,b]$ be an arbitrary closed interval on time scale $\mathbb{T}$. The time scale interval $[a,b]_{\mathbb{T}}$ is denoted by $[a,b] \cap \mathbb{T}$ (see p. 7 [42]).

Definition 3. [19] *The mappings $\sigma, \rho : \mathbb{T} \to \mathbb{T}$ are defined by $\sigma(t) = inf\{s \in T : s > t\}$, $\rho(t) = \sup\{s \in \mathbb{T} : s > t\}$ for $t \in \mathbb{T}$. Respectively, $\sigma(t)$ is forward jump operator and $\rho(t)$ is backward jump operator.*

If $\sigma(t) > t$, then t is right-scattered and if $\sigma(t) = t$, then t is called right-dense. If $\rho(t) < t$, then t is left-scattered and if $\rho(t) = t$, then t is called left-dense.

Definition 4. [19] *Let two mappings $\mu, \vartheta : \mathbb{T} \to \mathbb{R}^+$, such that $\mu(t) = \sigma(t) - t$, $\vartheta(t) = t - \rho(t)$. Here, the mappings $\mu(t)$ and $\vartheta(t)$ are called graininess mappings.*

If $\mathbb{T}$ has a left-scattered maximum m, then $\mathbb{T}^k = \mathbb{T} - \{m\}$. Otherwise $\mathbb{T}^k = \mathbb{T}$.

$\mathbb{T}^k$ is defined as follows (for details, see [19,20,42])

$$\mathbb{T}^k = \begin{cases} \mathbb{T} \smallsetminus (\rho\sup\mathbb{T}, \sup\mathbb{T}], & if \quad \sup\mathbb{T} < \infty, \\ \mathbb{T}, \quad if & \sup\mathbb{T} = \infty, \end{cases}$$

by the same way

$$\mathbb{T}_k = \begin{cases} \mathbb{T} \smallsetminus [\inf\mathbb{T}, \sigma(\inf\mathbb{T})], & |\inf\mathbb{T}| < \infty, \\ \mathbb{T}, & \inf\mathbb{T} = -\infty. \end{cases}$$

Assume that $h : \mathbb{T} \to \mathbb{R}$ is a function.

(i) If h is Δ-differentiable at point t ($t \in \mathbb{T}^k (t \neq \min\mathbb{T})$), then h is continuous at point t.

(ii) If h is left continuous at point t and t is right-scattered, then h is Δ-differentiable at point t,

$$h^{\Delta}(t) = \frac{h^{\sigma}(t) - h(t)}{\mu(t)}$$

Let t be right-dense.

(iii) If h is Δ-differentiable at point t and $\lim\limits_{s\to t} \frac{h(t)-h(s)}{t-s}$, then

$$h^{\Delta}(t) = \lim_{s\to t} \frac{h(t) - h(s)}{t - s}.$$

(iv) If h is Δ-differentiable at point t, then $h^{\sigma}(t) = h(t) + \mu(t)h^{\Delta}(t)$.

Remark 1. *(For details, see page 3 in [42]) If $\mathbb{T} = \mathbb{R}$, then $h^{\Delta}(t) = h'(t)$, and if $\mathbb{T} = \mathbb{Z}$, then $h^{\Delta}(t)$ reduces to $\Delta h(t)$.*

Definition 5. [20] *If* $H : \mathbb{T} \to \mathbb{R}$ *is defined as* Δ*-antiderivative of* $h : \mathbb{T} \to \mathbb{R}$, *then* $H^{\Delta} = h(t)$ *holds for* $\forall t \in \mathbb{T}$ *and we define the* Δ*-integral of* h *by*

$$\int_{s}^{t} h(\tau)\Delta\tau = H(t) - H(s),$$

for $s, t \in \mathbb{T}$.

We now give similar definitions for the nabla operator.

Definition 6. [20] *Where* $h : \mathbb{T}_k \to \mathbb{R}$ *is called* ∇*-differentiable at* $t \in \mathbb{T}_k$. *If* $\varepsilon > 0$, *then there exists a neighborhood* V *of* t *such that*

$$\left|h(\rho(t)) - h(s) - h^{\nabla}(t)(\rho(t) - s)\right| \leq \varepsilon|\rho(t) - s|,$$

for $\forall s \in V$.

Definition 7. [20] *Where* $H : \mathbb{T} \to \mathbb{R}$ *is called a* ∇*-antiderivative of* $h : \mathbb{T} \to \mathbb{R}$, *then we define*

$$\int_{s}^{t} h(\tau)\nabla\tau = H(t) - H(s),$$

for $s, t \in \mathbb{T}$. *Let* $f(t)$ *be differentiable on* $\mathbb{T}$ *for* $\alpha, t \in \mathbb{T}$. *Then, we define* $f^{\diamond_\alpha}(t)$ *by*

$$f^{\diamond_\alpha}(t) = \alpha f^{\Delta}(t) + (1 - \alpha)f^{\nabla}(t)$$

for $0 \leq \alpha \leq 1$.

Proposition 1. [20] *If we have* $f, h : \mathbb{T} \to \mathbb{R}$, $\diamond_\alpha$ *-differentiable for* $\alpha, t \in \mathbb{T}$, *then*

(i) $f + h : \mathbb{T} \to \mathbb{R}$ *is* $\diamond_\alpha$*-differentiable for* $t \in \mathbb{T}$ *with* $(f + h)^{\diamond_\alpha}(t) = f^{\diamond_\alpha}(t) + h^{\diamond_\alpha}(t)$.
(ii) *Let* $k \in \mathbb{R}$, $kf : \mathbb{T} \to \mathbb{R}$ *is* $\diamond_\alpha$*-differentiable for* $\alpha, t \in \mathbb{T}$ *with* $(kf)^{\diamond_\alpha}(t) = kf^{\diamond_\alpha}(t)$.
(iii) $f, h : \mathbb{T} \to \mathbb{R}$ *is* $\diamond_\alpha$*-differentiable for* $\alpha, t \in \mathbb{T}$ *with*

$$(fh)^{\diamond_\alpha}(t) = f^{\diamond_\alpha}(t)h(t) + \alpha f^{\sigma}(t)h^{\Delta}(t) + (1 - \alpha)f^{\rho}(t)h^{\nabla}(t).$$

Definition 8. [20] *If* $f : \mathbb{T} \to \mathbb{R}$ *is integrable and* $\alpha, b, t \in \mathbb{T}$, *then*

$$\int_{b}^{t} f(\delta) \diamond_\alpha \delta = \alpha \int_{b}^{t} f(\delta)\Delta\delta + (1 - \alpha) \int_{b}^{t} f(\delta)\nabla\delta$$

for $0 \leq \alpha \leq 1$.

Definition 9. [12,25] *If* $f \in C_{rd}(\mathbb{T}, \mathbb{R})$ *and* $t \in \mathbb{T}^k$, *then*

$$\int_{t}^{\sigma(t)} f(\tau) \diamond_\alpha \tau = \mu(t)f(t).$$

Here, we can define the fractional maximal diamond-α *integral*

$$M_a f(t) = \sup_{B \ni t} \frac{1}{|B|^{\frac{m-a}{m}}} \int_{a}^{t} f(x) \diamond_\alpha x,$$

where $f \in L_1([a,t] \cap \mathbb{T})$ *and* $M_a f \in L([a,t] \cap \mathbb{T})$.

Now, we can define the restricted centered fractional maximal diamond-α integral operator and the restricted uncentered fractional maximal diamond-α integral operator,

$$M^c_{a,\delta} f(t) = \sup_{\delta > r > 0} \frac{1}{|B(t,r)|^{1-\frac{a}{m}}} \int_{B(t,r)\cap\Omega} |f(\tau)| \diamond_\alpha \tau$$

and

$$M_{a,\delta} f(t) = \sup_{\delta > r > 0, |x-t|<r} \frac{1}{|B|^{1-\frac{a}{m}}} \int_{B(x,r)\cap\Omega} |f(\tau)| \diamond_\alpha \tau,$$

for $t \in \mathbb{R}^m$ and $\delta \in \mathbb{R}_+$ (for details, see [28]).

Definition 10. [35] *Let* $p : \Phi \to [1,\infty)$ *be a measurable function for* $\Phi \subset \mathbb{R}^m$ *and* $L^{p(.)}$ *be the space of all measurable functions on open set* Φ, *such that*

$$\int_\Phi \left(\frac{|f(t)|}{\lambda} \right)^{p(t)} dt \leq \infty,$$

for some $\lambda > 0$. *The norm in* $L^{p(x)}$ *is the generalization of the norm in* L^p *(p is constant). The Luxemburg norm in* $L^{p(x)}$ *is defined as follows:*

$$\|f\|_{L^{p(.)}} = \inf\left\{ \lambda > 0 : \int_\Phi \left(\frac{|f(t)|}{\lambda} \right)^{p(t)} dt \leq 1 \right\}.$$

Theorem 1. *(See [Theorem 2, in [21]) If* h *is* Δ*-integrable on* $[a,b]$, *then* $|h|$ *is* Δ*-integrable on* $[a,b]$ *and we have*

$$\left| \int_a^b h(\tau)\Delta\tau \right| \leq \int_a^b |h(\tau)|\Delta\tau.$$

Theorem 2. [40] *Let* $M_{a,\delta} f$ *be defined by (6), and let* $\delta > 0$. *Then*

$$\|M_{a,\delta} f\|_{L^{p(x)}(\mathbb{R}^m) \to L^{p(x)}(\mathbb{R}^m)} = \|M_a f\|_{L^{p(x)}(\mathbb{R}^m) \to L^{p(x)}(\mathbb{R}^m)}$$

holds for $1 \leq p(x) < \infty$.

Proof. From the definition of the operator $M_{a,\delta} f$ in (6), we obtain

$$\begin{aligned} M_{a,\delta} f(\delta x) &= \sup_{\delta > r > 0, |t-\delta x|<r} \frac{1}{|B|^{1-\frac{a}{m}}} \int_{B(t,r)} |f(y)|\Delta y \\ &= \sup_{\delta > r > 0, |t-x|<\frac{r}{\delta}} \frac{1}{v_m r^{1-\frac{a}{m}}} \int_{|t|<r} |f(\delta t - y)|\Delta y \\ &= \sup_{\delta > r > 0, |t-x|<\frac{r}{\delta}} \frac{\delta^{1-\frac{a}{m}}}{v_m r^{1-\frac{a}{m}}} \int_{|t|<\frac{r}{\delta}} |f(\delta(t-y))|\Delta y \\ &= \sup_{1 > \frac{r}{\delta} > 0, |t-x|<\frac{r}{\delta}} \frac{1}{v_m \left(\frac{r}{\delta}\right)^{1-\frac{a}{m}}} \int_{|t|<\frac{r}{\delta}} |(\tau_\delta f)(t-y)|\Delta y \\ &= \sup_{1 > r > 0, |t-x|<r} \frac{1}{v_m r^{1-\frac{a}{m}}} \int_{|t|<r} |(\tau_\delta f)(x-y)|\Delta y \\ &= M_{a,1}(\tau_\delta f)(x), \end{aligned} \tag{12}$$

where v_m is the volume of the unit ball in R^m and the dilation operator τ_δ *is defined as follows:*

$$(\tau_\delta f)(x) = f(\delta x),$$

for $\delta > 0$ and $x \in R^m$. It follows from (12) that

$$\frac{\|M_{a,\delta} f\|_{L^{p(x)}(\mathbb{R}^m)}}{\|f\|_{L^{p(x)}(\mathbb{R}^m)}} = \frac{\|M_{a,\delta} f(\delta)\|_{L^{p(x)}(\mathbb{R}^m)}}{\|f(\delta)\|_{L^{p(x)}(\mathbb{R}^m)}} = \frac{\|M_{a,1}(\tau_\delta f)\|_{L^{p(x)}(\mathbb{R}^m)}}{\|\tau_\delta f\|_{L^{p(x)}(\mathbb{R}^m)}}.$$

□

Taking the supremum over all $f \in L^{p(x)}(\mathbb{R}^m)$ with $\|f\|_{L^{p(x)}(\mathbb{R}^m)} \neq 0$ for the two sides of the above equation, we have

$$\|M_{a,\delta} f\|_{L^{p(x)}(\mathbb{R}^m) \to L^{p(x)}(\mathbb{R}^m)} = \|M_{a,1} f\|_{L^{p(x)}(\mathbb{R}^m) \to L^{p(x)}(\mathbb{R}^m)}, \tag{13}$$

for all $\delta > 0$ and $1 \le p(x) < \infty$.

Next, we will prove that

$$\|M_{a,\delta} f\|_{L^{p(x)}(\mathbb{R}^m) \to L^{p(x)}(\mathbb{R}^m)} = \|M_a f\|_{L^{p(x)}(\mathbb{R}^m) \to L^{p(x)}(\mathbb{R}^m)}.$$

We will use Equation (13) for proof. If $f \in L^{p(x)}(\mathbb{R}^m)$, then we have $Mf \in L^{p(x)}(\mathbb{R}^m)$. From Lemma 1, Lemma 4 and Equation (13), we obtain

$$\begin{aligned}
\|M_a\|^{p(x)}_{L^{p(x)}(\mathbb{R}^m) \to L^{p(x)}(\mathbb{R}^m)} &= \int_0^\infty \mu^{p(x)-1} d_{M_a f}(\mu) \Delta\mu \\
&= \int_0^\infty \mu^{p(x)-1} \lim_{\delta \to \infty} d_{M_{a,\delta} f}(\mu) \Delta\mu \\
&= \lim_{\delta \to \infty} \int_0^\infty \mu^{p(x)-1} d_{M_{a,\delta} f}(\mu) \Delta\mu \\
&= \lim_{\delta \to \infty} \|M_{a,\delta}\|^{p(x)}_{L^{p(x)}(\mathbb{R}^m)} \\
&\le \lim_{\delta \to \infty} \|M_{a,\delta}\|^{p(x)}_{L^{p(x)}(\mathbb{R}^m) \to L^{p(x)}(\mathbb{R}^m)} \|f\|^{p(x)}_{L^{p(x)}(\mathbb{R}^m)} \\
&= \|M_{a,1}\|^{p(x)}_{L^{p(x)}(\mathbb{R}^m) \to L^{p(x)}(\mathbb{R}^m)} \|f\|^{p(x)}_{L^{p(x)}(\mathbb{R}^m)}.
\end{aligned} \tag{14}$$

Now, taking advantage of inequality (14), we get the following inequality

$$\|M_a\|^{p(x)}_{L^{p(x)}(\mathbb{R}^m) \to L^{p(x)}(\mathbb{R}^m)} \ge \|M_{a,1}\|^{p(x)}_{L^{p(x)}(\mathbb{R}^m) \to L^{p(x)}(\mathbb{R}^m)}. \tag{15}$$

Hence, we obtain from (14) that

$$\|M_a\|^{p(x)}_{L^{p(x)}(\mathbb{R}^m) \to L^{p(x)}(\mathbb{R}^m)} = \|M_{a,1}\|^{p(x)}_{L^{p(x)}(\mathbb{R}^m) \to L^{p(x)}(\mathbb{R}^m)}.$$

3. Main Results

In this section we give statements and proofs of our results.

Theorem 3. *Suppose that $M^c_{a,\delta} f(x)$ is defined by (5). Then*

$$\|M^c_{a,\delta}\|_{L^{p(x)}(\mathbb{R}^m) \to L^{p(x)}(\mathbb{R}^m)} = \|M^c_a\|_{L^{p(x)}(\mathbb{R}^m) \to L^{p(x)}(\mathbb{R}^m)}$$

holds for $\delta > 0$ and $1 \le p(x) < \infty$.

Proof. For $0 < \delta < \infty$, we first prove

$$\|M^c_{a,\delta}\|_{L^{p(x)}(\mathbb{R}^m)\to L^{p(x)}(\mathbb{R}^m)} = \|M^c_{a,1}\|_{L^{p(x)}(\mathbb{R}^m)\to L^{p(x)}(\mathbb{R}^m)}.$$

If we use the definition of the operator $M^c_{a,\delta}$ in (5), then we have

$$M^c_{a,\delta}f(x) = \sup_{\delta>r>0} \frac{1}{|B(x,r)|^{1-\frac{a}{m}}} \int_{B(x,r)\cap\Omega} |f(y)| \diamond_\alpha y = \sup_{\delta>r>0} \frac{1}{v_m r^{1-\frac{a}{m}}} \int_{|y|\le r} |f(x-y)| \diamond_\alpha y, \quad (16)$$

for $0 < \delta < \infty$ and $x \in \mathbb{R}^m$, where v_m is the volume of the unit ball in $\mathbb{R}^m$. Hence, we have

$$\begin{aligned} M^c_{a,\delta}f(\delta x) &= \sup_{\delta>r>0} \frac{1}{v_m r^{1-\frac{a}{m}}} \int_{|y|\le r} |f(\delta x - y)| \diamond_\alpha y \\ &= \sup_{\delta>r>0} \frac{\delta^m}{v_m r^{1-\frac{a}{m}}} \int_{|y|\le \frac{r}{\delta}} |f(\delta x - \delta y)| \diamond_\alpha y \\ &= \sup_{1>\frac{r}{\delta}>0} \frac{1}{v_m (\frac{r}{\delta})^{1-\frac{a}{m}}} \int_{|y|\le \frac{r}{\delta}} |f(\delta x - \delta y)| \diamond_\alpha y \\ &= \sup_{1>r>0} \frac{1}{v_m r^{1-\frac{a}{m}}} \int_{|y|\le r} |f(\delta x - \delta y)| \diamond_\alpha y \\ &= M^c_{a,1}f(\delta x), \end{aligned} \quad (17)$$

for $0 < \delta < \infty$ and $x \in \mathbb{R}^m$. If we use (17), then we have

$$\frac{\|M^c_{a,\delta}\|_{L^{p(x)}(\mathbb{R}^m)}}{\|f\|_{L^{p(x)}(\mathbb{R}^m)}} = \frac{\|M^c_{a,\delta}f(\delta x)\|_{L^{p(x)}(\mathbb{R}^m)}}{\|f(\delta x)\|_{L^{p(x)}(\mathbb{R}^m)}} = \frac{\|M^c_{a,1}f(\delta x)\|_{L^{p(x)}(\mathbb{R}^m)}}{\|f(\delta x)\|_{L^{p(x)}(\mathbb{R}^m)}}. \quad (18)$$

If supremum is taken over all the $f \in L^{p(x)}(\mathbb{R}^m)$ for the two sides of (18), we have

$$\|M^c_{a,\delta}\|_{L^{p(x)}(\mathbb{R}^m)\to L^{p(x)}(\mathbb{R}^m)} = \|M^c_{a,1}\|_{L^{p(x)}(\mathbb{R}^m)\to L^{p(x)}(\mathbb{R}^m)}. \quad (19)$$

Next, we will use Equation (19) to prove

$$\|M^c_{a,\delta}\|_{L^{p(x)}(\mathbb{R}^m)\to L^{p(x)}(\mathbb{R}^m)} = \|M^c_{a}\|_{L^{p(x)}(\mathbb{R}^m)\to L^{p(x)}(\mathbb{R}^m)},$$

for $\forall\delta > 0$ and $1 \le p(x) < \infty$. We just need to prove

$$\|M^c_{a,\delta}\|_{L^{p(x)}(\mathbb{R}^m)\to L^{p(x)}(\mathbb{R}^m)} \ge \|M^c_{a}\|_{L^{p(x)}(\mathbb{R}^m)\to L^{p(x)}(\mathbb{R}^m)}.$$

If we use Lemma 5, for $\epsilon > 0$, then there exists a function $f \in C^\infty_c(\mathbb{R}^m)$, such that

$$\frac{\|M^c_a f\|_{L^{p(x)}(\mathbb{R}^m)}}{\|f\|_{L^{p(x)}(\mathbb{R}^m)}} = \|M^c_a\|_{L^{p(x)}(\mathbb{R}^m)\to L^{p(x)}(\mathbb{R}^m)} - \epsilon. \quad (20)$$

Since $f \in C^\infty_c(\mathbb{R}^m)$ implies $f \in L^{p(x)}(\mathbb{R}^m)$, we have $M^c_a f \in L^{p(x)}(\mathbb{R}^m)$. If $\mathbb{R}$ is a real integer, then we have

$$\|(M^c_a f)\chi_{(|.|\ge\mathbb{R})}\|_{L^{p(x)}(\mathbb{R}^m)} \le \epsilon\|f\|_{L^{p(x)}(\mathbb{R}^m)}. \quad (21)$$

Now we set $\delta_0 = \mathbb{Z}_+ + \mathbb{R}$ ($\mathbb{Z}_+$ is a positive integer and $\mathbb{R}$ is a real integer). Then it can be written from the definition of $M^c_{a,\delta}$ that

$$M^c_a f(x) = M^c_{a,\delta_0}f(x), \quad (22)$$

holds for $|x| < \mathbb{R}$. Hence, from (20)–(22), we obtain

$$\begin{aligned} ||M^c_{a,\delta_0}f||_{L^{p(x)}(\mathbb{R}^m)} &\geq ||\left(M^c_{a,\delta_0}f\right)\chi_{(|x|<R)}||_{L^{p(x)}(\mathbb{R}^m)} \\ &= ||(M^c_a f)\chi_{(|x|<R)}||_{L^{p(x)}(\mathbb{R}^m)} \\ &\geq ||M^c_a f||_{L^{p(x)}(\mathbb{R}^m)} - ||(M^c_a f)\chi_{(|x|\geq R)}||_{L^{p(x)}(\mathbb{R}^m)} \\ &\geq ||M^c_a||_{L^{p(x)}(\mathbb{R}^m)\to L^{p(x)}(\mathbb{R}^m)}||f||_{L^{p(x)}(\mathbb{R}^m)} - 2\epsilon||f||_{L^{p(x)}(\mathbb{R}^m)}. \end{aligned} \tag{23}$$

Obviously, (23) implies that

$$\frac{||M^c_{a,\delta_0}f||_{L^{p(x)}(\mathbb{R}^m)}}{||f||_{L^{p(x)}(\mathbb{R}^m)}} \geq ||M^c_a||_{L^{p(x)}(\mathbb{R}^m)\to L^{p(x)}(\mathbb{R}^m)} - 2\epsilon. \tag{24}$$

Here, the inequality (24) yields

$$||M^c_{a,\delta_0}||_{L^{p(x)}(\mathbb{R}^m)\to L^{p(x)}(\mathbb{R}^m)} \geq ||M^c_a||_{L^{p(x)}(\mathbb{R}^m)\to L^{p(x)}(\mathbb{R}^m)} - 2\epsilon. \tag{25}$$

From (19) and (25), we have

$$||M^c_{a,\delta}||_{L^{p(x)}(\mathbb{R}^m)\to L^{p(x)}(\mathbb{R}^m)} = ||M^c_a||_{L^{p(x)}(\mathbb{R}^m)\to L^{p(x)}(\mathbb{R}^m)},$$

for $\forall\delta > 0$ and $1 \leq p(x) < \infty$. Thus, proof of Theorem 3 is complete. □

Now, let us prove the weak (1,1) boundedness for the restricted centered diamond-α fractional maximal operator.

Theorem 4. *If $M^c_{a,\delta}$ is defined by (5) and $1 \leq p(x) < \infty$, then*

$$||M^c_{a,\delta}||_{L^1(\mathbb{R}^m)\to L^{1,\infty}(\mathbb{R}^m)} = ||M^c_a||_{L^1(\mathbb{R}^m)\to L^{1,\infty}(\mathbb{R}^m)}$$

holds for all $\delta > 0$.

Proof. Let $M^c_{a,\delta}$ be defined by (5) for $0 < \delta < \infty$. First, we prove that

$$||M^c_{a,\delta}||_{L^1(\mathbb{R}^m)\to L^{1,\infty}(\mathbb{R}^m)} = ||M^c_{a,1}||_{L^1(\mathbb{R}^m)\to L^{1,\infty}(\mathbb{R}^m)}.$$

From the identity (17), we get

$$M^c_{a,\delta}f(\delta x) = M^c_{a,1}(\tau_\delta f)(x). \tag{26}$$

For any $0 < \delta$, we obtain from (26) that

$$|\{x : M^c_{a,1}(\tau_\delta f) > \mu\}| = |\{x : M^c_{a,\delta}f(\delta x) > \mu\}| = \left|\left\{\frac{x}{y} : M^c_{a,\delta}f(x) > \mu\right\}\right| = \delta^{-m}\left|\left\{\frac{x}{y} : M^c_{a,\delta}f(x) > \mu\right\}\right|. \tag{27}$$

Thus (27) implies that

$$\sup_{\mu>0}\mu|\{x : M^c_{a,1}(\tau_\delta f) > \mu\}| = \delta^{-m}\sup_{\mu>0}\mu\left|\left\{\frac{x}{y} : M^c_{a,\delta}f(x) > \mu\right\}\right|. \tag{28}$$

If $||f||_{L^1(\mathbb{R}^m)} \neq 0$, then it follows from (28) that

$$\begin{aligned} \frac{\delta^{-m}\sup_{\mu>0}\mu|\{x:M^c_{a,\delta}f(x)>\mu\}|}{||f||_{L^1(\mathbb{R}^m)}} &= \frac{\sup_{\mu>0}\mu|\{x:M^c_{a,1}(\tau_\delta f)(x)>\mu\}|}{||f||_{L^1(\mathbb{R}^m)}} \\ &= \frac{\delta^{-m}\sup_{\mu>0}\mu|\{x:M^c_{a,\delta}f(x)>\mu\}|}{||\tau_\delta f||_{L^1(\mathbb{R}^m)}}. \end{aligned} \tag{29}$$

Now taking the supremum over all $f \in L^1(\mathbb{R}^m)$ with $\|f\|_{L^1(\mathbb{R}^m)} \neq 0$ for the two sides of (29), we obtain

$$\|M^c_{a,\delta}\|_{L^1(\mathbb{R}^m)\to L^{1,\infty}(\mathbb{R}^m)} = \|M^c_{a,1}\|_{L^1(\mathbb{R}^m)\to L^{1,\infty}(\mathbb{R}^m)}. \tag{30}$$

Next, we will use (30) to prove that

$$\|M^c_{a,\delta}\|_{L^1(\mathbb{R}^m)\to L^{1,\infty}(\mathbb{R}^m)} = \|M^c_{a}\|_{L^1(\mathbb{R}^m)\to L^{1,\infty}(\mathbb{R}^m)},$$

holds for $0 < \delta$. Now, let us prove the correctness of the following equation.

$$\sup_{\mu>0} \mu d_{M^c_a f}(\mu) = \lim_{\delta\to\infty} \sup_{\mu>0} \mu d_{M^c_{a,\delta} f}(\mu), \tag{31}$$

holds for any $f \in L^1(\mathbb{R}^m)$ with $\|f\|_{L^1(\mathbb{R}^m)} \neq 0$. Clearly, the right side of (31) is not bigger than the left side, so it is enough to show opposite inequality. From Lemma 3, we have

$$\sup_{\mu>0} \mu d_{M^c_a f}(\mu) = \sup_{\mu>0} \mu \left(\lim_{\delta\to\infty} d_{M^c_{a,\delta} f}(\mu) \right).$$

Let $A = \sup_{\mu>0} \mu d_{M^c_a f}(\mu)$. For $0 < \epsilon$, there must be a $\mu_0 \in \mathbb{R}^+$ such that

$$A \geq \mu_0 d_{M^c_a f}(\mu_0) \geq A - \epsilon.$$

We conclude that

$$A - \epsilon \leq \mu_0 d_{M^c_a f}(\mu_0) = \lim_{\delta\to\infty} d_{M^c_{a,\delta} f}(\mu) \leq \sup_{\mu>0} \mu \left(\lim_{\delta\to\infty} d_{M^c_{a,\delta} f}(\mu) \right).$$

This is equivalent to $A \leq \sup_{\mu>0} \mu \left(\lim_{\delta\to\infty} d_{M^c_{a,\delta} f}(\mu) \right)$.

Herewith, (31) holds. If we use Equation (31), we obtain that

$$\begin{aligned} \|M^c_a\|_{L^1(\mathbb{R}^m)\to L^{1,\infty}(\mathbb{R}^m)} &= \sup_{\|f\|_{L^1(\mathbb{R}^m)}\neq 0} \frac{\sup_{\mu>0} \mu d_{M^c_a f}(\mu)}{\|f\|_{L^1(\mathbb{R}^m)}} \\ &= \sup_{\|f\|_{L^1(\mathbb{R}^m)}\neq 0} \frac{\lim_{\delta\to\infty} \sup_{\mu>0} \mu d_{M^c_{a,\delta} f}(\mu)}{\|f\|_{L^1(\mathbb{R}^m)}} \\ &= \lim_{\delta\to\infty} \sup_{\|f\|_{L^1(\mathbb{R}^m)}\neq 0} \frac{\sup_{\mu>0} \mu d_{M^c_{a,\delta} f}(\mu)}{\|f\|_{L^1(\mathbb{R}^m)}} \\ &= \lim_{\delta\to\infty} \|M^c_{a,\delta}\|_{L^1(\mathbb{R}^m)\to L^{1,\infty}(\mathbb{R}^m)}. \end{aligned} \tag{32}$$

Thus, we get the result we want to achieve. □

Remark 2. *Let M_a be the uncentered fractional maximal operator defined by (3). Define the iterated fractional maximal operator denoted by M_a^{i+1} as follows:*

$$M_a^{i+1} g(y) = M_a \left(M_a^i g \right)(y) \tag{33}$$

for $i = 1, 2, 3, \ldots$ and $y \in \mathbb{R}^m$. Set $\left(M_a^1 g\right)(y) = (M_a g)(y)$.

Lemma 6. *Assume that a sequence $\{d_k\}_{k=1}^{\infty}$ satisfies the following two conditions simultaneously:*

(a) $d_1 = s \in (0.1)$,

(b) *for any* $i \geq 1$, $d_{i+1} = (1-s)d_i + s$.
Then $\{d_k\}_{k=1}^{\infty}$ *is strictly monotone increasing and we have*

$$\lim_{i\to\infty} d_i = 1.$$

Proof. By the mathematical induction and the two conditions (a) and (b), we can easily obtain $0 < d_i < 1$ for each $i \in \mathbb{N}$. Furthermore, the condition (b) implies

$$d_{i+1} - d_i = (1-s)d_i + s - d_i = s(1-d_i) > 0.$$

This shows that $\{d_k\}_{k=1}^{\infty}$ is strictly monotone increasing. Since $\{d_k\}_{k=1}^{\infty}$ is monotone increasing and has the upper bound, the limit of $\{d_k\}_{k=1}^{\infty}$ exists, and we can easily get

$$\lim_{i\to\infty} d_i = 1.$$

By Lemma 6, we have the following corollary. □

Corollary 1. *For any* $g \in L^{\infty}(\mathbb{R}^m)$, *the equation*

$$\lim_{i\to\infty} M_a^i g(y) = \|g\|_{\infty}$$

holds for $i = 1, 2, 3, \ldots$ *and* $y \in \mathbb{R}^m$.

4. Conclusions

For more than a quarter century, the concept of time scales has taken an important place in the literature. Mathematicians and scientists working in other disciplines have demonstrated many applications of dynamic equations and integral inequalities; for example, transformations, inverse conversions, extensions, wave equations, heat transfer, optics, fluid dynamics, quantum calculus, economy, etc. The boundedness and compactness of the integral operators we know from harmonic analysis occupy an important place in the literature. Norms in variable exponential spaces are used to solve these problems. Previously, studies on the concept of the equivalence of norms in variable exponential spaces were conducted. In this way, we obtain the boundedness and compactness of integral operators that we do not have any information about. For more detailed information, we refer the reader to references.

In this study, we wanted to relate the norms of integral operators with time scales. In this article, we showed the equivalence of the norm variable exponent $L^{p(x)}$ of the restricted centered fractional maximal diamond-α integral $M_{a,\delta}^c$ with norm variable exponent $L^{p(x)}$ of centered fractional maximal diamond-α integral M_a^c for all $0 < \delta < \infty$ and $1 \leq p(x) < \infty$ on time scales. Hereby, we will be able to establish the boundedness and compactness conditions of fractional integral operators. In the future, we plan to carry these studies to variable exponent grand Lebesgue spaces, which is more general.

Author Contributions: The author has read and agreed to the published version of the manuscript.

Funding: This work received no external funding.

Institutional Review Board Statement: Not applicable.

Informed Consent Statement: Not applicable.

Acknowledgments: The author would like to thank the editor and the referees for his/her careful reading and valuable comments.

Conflicts of Interest: The author declares that there is no conflict of interest.

References

1. Hilger, S. Ein Maßkettenkalkül mit Anwendung auf Zentrmsmannigfaltingkeiten. Ph.D. Thesis, University Würzburg, Wuerzburg, Germany, 1988.
2. Agarwal, R.P.; Bohner, M.; Peterson, A. Inequalities on time scales: A survey. *Math. Inequal. Appl.* **2001**, *2001*, 535–555. [CrossRef]
3. Akin-Bohner, E.; Bohner, M.; Akin, F. Pachpatte inequalities on time scales. *J. Inequalities Pure Appl. Math.* **2005**, *6*, 1–23.
4. Li, W.N. Nonlinear integral inequalities in two independent variables on time scales. *Adv. Differ. Equ.* **2011**, *2011*, 283926. [CrossRef]
5. Anastassiou, G.A. Principles of delta fractional calculus on time scales and inequalities. *Math. Comput. Model.* **2010**, *52*, 556–566. [CrossRef]
6. Wong, F.-H.; Yeh, C.-C.; Yu, S.-L.; Hong, C.-H. Young's inequality and related results on time scales. *Appl. Math. Lett.* **2005**, *18*, 983–988. [CrossRef]
7. Wong, F.-H.; Yeh, C.-C.; Lian, W.-C. An extension of Jensen's inequality on time scales. *Adv. Dynam. Syst. Appl.* **2006**, *1*, 113–120.
8. Kuang, J. *Applied İnequalities*; Shandong Science Press: Jinan, China, 2003.
9. Uçar, D.; Hatipoğlu, V.F.; Akincali, A. Fractional integral inequalities on time scales. *Open J. Math. Sci.* **2018**, *2*, 361–370. [CrossRef]
10. Özkan, U.M.; Sarikaya, M.Z.; Yildirim, H. Extensions of certain integral inequalities on time scales. *Appl. Math. Lett.* **2008**, *2*, 993–1000. [CrossRef]
11. Tian, J.-F.; Ha, M.-H. Extensions of Hölder-type inequalities on time scales and their applications. *J. Nonlinear Sci. Appl.* **2017**, *10*, 937–953. [CrossRef]
12. Kac, V.; Cheung, P. *Quantum Calculus*; Universitext Springer: New York, NY, USA, 2002.
13. Yang, W.-G. A functional generalization of diamond-α integral Hölder's inequality on time scales. *Appl. Math. Lett.* **2010**, *23*, 1208–1212. [CrossRef]
14. Spedding, V. Taming nature's numbers. *New Sci.* **2003**, *179*, 28–31.
15. Tisdell, C.C.; Zaidi, A. Basic qualitative and quantitative results for solutions to nonlinear dynamic equations on time scales with an application to economic modelling. *Nonlinear Anal.* **2008**, *68*, 3504–3524. [CrossRef]
16. Bohner, M.; Heim, J.; Liu, A. Qualitative analysis of Solow model on time scales. *J. Concr. Appl. Math.* **2015**, *13*, 183–197.
17. Brigo, D.; Mercurio, F. Discrete time vs continuous time stock-price dynamics and implications for option pricing. *Financ. Stochast* **2000**, *4*, 147–159. [CrossRef]
18. Seadawy, A.R.; Iqbal, M.; Lu, D. Nonlinear wave solutions of the Kudryashov–Sinelshchikov dynamical equation in mixtures liquid-gas bubbles under the consideration of heat transfer and viscosity. *J. Taibah Univ. Sci.* **2019**, *13*, 1060–1072. [CrossRef]
19. Bohner, M.; Agarwal, R.P. Basic calculus on time scales and some of its applications. *Result. Der Math.* **1999**, *35*, 3–22.
20. Bohner, M.; Peterson, A. *Dynamic Equations on Time Scales, An Introduction with Applications*; Birkhauser: Boston, MA, USA, 2001.
21. Tuna, A.; Kutukcu, S. Some integral inequalities on time scales. *Appl. Math. Mech. (Engl. Ed.)* **2008**, *29*, 23–28. [CrossRef]
22. D'Ovidio, M.; Loreti, P.; Momenzadeh, A.; Ahrabi, S.S. Determination of Order in Linear Fractional Differential Equations. *Fract. Calc. Appl. Anal.* **2018**, *21*, 937–948. [CrossRef]
23. Heris, J.M.; Aghdaei, M.F. Equivalent HPM with ADM and Convergence of the HPM to a Class of Nonlinear Integral Equations. *J. Math. Ext.* **2013**, *7*, 33–49.
24. Heris, J.M.; Bagheri, M. Exact Solutions for the Modified KdV and the Generalized KdV Equations via Exp-Function Method. *J. Math. Ext.* **2010**, *4*, 75–95.
25. Akin, L. On the Fractional Maximal Delta Integral Type Inequalities on Time Scales. *Fractal Fract.* **2020**, *4*, 26. [CrossRef]
26. Higgins, R. Asymptotic behavior of second-order nonlinear dynamic equations on time scales. *Discret. Contin. Dyn. Syst. Ser. B* **2010**, *13*, 609–622. [CrossRef]
27. Ozturk, O.; Higgins, R. Limit behaviors of nonoscillatory solutions of three-dimensional time scale systems. *Turk. J. Math.* **2018**, *42*, 2576–2587. [CrossRef]
28. Shi, Z.S.H.; Yan, D.Y. Criterion on $L^{P_1} \times L^{P_2} \to L^q$-boundedness for oscillatory bilinear Hilbert transform. *Abstr. Appl. Anal.* **2014**, *2014*, 712051. [CrossRef]
29. Mingquan, W.; Xudong, N.; Di, W.; Dunyan, Y. A note on Hardy-Littlewood maximal operators. *J. Inequalities Appl.* **2016**, *2016*, 1–13.
30. Grafakos, L. *Classical and Modern Fourier Analysis*; China Machine Press: Beijing, China, 2005.
31. Rudin, W. *Real and Complex Analysis*, 3rd ed.; McGraw-Hill: Singapore, 1987.
32. Mamedov, F.I.; Zeren, Y.; Akin, L. Compactification of weighted Hardy operator in variable exponent Lebesgue spaces. *Asian J. Math. Comput. Sci.* **2017**, *17*, 38–47.
33. Akin, L. A Characterization of Approximation of Hardy Operators in VLS. *Celal Bayar Univ. J. Sci.* **2018**, *14*, 333–336. [CrossRef]
34. Akin, L.; Zeren, Y. Some properties for higher order commutators of Hardy-type integral operator on Herz–Morrey spaces with variable exponent. *Sigma J. Eng. Nat. Sci.* **2019**, *10*, 157–163.
35. Capone, C.; David Cruz-Uribe, S.F.O.; Fiorenza, A. The fractional maximal operator and fractional integrals on variable L^p spaces. *Rev. Mat. Iberoam.* **2007**, *23*, 743–770. [CrossRef]
36. Zhang, P.; Wu, J. Commutators of the fractional maximal function on variable exponent Lebesgue spaces. *Czechoslov. Math. J.* **2014**, *64*, 183–197. [CrossRef]

37. Beltran, D.; Madrid, J. Regularity of the centered fractional maximal Function on radial functions. *J. Funct. Anal.* **2020**, 108686. [CrossRef]
38. Akin, L.; Dusunceli, F. A New Approach for Weighted Hardy's Operator in VELS. *Appl. Math. Nonlinear Sci.* **2019**, *4*, 417–432. [CrossRef]
39. Agarwal, R.P.; Otero–Espinar, V.; Perera, K.; Vivero, D.R. Basic properties of Sobolev's spaces on time scales. *Adv. Differ. Equ.* **2006**, *2006*, 38121.
40. Akin, L.; Zeren, Y. An investigation on fractional maximal operator in time scales. In Proceedings of the 3rd International E-Conference On Mathematical Advances And Applications, Yildiz Technical University, Istanbul, Turkey, 24–27 June 2020.
41. Lu, S.Z.; Yan, D.Y. L^p Boundedness of multilinear oscillatory singular integrals with Calderón-Zygmund kernel. *Sci. China Ser. A* **2002**, *45*, 196–213.
42. Agarwal, R.P.; O'Regan, D.; Saker, S.H. *Hardy Type Inequalities on Time Scales*; Springer: Cham, Switzerland, 2016.
43. Akin, L. On some results of weighted Hölder type inequality on time scales. *Middle East J. Sci.* **2020**, *6*, 15–22. [CrossRef]

fractal and fractional

MDPI

Article

Stability Analysis and Numerical Computation of the Fractional Predator–Prey Model with the Harvesting Rate

Mehmet Yavuz [1,2,*] and Ndolane Sene [3,*]

1 Department of Mathematics and Computer Sciences, Necmettin Erbakan University, 42090 Konya, Turkey
2 Department of Mathematics, College of Engineering, Mathematics and Physical Sciences, University of Exeter, Penryn Campus, Cornwall TR10, UK
3 Laboratoire Lmdan, Département de Mathématiques de la Décision, Université Cheikh Anta Diop de Dakar, Faculté des Sciences Economiques et Gestion, Dakar Fann BP 5683, Senegal
* Correspondence: m.yavuz@exeter.ac.uk (M.Y.); ndolanesene@yahoo.fr (N.S.)

Received: 23 May 2020; Accepted: 14 July 2020; Published: 16 July 2020

Abstract: In this work, a fractional predator-prey model with the harvesting rate is considered. Besides the existence and uniqueness of the solution to the model, local stability and global stability are experienced. A novel discretization depending on the numerical discretization of the Riemann–Liouville integral was introduced and the corresponding numerical discretization of the predator–prey fractional model was obtained. The net reproduction number $\mathcal{R}_0$ was obtained for the prediction and persistence of the disease. The dynamical behavior of the equilibria was examined by using the stability criteria. Furthermore, numerical simulations of the model were performed and their graphical representations are shown to support the numerical discretizations, to visualize the effectiveness of our theoretical results and to monitor the effect of arbitrary order derivative. In our investigations, the fractional operator is understood in the Caputo sense.

Keywords: caputo fractional derivative; predator–prey model; harvesting rate; stability analysis; equilibrium point; implicit discretization numerical scheme

1. Introduction

Fractional calculus (FC) is a common field trying to understand the real-world phenomena that are modeled with non-integer-order derivatives and it is a field wherein the differentiation and the integrations are done with non-integer order derivatives as well. A fractional derivative, one can understand, is a type of derivative in which the order is non-integer-based but satisfies certain conditions: when the order of the derivative is zero we have the primary function, and when the order is one we converge to the first order integer order derivative [1]. The advantages of the fractional derivatives are the memory impact and the illustrative physical properties that are conserved. Using these types of operators, more effective and up-to-date studies have been revealing over time. In this context, fractional calculus theory and its illustrative applications are attracting attention all over the world day by day. New fractional operators that have different features have been defined and have been used extensively to model real-life problems. The emergence of the new operators in the literature can be considered as a result of the reproduction of new problems that model different types of real-life events. Fractional derivative operators that address the kind of nonlinear differential equations can be stated as non-local. There exist nowadays, many types of fractional derivatives with and without singular kernels. The fractional derivative begins with Leibniz's question in 1695. The list of the existing fractional derivatives is very long. With singular kernels, we have the Caputo–derivative [2], the Riemann–Liouville derivative [2] and the Katugampola derivative [3].

Without singular kernels, we have two types: the fractional derivative with an exponential kernel known as the Caputo–Fabrizio fractional derivative (CF) [4] and the fractional derivative with a Mittag–Leffler kernel known as the Atangana–Baleanu fractional derivative (ABC) [5]. Due to the memory effect, the non-integer models integrate all previous information from the past that makes it easier for them to predict and translate the epidemic models more accurately. Because of effective properties, fractional order calculus has found wide applications to model dynamics processes in many well-known fields, such as biology [6–11], physics [12–16], finance and economics [17,18], science and engineering [19,20], mechanics and mathematical modeling [21,22]. We enumerate numerous fractional operators in the literature [23–27]. Moreover, some numerical and approximate solution methods and their illustrative applications have been stated in [28–50].

Regarding modeling the predator–prey model (P–PM) with a fractional-order derivative, the numerical discretizations and the simulations are the subjects of research in this present paper. The P–PM has been considered in the context of the Caputo fractional derivative [1,51,52]. There exist many investigations related to the predator–prey models. In [53], Li et al. have proposed the stability analysis of the P–PM with harvesting. They have also provided graphical representations to support their results. In [54], the authors presented the predator–prey model under a reserved area. The authors have provided a new predator–prey model, proposed the equilibrium points, and investigated their stability analysis. In [55], Seo et al. have presented the P–PM with a Holling type functional response. In [56], Suryando et al. have proposed investigations related to the fractional P–PM with the functional response and harvesting. The authors have proposed as well the stability analysis of the equilibrium points of their proposed model. In [57], Tang presented a scientific report on predator–prey dynamics. In [58], Elettreby et al. have presented the stability analysis and the numerical simulations of the P–PM with a fractional order derivative and with a two prey, one predator system. In [59], Liu et al. have proposed the numerical solutions of a fractional P–PM and many others [60–67].

In this paper, we consider the predator–prey model with the Caputo fractional derivative and with the harvesting rate. The main objective of this paper is to propose a new numerical scheme base on the numerical scheme of the Riemann–Liouville integral to construct numerical discretizations of the fractional predator–prey model with the harvesting rate. The graphics of the solutions of the fractional equations will be proposed to support the numerical discretizations. We are mainly motivated by the fact in the literature, many investigations related to the predator–prey models investigate stability analysis. Here, after stability analysis, we propose a new numerical scheme. This issue will permit us to analyze the impact of the harvesting rate on the processes carefully.

The paper is divided as follows: In Section 2, we recall the fractional tools for our investigations. We deal with the Caputo derivative and Riemann–Liouville integral in our investigations throughout the paper. We also recall some properties related to the fractional derivatives. In Section 3, we present the predator–prey model in the context of the Caputo derivative. We focus on the qualitative properties of the solution in Section 4. In Section 5, we investigate the both local and global stability analyses of the equilibrium points of the predator–prey model. In Section 6, the novel numerical discretization of the fractional P–PM is proposed. In Section 7, we support the numerical discretizations by graphical representations. Final remarks are assigned in Section 8.

2. Some Preliminaries

In this section, we give the fundamental definitions that can be used throughout the paper. These definitions generally explain the fractional derivative in the power kernel sense.

Definition 1 ([1]). *The Riemann–Liouville (R–L) representation of fractional integral operator of order $\gamma > 0$ of a function $\varphi : (0, \infty) \to \mathbb{R}$ is given by*

$$ {}_{0}^{RL}D_t^{-\gamma}\varphi(t) = {}_{0}^{RL}I_t^{\gamma}\varphi(t) = \frac{1}{\Gamma(\gamma)} \int_0^t (t-\tau)^{\gamma-1}\varphi(\tau)d\tau, t > 0, \tag{1}$$

$$ {}_{0}^{RL}I_{t}^{0}\psi(\tau) = \psi(\tau), $$

where $\gamma > 0$ and $\Gamma(.)$ is the Gamma function.

Definition 2 ([1]). *The R–L representation of fractional operator of order $\gamma > 0$ of a function $\varphi : (0,\infty) \to \mathbb{R}$ is given by*

$$ {}_{0}^{RL}D_{t}^{\gamma}\varphi(t) = \begin{cases} \frac{1}{\Gamma(n-\gamma)}\left(\frac{d}{dt}\right)^{n}\int_{0}^{t}\frac{\varphi(\tau)}{(t-\tau)^{\gamma-n+1}}d\tau, & 0 \leq n-1 < \gamma < n, n = [\gamma], \\ \left(\frac{d}{dt}\right)^{n}\varphi(t), & \gamma = n \in \mathbb{N}. \end{cases} \tag{2} $$

Definition 3 ([1]). *The Caputo fractional operator of order $\gamma > 0$ of a function $\varphi : (0,\infty) \to \mathbb{R}$ is given by*

$$ {}_{0}^{C}D_{t}^{\gamma}\varphi(t) = \begin{cases} \frac{1}{\Gamma(n-\gamma)}\int_{0}^{t}\frac{(d/d\tau)^{n}\varphi(\tau)}{(t-\tau)^{\gamma-n+1}}d\tau, & 0 \leq n-1 < \gamma < n, n = [\gamma], n \in \mathbb{N}, \\ \left(\frac{d}{dt}\right)^{n}\varphi(t), & \gamma = n, n \in \mathbb{N}. \end{cases} \tag{3} $$

where the operator ${}_{0}^{C}D_{t}^{\gamma}$ satisfies:
${}_{0}^{C}D_{t}^{\gamma}{}_{0}^{RL}I_{t}^{\gamma}\varphi(t) = \varphi(t)$ *and* ${}_{0}^{RL}I_{t}^{\gamma}{}_{0}^{C}D_{t}^{\gamma}\varphi(t) = \varphi(t) - \sum_{v=0}^{n-1}\frac{\varphi^{(v)}(u)}{v!}(t-u)^{v}, t > u.$

Definition 4 ([1]). *The Laplace of the Caputo fractional operator of a function $\varphi(t)$ of order $\gamma > 0$ is presented with*

$$ \mathcal{L}\left[{}_{0}^{C}D_{t}^{\gamma}\varphi(t)\right] = s^{\gamma}\varphi(s) - \sum_{v=0}^{n-1}\varphi^{(v)}(0)s^{\gamma-v-1}. \tag{4} $$

We introduce two lemmas which will be used to establish local stability and global stability, respectively. The first lemma is called the Matignon criterion and the second one is the Lyapunov characterization for global stability.

Lemma 1 ([68]). *The fractional differential equation ${}_{0}^{C}D_{t}^{\gamma}x = Px$, with $P \in \mathbb{R}^{n\times n}$, $x(t_0) = x_0$, $0 < \gamma < 1$ and $x \in \mathbb{R}^{n}$, is local asymptotically stable if only if*

$$ |\arg(spc(P))| > \frac{\gamma\pi}{2}, \tag{5} $$

where $spc(P)$ is considered as the spectrum of the matrix P.

Lemma 2 ([69]). *We assume the vectors $w \in \mathbb{R}^{n}$ which are differentiables. Under the assumption $t \geq t_0$, we have the following condition*

$$ {}_{0}^{C}D_{t}^{\gamma}\left[w - w^{*} - w^{*}\ln\left(\frac{w}{w^{*}}\right)\right] \leq \left[1 - \frac{w}{w^{*}}\right]{}_{0}^{C}D_{t}^{\gamma}w, \text{ with } w^{*} \in \mathbb{R}_{+}^{n}. \tag{6} $$

3. Fractional Predator–Prey Model with Caputo Derivative

In this paper, we present the predator–prey model in the context of the fractional operator. Note that the fractional-order derivatives are more accurate at modeling biological processes since these types of operators consider the memory impact which gives more realistic results in real-life models. It is the deterministic property of the dynamical system. The following dynamics represent the fractional equation proposed in this section [53,70,71]

$$ {}_{0}^{C}D_{t}^{\gamma}x = rx\left(1 - \frac{x}{k}\right) - axy, \tag{7} $$

$$ {}_{0}^{C}D_{t}^{\gamma}y = acxy - dy - \mathcal{H}(y), \tag{8} $$

where ${}_{0}^{C}D_{t}^{\gamma}$ represents the Caputo fractional derivative which is given in Definition 3. We consider the initial conditions defined by

$$x(0) = x_0, \qquad y(0) = y_0, \tag{9}$$

where x denotes the prey species; y represents the predator species; the prey increases logistically with the growth rate denoted by r and the carrying capacity k; a represents the rate of predation; c denotes the efficiency of predation; d is the mortality rate of the predator species; and $\mathcal{H}(y)$ represents the harvesting function.

Now, we consider the model of Equations (7) and (8). Firstly, we describe harvesting function $\mathcal{H}(y)$ of the predators in our model, Equations (7) and (8), which has the following form

$$\mathcal{H}(y) = \begin{cases} my, & 0 \leq y \leq y_0, \\ h, & y_0 < y. \end{cases} \tag{10}$$

Using the model in Equations (7) and (8) as our baseline model, we suppose that harvesting takes place, but only the predator population is under harvesting, and introduce harvesting function $\mathcal{H}(y)$ of the predator to prey-predator model in Equations (7) and (8) for discussing its dynamical features. We assume that the harvesting rate is proportional to the predator population size until it reaches a threshold value due to limited facilities of harvesting or resource protection. Let us show the harvesting threshold value as $h = my_0$; thus Equations (7) and (8) can be written as the following equations for $0 \leq y \leq y_0$

$$\begin{aligned} {}_{0}^{C}D_{t}^{\gamma}x &= rx\left(1 - \frac{x}{k}\right) - axy, \\ {}_{0}^{C}D_{t}^{\gamma}y &= acxy - dy - my. \end{aligned} \tag{11}$$

When $y_0 < y$, then the system in Equations (7) and (8) turns to the following

$$\begin{aligned} {}_{0}^{C}D_{t}^{\gamma}x &= rx\left(1 - \frac{x}{k}\right) - axy, \\ {}_{0}^{C}D_{t}^{\gamma}y &= acxy - dy - h. \end{aligned} \tag{12}$$

Positivity and Boundedness

In this subsection, the positivity and boundedness of the solution for the proposed model (Equations (7) and (8)) are given. Let $\mathbb{R}_{+}^{2} = \{\chi(t) \in \mathbb{R}^{2} : \chi(t) \geq 0\}$ and $\chi(t) = [x(t), y(t)]^{T}$.

Theorem 1. *The solution of the proposed fractional-order model (Equations (7) and (8)) along initial conditions (9) is bounded in $\mathbb{R}_{+}^{2}$. Moreover, the density of the population remains in a nonnegative region.*

Proof. Let the function $W(t) = x + \frac{1}{c}y$ and λ be a positive constant. Applying the Caputo derivative, we have the following relationship

$$\begin{aligned} {}_{0}^{C}D_{t}^{\gamma}W + \lambda W &= -\frac{rx^2}{k} + rx - \frac{dy}{c} - \frac{\mathcal{H}(y)}{c} + \lambda x + \frac{\lambda}{c}y \\ &= -\frac{rx^2}{k} + (r+\lambda)x + \left(\frac{\lambda}{c} - \frac{d}{c}\right)y - \frac{\mathcal{H}(y)}{c} \\ &= -\frac{r}{k}\left(x^2 - \frac{k(r+\lambda)}{r}x\right) + \left(\frac{\lambda}{c} - \frac{d}{c}\right)y - \frac{\mathcal{H}(y)}{c} \\ &\leq -\frac{r}{k}\left(x - \frac{k(r+\lambda)}{2r}\right)^2 + \frac{k(r+\lambda)^2}{4r}, \end{aligned} \tag{13}$$

where $\lambda < d + m$. From the property in [72] and using comparison principle, since t converges to infinity, we have the following relationship

$$W(t) \leq W(0)\mathbb{E}_{\gamma}\left(-\lambda t^{\gamma}\right) + \frac{k(r+\lambda)^2}{4r} t^{\gamma}\mathbb{E}_{\gamma,\gamma+1}\left(-\lambda t^{\gamma}\right) \leq \frac{k(r+\lambda)^2}{4r}, \tag{14}$$

where $\mathbb{E}_{\gamma,\beta}(.)$ is the Mittag–Leffer function of two parameters. Finally, the following set in the domain $\mathbb{R}^2_+$ is positively invariant

$$\mathcal{A} = \left\{(x(t), y(t)) \in \mathbb{R}^2_+ |\ x(t) \geq 0, y(t) \geq 0, x + \frac{1}{c}y \leq \frac{k(r+\lambda)^2}{4r}\right\}.$$

□

We have replaced the classical derivative by the Caputo derivative in the study. It is important to justify the replacement and to prove the physical meanings of the new model. Another point is also to show that the solution to the new model exists and is unique. All these points will be discussed in the next sections.

4. Qualitative Properties of the P–PM

In this Part, we give the qualitative properties of the solutions of the predator–prey model which is given in the system (7) and (8). Firstly we start by taking the Riemann–Liouville integral which is given in Definition 1 of both sides the mentioned system and we get

$$\begin{aligned} x(t) - x(0) &= {}^{RL}_{0}I^{\gamma}_{t}\left(rx\left(1-\tfrac{x}{k}\right) - axy\right), \\ y(t) - y(0) &= {}^{RL}_{0}I^{\gamma}_{t}\left(acxy - dy - \mathcal{H}(y)\right), \end{aligned} \tag{15}$$

which gives the following Volterra-type integral equations:

$$\begin{aligned} x(t) - x(0) &= \frac{1}{\Gamma(\gamma)}\int_0^t (t-\tau)^{\gamma-1}\left(rx(\tau)\left(1-\frac{x(\tau)}{k}\right) - ax(\tau)y(\tau)\right)d\tau, \\ y(t) - y(0) &= \frac{1}{\Gamma(\gamma)}\int_0^t (t-\tau)^{\gamma-1}\left(acx(\tau)y(\tau) - dy(\tau) - \mathcal{H}(y)\right)d\tau. \end{aligned} \tag{16}$$

Let us define the following kernels as

$$\begin{aligned} \varphi(t,x,y) &= rx(t)\left(1-\frac{x(t)}{k}\right) - ax(t)y(t), \\ \phi(t,x,y) &= acx(t)y(t) - dy(t) - \mathcal{H}(y). \end{aligned} \tag{17}$$

Then the following theorem arises:

Theorem 2. *The kernels φ and ϕ satisfy the Lipschitz assumptions and contractions if the following inequality is verified:*

$$0 \leq z_1, z_2 < 1. \tag{18}$$

where $\|x\| \leq q$, $\|y\| \leq l$, $z_1 = r + al + 2qr/k$, $q, l \geq 0$ and $z_2 = acq + d$, or $z_2 = acq + d + m$, for the constant harvesting rate or depending on the predator population, respectively.

Proof. Let x_1 and x_2 be two functions for the kernel φ; and y_1 and y_2 be two functions for the kernel ϕ. Then we have

$$\begin{aligned} \|\varphi(t,x_1,y)-\varphi(t,x_2,y)\| &= \left\|rx_1\left(1-\frac{x_1}{k}\right)-ax_1y-rx_2\left(1-\frac{x_2}{k}\right)+ax_2y\right\|, \\ &\leq \left(r+al+\frac{2qr}{k}\right)\|x_1-x_2\|, \\ &\leq z_1\|x_1-x_2\|, \end{aligned} \tag{19}$$

and

$$\begin{aligned} \|\varphi(t,x,y_1)-\varphi(t,x,y_2)\| &= \|acxy_1-dy_1-h-acxy_2+dy_2+h\|, \\ &\leq (acq+d)\|y_1-y_2\|, \\ &\leq z_2\|y_1-y_2\|, \end{aligned} \tag{20}$$

or

$$\begin{aligned} \|\varphi(t,x,y_1)-\varphi(t,x,y_2)\| &= \|acxy_1-dy_1-my_1-acxy_2+dy_2+my_2\|, \\ &\leq (acq+d+m)\|y_1-y_2\|, \\ &\leq z_2\|y_1-y_2\|, \end{aligned} \tag{21}$$

where $\|.\|$ is the Euclidean norm, $\|x\| \leq q$, $\|y\| \leq l$, $z_1 = r+al+2qr/k$ and $z_2 = acq+d$, or $z_2 = acq+d+m$, for the constant harvesting rate or depending on the predator population, respectively. Therefore, the Lipschitz conditions are satisfied for kernels φ and ϕ, and if $0 \leq z_1, z_2 < 1$, then z_1 and z_2 are also contractions for φ and ϕ, respectively. This proofs the theorem. □

By considering the kernels φ and ϕ, we can rewrite the system which is given in Equation (16) as follows:

$$\begin{aligned} x(t) &= x(0)+\frac{1}{\Gamma(\gamma)}\int_0^t (t-\tau)^{\gamma-1}\varphi(\tau,x,y)\,d\tau, \\ y(t) &= y(0)+\frac{1}{\Gamma(\gamma)}\int_0^t (t-\tau)^{\gamma-1}\phi(\tau,x,y)\,d\tau. \end{aligned} \tag{22}$$

We can proceed with the following recursive formula

$$\begin{aligned} x_n(t) &= x(0)+\frac{1}{\Gamma(\gamma)}\int_0^t (t-\tau)^{\gamma-1}\varphi(\tau,x_{n-1},y)\,d\tau, \\ y_n(t) &= y(0)+\frac{1}{\Gamma(\gamma)}\int_0^t (t-\tau)^{\gamma-1}\phi(\tau,x,y_{n-1})\,d\tau, \end{aligned} \tag{23}$$

where $x_0(t) = x(0)$ and $y_0(t) = y(0)$. Then we can write

$$\begin{aligned} \Psi_n(t) &= x_n(t)-x_{n-1}(t) = \frac{1}{\Gamma(\gamma)}\int_0^t (t-\tau)^{\gamma-1}\left[\varphi(\tau,x_{n-1},y)-\varphi(\tau,x_{n-2},y)\right]d\tau, \\ \Phi_n(t) &= y_n(t)-y_{n-1}(t) = \frac{1}{\Gamma(\gamma)}\int_0^t (t-\tau)^{\gamma-1}\left[\phi(\tau,x,y_{n-1})-\phi(\tau,x,y_{n-2})\right]d\tau, \end{aligned} \tag{24}$$

where $x_n(t) = \sum_{j=1}^{n} \Psi_n(t)$ and $y_n(t) = \sum_{j=1}^{n} \Phi_n(t)$. By taking the norm of both sides of Equation (24), we have

$$\begin{aligned} \|\Psi_n(t)\| &= \|x_n(t) - x_{n-1}(t)\| \leq \frac{1}{\Gamma(\gamma)} \left\| \int_0^t (t-\tau)^{\gamma-1} [\varphi(\tau, x_{n-1}, y) - \varphi(\tau, x_{n-2}, y)] \, d\tau \right\|, \\ \|\Phi_n(t)\| &= \|y_n(t) - y_{n-1}(t)\| \leq \frac{1}{\Gamma(\gamma)} \left\| \int_0^t (t-\tau)^{\gamma-1} [\phi(\tau, x, y_{n-1}) - \phi(\tau, x, y_{n-2})] \, d\tau \right\|. \end{aligned} \quad (25)$$

Since the kernels satisfy the Lipschitz condition (see Theorem 2), we get

$$\begin{aligned} \|x_n(t) - x_{n-1}(t)\| &\leq \frac{z_1}{\Gamma(\gamma)} \int_0^t (t-\tau)^{\gamma-1} \|x_{n-1} - x_{n-2}\| \, d\tau, \\ \|y_n(t) - y_{n-1}(t)\| &\leq \frac{z_2}{\Gamma(\gamma)} \int_0^t (t-\tau)^{\gamma-1} \|y_{n-1} - y_{n-2}\| \, d\tau. \end{aligned} \quad (26)$$

Then we achieve from the last inequality

$$\begin{aligned} \|\Psi_n(t)\| &\leq \frac{z_1}{\Gamma(\gamma)} \int_0^t (t-\tau)^{\gamma-1} \|\Psi_{n-1}(\tau)\| \, d\tau, \\ \|\Phi_n(t)\| &\leq \frac{z_2}{\Gamma(\gamma)} \int_0^t (t-\tau)^{\gamma-1} \|\Phi_{n-1}(\tau)\| \, d\tau. \end{aligned} \quad (27)$$

These results give us the following theorem:

Theorem 3. *The predator–prey model defined by the fractional operator with the power kernel has a solution under the condition that we are able to find t_{max} holding:*

$$\frac{z_i t_{max}^{\gamma}}{\Gamma(\gamma+1)} < 1, \quad i = 1, 2. \quad (28)$$

Proof. Considering the functions $x(t)$ and $y(t)$ are bounded and their kernels φ and ϕ hold the Lipschitz condition, we can give the following by taking Equation (27) into account,

$$\begin{aligned} \|\Psi_n(t)\| &\leq \|x_0(t)\| \left\{ \frac{z_1 t_{max}^{\gamma}}{\Gamma(\gamma+1)} \right\}^n, \\ \|\Phi_n(t)\| &\leq \|y_0(t)\| \left\{ \frac{z_2 t_{max}^{\gamma}}{\Gamma(\gamma+1)} \right\}^n. \end{aligned} \quad (29)$$

Now we show that the functions in Equation (29) are the solutions of the given predator–prey model. We suppose

$$\begin{aligned} x(t) - x(0) &= x_n(t) - p_n(t), \\ y(t) - y(0) &= y_n(t) - q_n(t), \end{aligned} \quad (30)$$

where p_n and q_n are remaining terms. Then we will demonstrate that the terms which are given in Equation (30) hold that $\|p_\infty(t)\| \to 0$ and $\|q_\infty(t)\| \to 0$. Since we have

$$\begin{aligned} \|p_n(t)\| &\leq \left\| \frac{1}{\Gamma(\gamma)} \int_0^t (t-\tau)^{\gamma-1} [\varphi(\tau, x, y) - \varphi(\tau, x_{n-1}, y)] \, d\tau \right\| \\ &\leq \frac{1}{\Gamma(\gamma)} \int_0^t (t-\tau)^{\gamma-1} \|\varphi(\tau, x, y) - \varphi(\tau, x_{n-1}, y)\| \, d\tau \\ &\leq \frac{t^{\gamma} z_1}{\Gamma(\gamma+1)} \|x - x_{n-1}\|, \end{aligned} \quad (31)$$

and

$$\begin{aligned} \|q_n(t)\| &\leq \left\| \frac{1}{\Gamma(\gamma)} \int_0^t (t-\tau)^{\gamma-1} [\phi(\tau,x,y) - \phi(\tau,x,y_{n-1})]\, d\tau \right\| \\ &\leq \frac{1}{\Gamma(\gamma)} \int_0^t (t-\tau)^{\gamma-1} \|\phi(\tau,x,y) - \phi(\tau,x,y_{n-1})\|\, d\tau \\ &\leq \frac{t^\gamma z_2}{\Gamma(\gamma+1)} \|y - y_{n-1}\|, \end{aligned} \tag{32}$$

repeating this process recursively, we get

$$\|p_n(t)\| \leq \left\{ \frac{t^\gamma}{\Gamma(\gamma+1)} \right\}^{n+1} z_1^n N,$$

and

$$\|q_n(t)\| \leq \left\{ \frac{t^\gamma}{\Gamma(\gamma+1)} \right\}^{n+1} z_2^n N.$$

Considering these last two inequalities at t_{max} point, we have

$$\|p_n(t)\| \leq \left\{ \frac{t_{max}^\gamma}{\Gamma(\gamma+1)} \right\}^{n+1} z_1^n N,$$

and

$$\|q_n(t)\| \leq \left\{ \frac{t_{max}^\gamma}{\Gamma(\gamma+1)} \right\}^{n+1} z_2^n N.$$

For the last step, after applying the limit to both sides of the last inequalities as $n \to \infty$, and by taking into account the results of Theorem 2, we get $\|p_\infty(t)\| \to 0$ and $\|q_\infty(t)\| \to 0$. □

Theorem 4. *The predator–prey model defined by the fractional operator with the power kernel in Equations (7) and (8) has a unique solution.*

Proof. Let say there exists another solution of the system, namely, $x_1(t)$ and $y_1(t)$. Then we can write

$$\begin{aligned} x(t) - x_1(t) &= \frac{1}{\Gamma(\gamma)} \int_0^t (t-\tau)^{\gamma-1} [\varphi(\tau,x,y) - \varphi(\tau,x_1,y)]\, d\tau, \\ y(t) - y_1(t) &= \frac{1}{\Gamma(\gamma)} \int_0^t (t-\tau)^{\gamma-1} [\phi(\tau,x,y) - \phi(\tau,x,y_1)]\, d\tau. \end{aligned} \tag{33}$$

If we apply the norm to both sides of Equation (33), we obtain

$$\begin{aligned} \|x(t) - x_1(t)\| &\leq \frac{1}{\Gamma(\gamma)} \int_0^t (t-\tau)^{\gamma-1} \|\varphi(\tau,x,y) - \varphi(\tau,x_1,y)\|\, d\tau, \\ \|y(t) - y_1(t)\| &\leq \frac{1}{\Gamma(\gamma)} \int_0^t (t-\tau)^{\gamma-1} \|\phi(\tau,x,y) - \phi(\tau,x,y_1)\|\, d\tau. \end{aligned} \tag{34}$$

Since the Lipschitz condition is satisfied by the kernels φ and ϕ, we can write

$$\begin{aligned} \|x(t) - x_1(t)\| &\leq \frac{z_1 t^\gamma}{\Gamma(\gamma+1)} \|x(t) - x_1(t)\|, \\ \|y(t) - y_1(t)\| &\leq \frac{z_2 t^\gamma}{\Gamma(\gamma+1)} \|y(t) - y_1(t)\|, \end{aligned} \tag{35}$$

which gives

$$\begin{aligned} \|x(t) - x_1(t)\| \left(1 - \frac{z_1 t^\gamma}{\Gamma(\gamma+1)}\right) &\leq 0, \\ \|y(t) - y_1(t)\| \left(1 - \frac{z_2 t^\gamma}{\Gamma(\gamma+1)}\right) &\leq 0. \end{aligned} \tag{36}$$

Hence, we have $\|x(t) - x_1(t)\| = 0$ and $\|y(t) - y_1(t)\| = 0$ which gives $x(t) = x_1(t)$ and $y(t) = y_1(t)$. This concludes that the model has a unique solution and proofs the theorem. □

5. Stability Analysis of the Predator–Prey Model

In this section, we determine the equilibrium points and study their stability. The local stability of the equilibrium points will be examined by using the Jacobian matrix, and the global asymptotic stability will be studied by constructing a Lyapunov function.

5.1. Existence of Equilibria

In this subsection, we examine the existence of all nonnegative equilibria and present our results of the existence of positive equilibria as follows. The equilibrium points of the P–PM described by Equations (7) and (8) are obtained by solving the equations represented by

$${}_0^C D_t^\gamma x = 0, \qquad {}_0^C D_t^\gamma y = 0. \tag{37}$$

Before going further, we proceed with the net reproduction number for the predator population as the expected number of predator individuals producing as the predator population is introduced into a stable prey population [53]. Thus we adopt the following procedure. Fractional differential Equations (7) and (8) can be written in the form

$${}_0^C D_t^\gamma \xi = \mathcal{F}(\xi) - \mathcal{V}(\xi), \tag{38}$$

where $\xi = (y, x)$ and the matrix $\mathcal{F}$ and $\mathcal{V}$ are described as follows

$$\mathcal{F} = \begin{pmatrix} acxy \\ 0 \end{pmatrix}, \qquad \mathcal{V} = \begin{pmatrix} dy + my \\ -rx\left(1 - \frac{x}{k}\right) + axy \end{pmatrix}. \tag{39}$$

The Jacobian matrixes of the functions $\mathcal{F}$ and $\mathcal{V}$ at the predator-free point $(k, 0)$ gives the following matrixes F and V. We have the following

$$F = \begin{pmatrix} ack & 0 \\ 0 & 0 \end{pmatrix}, \qquad V^{-1} = \begin{pmatrix} 1/(d+m) & 0 \\ 0 & 1/r \end{pmatrix}. \tag{40}$$

Finally, the reproduction number is obtained by determining the spectral radius of the matrix FV^{-1}:

$$\mathcal{R}_0 = \frac{ack}{d+m}. \tag{41}$$

The reproduction number is significant in the classification of the biological models. This number, in general, tells us the number of species that can be infected by a single infected person. For the control of the biological model, notably, its usage in the stability analysis is essential. As we will notice, for the rest of the paper, the stability analysis of the extinction point, the predator-free equilibrium and the non-trivial equilibrium will be focused according to the reproduction number $\mathcal{R}_0$. Many other interpretations of the net reproduction number exist as well.

Now we proceed with the system in Equation (11) which considers the linear predator harvesting strategy to present its equilibria. The resolution of Equation (11) gives three different equilibrium points, which are the extinction point $(0,0)$, the predator-free equilibrium $(k,0)$ and the non-trivial predator–prey equilibrium point $\left(\frac{d+m}{ac}, \frac{r}{a}\left(1 - \frac{d+m}{akc}\right)\right)$; it is straightforward to reach to the first two equilibria. In the subregion $\mathcal{A}$ with the linear predator harvest strategy, i.e., when $0 \leq y \leq y_0$, a positive equilibrium, satisfies the following system

$$\begin{aligned} rx^*\left(1 - \frac{x^*}{k}\right) - ax^*y^* &= 0, \\ acx^*y^* - dy^* - my^* &= 0, \end{aligned} \tag{42}$$

which follows $x^* = \dfrac{d+m}{ac} = \dfrac{k}{\mathcal{R}_0}$ and $y^* = \dfrac{r}{a}\left(1 - \dfrac{1}{\mathcal{R}_0}\right) > 0$, if $\mathcal{R}_0 > 1$. Meanwhile, we get from $y^* = \dfrac{r}{a}\left(1 - \dfrac{1}{\mathcal{R}_0}\right) \leq y_0$, thus $\dfrac{1}{\mathcal{R}_0} \geq \dfrac{r - ay_0}{r}$ which means that there exists a positive coexistence equilibrium in the region when $0 \leq y \leq y_0$ if $\dfrac{r - ay_0}{r} \leq 0$, or $\dfrac{r - ay_0}{r} > 0$ and $\mathcal{R}_0 \leq \dfrac{1}{1 - \frac{ay_0}{r}} = \dfrac{r}{r - ay_0}$.

5.2. Stability of Equilibria

For the investigation related to the stability of the equilibrium points, we give the form of the Jacobian matrix; that is,

$$J = \begin{pmatrix} r\left(1 - \frac{2x}{k}\right) - ay & -ax \\ acy & acx - d - m \end{pmatrix}. \tag{43}$$

For the extinction point $(0,0)$, we fix $x = 0$ and $y = 0$, substituting them into the Equation (43), andwe obtain the Jacobian matrix computed at the $(0,0)$ given by the following matrix

$$J_{(0,0)} = \begin{pmatrix} r & 0 \\ 0 & -d - m \end{pmatrix}. \tag{44}$$

The eigenvalues of the Jacobian matrix are given by $\lambda_1 = r$ and $\lambda_2 = -d - m$. In the context of fractional order derivative, we evaluate $\arg(\lambda_1) = 0 < \gamma\pi/2$ and $\arg(\lambda_2) = \pi > \gamma\pi/2$, for all $\gamma \in (0,1)$. Therefore, the condition described in Lemma 1 is not satisfied; that is, the extinction point $(0,0)$ is unstable.

The local stability of the predator-free equilibrium is described in the following procedure. The Jacobian matrix defined in Equation (43) evaluated at the point $(k,0)$ is determined by the matrix

$$J_{(k,0)} = \begin{pmatrix} -r & -ak \\ 0 & ack - d - m \end{pmatrix}. \tag{45}$$

Thus, the eigenvalues of the Jacobian matrix are given by $\lambda_1 = -r$ and $\lambda_2 = ack - d - m = (d+m)\left[\mathcal{R}_0 - 1\right]$. Now, in the context of fractional order derivative, we evaluate $\arg(\lambda_1) = \pi > \gamma\pi/2$ and $\arg(\lambda_2) = \pi > \gamma\pi/2$, for all $\gamma \in (0,1)$, and when the reproduction number satisfies the condition $\mathcal{R}_0 < 1$. Thus, the predator-free equilibrium is locally asymptotically stable if the condition $\mathcal{R}_0 < 1$ is held. We also notice when $\mathcal{R}_0 > 1$, then $\arg(\lambda_2) = 0 > \gamma\pi/2$, which in turn is impossible. Thus, the predator free-equilibrium should be unstable for all fractional time order satisfying the condition $\gamma \in (0,1)$.

Theorem 5. *The coexistence equilibrium $E^*(x^*, y^*)$ of the proposed fractional predator–prey model is locally asymptotically stable if $\mathcal{R}_0 > 1$; otherwise, it is unstable.*

Proof. To study the stability criterion of coexistence equilibrium, the Jacobian matrix which has been calculated in Equation (43) is considered in the equilibrium point $E^*\,(x^*, y^*)$. Thus, it follows

$$J_{(x^*,y^*)} = \begin{pmatrix} \frac{-r\,(d+m)}{akc} & \frac{-\,(d+m)}{c} \\ cr\left(1-\frac{d+m}{ack}\right) & 0 \end{pmatrix}. \tag{46}$$

We can evaluate the eigenvalues by solving the following corresponding characteristic equation

$$\left|J_{(x^*,y^*)} - \kappa I\right| = 0, \tag{47}$$

which gives the equation of the form

$$\kappa^2 + \kappa\frac{r\,(d+m)}{ack} + r\,(d+m)\left(1-\frac{d+m}{ack}\right) = 0, \tag{48}$$

and we then get from the last equation the roots as $\kappa_{1,2} = \frac{-\frac{r}{\mathcal{R}_0} \mp \sqrt{\frac{r^2}{\mathcal{R}_0^2} - 4r(d+m)\left(1-\frac{1}{\mathcal{R}_0}\right)}}{2}$. This means that all two eigenvalues have negative real parts as long as $\mathcal{R}_0 > 1$. Therefore, we conclude from this fact that the coexistence equilibrium $E^*\,(x^*, y^*)$ is locally asymptotically stable if $\mathcal{R}_0 > 1$. Moreover, if $\mathcal{R}_0 < 1$, one of the eigenvalues is positive which means that the coexistence equilibrium is unstable. □

Now, we prove that the coexistence equilibrium point is globally asymptotically stable. For that proof we take into account the Lyapunov direct technique. To arrive at our end, we propose the following Lyapunov function

$$V(x,y) = c\left[x - x^* - x^*\ln\left(\frac{x}{x^*}\right)\right] + y - y^* - y^*\ln\left(\frac{y}{y^*}\right). \tag{49}$$

Using Lemma 2, the fractional derivative along the trajectories of the Lyapunov function yields that

$$\begin{aligned} {}_0^C D_t^\gamma V &\le c\left[1-\frac{x^*}{x}\right] {}_0^C D_t^\gamma x + \left[1-\frac{y^*}{y}\right] {}_0^C D_t^\gamma y \\ &\le c\left[1-\frac{x^*}{x}\right]\left[rx\left(1-\frac{x}{k}\right) - axy\right] + \left[1-\frac{y^*}{y}\right][acxy - dy - my] \\ &\le crx - \frac{crx^2}{k} - crx^* + \frac{crxx^*}{k} - acxy^* + (d+m)\,y^*. \end{aligned} \tag{50}$$

Using the fact that $x^* = \frac{d+m}{ac}$ and $y^* = \frac{r}{a}\left(1-\frac{d+m}{akc}\right)$, Equation (50) can be written in the following form:

$${}_0^C D_t^\gamma V \le -\frac{cr}{k}\left[x - \frac{d+m}{ac}\right]^2 \le 0, \tag{51}$$

which implies that the non-trivial equilibrium point $\left(\frac{d+m}{ac}, \frac{r}{a}\left(1-\frac{d+m}{akc}\right)\right)$ is globally asymptotically stable.

6. Numerical Scheme of the Predator–Prey Model

This section addresses the numerical discretizations of the fractional predator–prey equations represented by Equations (7) and (8). The algorithm adopted in this section begins with the solutions of the fractional differential equation of Equations (7) and (8) in terms of the R–L integral. We mainly use the implicit discretization method to construct the scheme. The solutions of the fractional predator–prey model described by Equations (7) and (8) are represented as follows:

$$x(t) = x(0) + I^{\gamma}\Psi(t,x), \quad (52)$$
$$y(t) = y(0) + I^{\gamma}\Phi(t,y). \quad (53)$$

At the point t_n, the solutions represented by Equations (52) and (53) can be discretized as the following form

$$x(t_n) = x(0) + I^{\gamma}\Psi(t_n,x), \quad (54)$$
$$y(t_n) = y(0) + I^{\gamma}\Phi(t_n,y). \quad (55)$$

We set the step-size as z and the grid step as $t_n = nz$. Thus the Riemann–Liouville integral can be discretized in an implicit sense to the following form.

$$I^{\gamma}\Psi(t_n,x) = z^{\gamma}\left[\bar{a}_n^{(\gamma)}\Psi(0) + \sum_{i=1}^{n}\bar{a}_{n-i}^{(\gamma)}\Psi(t_i,x_i)\right], \quad (56)$$
$$I^{\gamma}\Phi(t_n,y) = z^{\gamma}\left[\bar{a}_n^{(\gamma)}\Phi(0) + \sum_{i=1}^{n}\bar{a}_{n-i}^{(\gamma)}\Phi(t_i,x_i)\right], \quad (57)$$

where the parameters are represented by the expressions enumerated as follows

$$\bar{a}_n^{(\gamma)} = \frac{(n-1)^{\gamma} - n^{\gamma}(n-\gamma-1)}{\Gamma(2+\gamma)}, \quad (58)$$

and for $n = 1, 2, \ldots$, we set the following parameters in other cases as the following form:

$$a_0^{(\gamma)} = \frac{1}{\Gamma(2+\gamma)} \text{ and } a_n^{(\gamma)} = \frac{(n-1)^{\gamma+1} - 2n^{\gamma+1} + (n+1)^{\gamma+1}}{\Gamma(2+\gamma)}. \quad (59)$$

Substituting Equations (56) and (57) into Equations (54) and (55), respectively, the final numerical discretization of the P–PM in the context of the Caputo derivative is presented by the following form [73].

$$x(t_n) = x(0) + z^{\gamma}\left[\bar{a}_n^{(\gamma)}\Psi(0) + \sum_{i=1}^{n}\bar{a}_{n-i}^{(\gamma)}\Psi(t_i,x_i)\right], \quad (60)$$
$$y(t_n) = y(0) + z^{\gamma}\left[\bar{a}_n^{(\gamma)}\Phi(0) + \sum_{i=1}^{n}\bar{a}_{n-i}^{(\gamma)}\Phi(t_i,x_i)\right], \quad (61)$$

where the following relationships describe the numerical discretizations of the intermediary functions Ψ and Φ.

$$\Psi(t_i,x_i) = rx_i\left(1 - \frac{x_i}{k}\right) - ax_iy_i, \quad (62)$$
$$\Phi(t_i,y_i) = acx_iy_i - dy_i - \mathcal{H}(y_i). \quad (63)$$

We set $x(t_n)$ and $y(t_n)$, the numerical approximations of the fractional predator–prey model, and x_n and y_n, their associated exact solutions. Note that our numerical discretization follow the following errors terms:

$$|x(t_n) - x_n| = \mathcal{O}\left(z^{\min\{\gamma+1,2\}}\right), \tag{64}$$

$$|y(t_n) - y_n| = \mathcal{O}\left(z^{\min\{\gamma+1,2\}}\right), \tag{65}$$

which converge to zero as the step-size z converge to zero too. In the next section, we give the graphical representations to support our implicit numerical discretization for the fractional predator–prey model constructed with the Caputo derivative.

7. Numerical Simulation of the Implicit Scheme

We illustrate the numerical discretizations of the predator–prey model described in the previous section. For the graphical representations, we consider different contexts by considering the different values of the parameters of the model. We, firstly, analyze the solution according to the fixed harvesting rate (case 1). In first cases, we fix the following assumptions [53]: the growth rate $r = 0.03$ and the carrying capacity $k = 0.25$, the rate of predation is $a = 0.5$, the efficiency of predation is $c = 0.4$, $d = 0.01$ is death rate of the predator species and $\gamma = 0.95$ is the order. In the first subcase, we fix the harvesting rate as $h = 0.00033$; in Figure 1, we depict the evolutions of the predator and the prey species in time. We notice the trajectory describes a cycle and converges to the non-trivial equilibrium point.

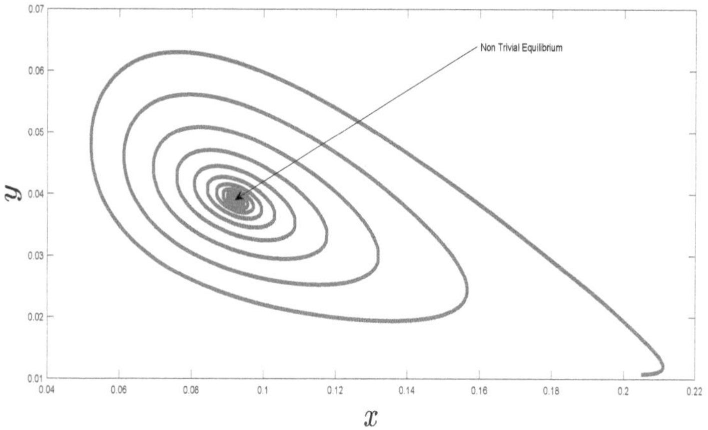

Figure 1. Phase diagram of fractional P–PM with $\gamma = 0.95$.

In Figure 2, we depict the dynamics of the P–PM under no harvesting rate $(h = 0)$. We notice the same dynamics as in the presence of harvesting rate; the solutions describe a cycle and converge to a non-trivial equilibrium point.

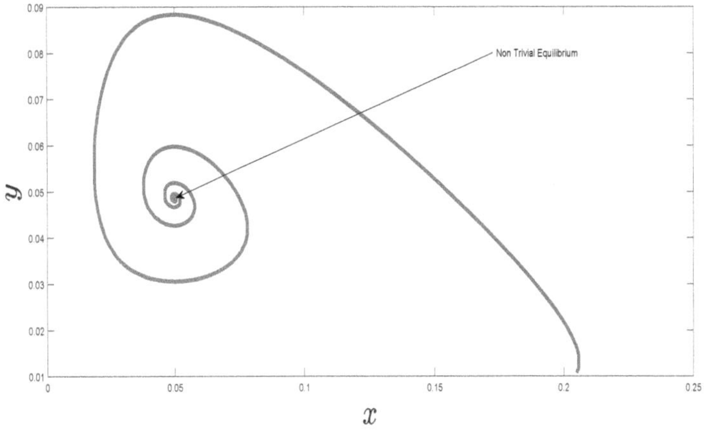

Figure 2. Dynamical behavior of fractional P–PM under no harvesting rate with $\gamma = 0.95$.

We notice when the harvesting rate varies and exceeds $h = 0.00035$, in Figure 3, we see the line instead of the cycle. It corresponds that the non-trivial equilibrium point is not stable. Furthermore, the obtained solutions for the predator–prey model are unrealistic, since the species can not be negative; they do not make sense.

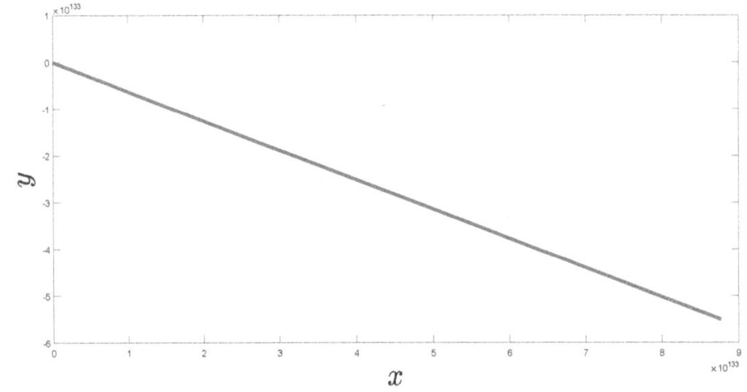

Figure 3. Dynamical behavior of fractional P–PM with $\gamma = 0.95$.

In conclusion, the harvesting rate has a significant impact on the dynamics of the P–PMs. We note after certain values that the behaviors of the solutions are in contradiction with the real possible phenomena. Thus, it is crucial to control the harvesting rate into the predator–prey models. There exist many methods to control it, such as the maximization principle using the Hamiltonian approach. This problem is not addressed in this paper.

Let us give illustrative results to support our results. We change the values of the parameters, and we suppose the following assumptions [53]: the growth rate $r = 0.004$ and the carrying capacity $k = 0.25$, the rate of predation $a = 0.1$, the efficiency of predation $c = 0.4$, the death rate of the predator species $d = 0.001$, the harvesting rate $h = 0.000005$ and the order is maintained at $\gamma = 0.95$.

We notice in Figure 4 that the evolutions of the predator and the prey species have been depicted in time. We see the trajectory describes a cycle and converges to the non-trivial equilibrium point. In conclusion, after variation in the parameters, the solutions respect the cycles; there are not many changes in the behaviors of the solutions. Our fractional model is, in general, stable but strongly depends on the values of the harvesting rate, because when the harvesting rate value exceeds certain values, the cycle is displayed.

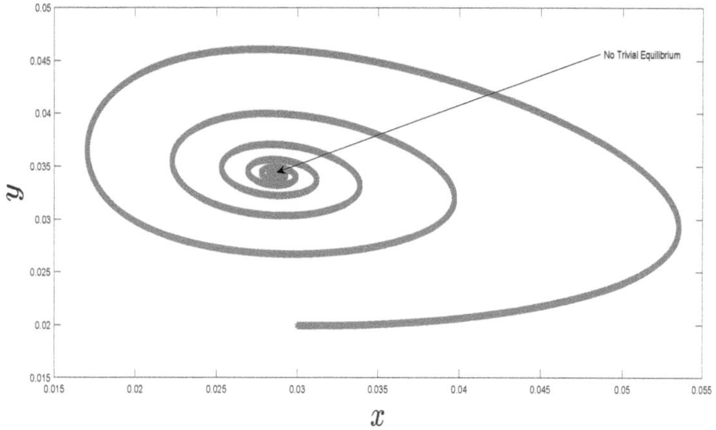

Figure 4. Dynamical behavior of fractional P–PM with $\gamma = 0.95$.

To support our numerical scheme, we consider the second case where the harvesting rate is expressed as the linear representation of the predator population, i.e., $h = my$. We set the following assumptions [53]: the growth rate $r = 0.1$ and the carrying capacity $k = 0.5$, $a = 0.25$ represents the rate of predation, $c = 0.8$ denotes the efficiency of predation, $d = 0.01$ is death rate of the predator species, the order $\gamma = 0.95$ and $m = 0.0003$. In Figure 5, we represent graphically the dynamics of the predator versus prey.

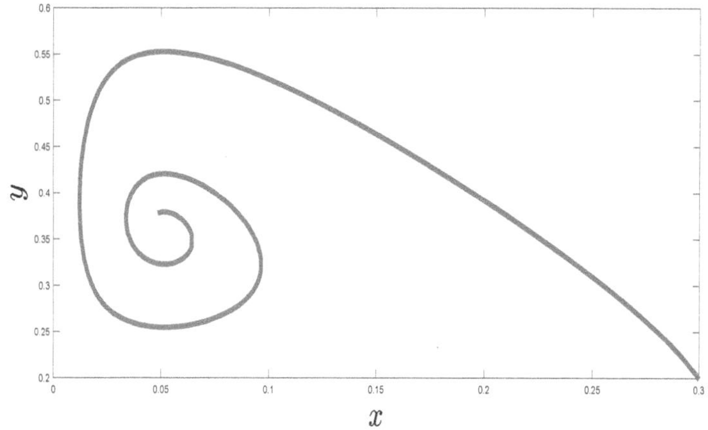

Figure 5. Dynamics of the predator and prey in the model for $\gamma = 0.95$.

In Figure 6, we represent graphically the dynamics of the predator in time.

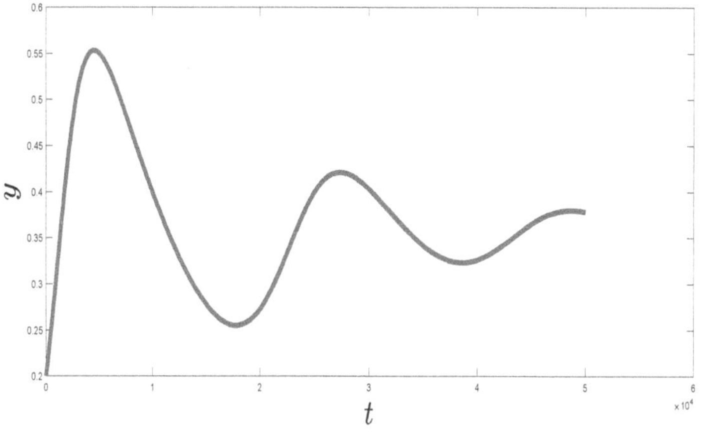

Figure 6. Dynamics of the predator in the model for $\gamma = 0.95$.

In Figure 7, we represent graphically the dynamics of the prey in time.

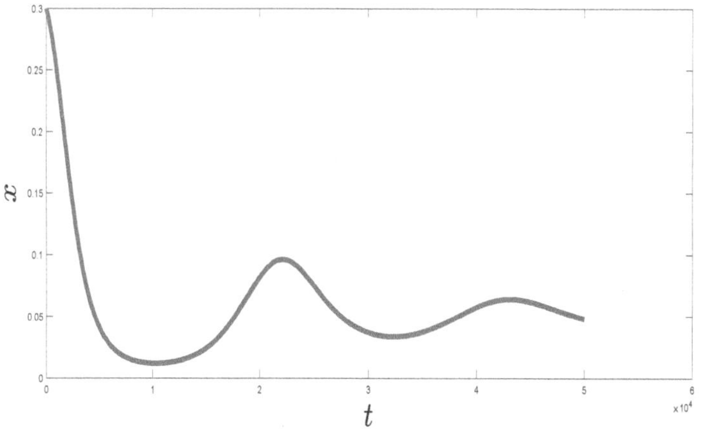

Figure 7. Dynamics of the prey in the model for $\gamma = 0.95$.

In the figures of the first case, the order converges to the classical order, i.e., to 1. We now depict the figures when the order is arbitrary in the interval $(0, 1)$ which we consider it as $\gamma = 0.85$. In Figure 8, we represent graphically the dynamics of the predator versus the prey.

In Figure 9, we represent graphically the dynamics of the predator in time.

In Figure 10, we represent graphically the dynamics of the prey in time.

We notice by comparing the plots in Figures 6, 7, 9 and 10 that the fractional order derivative has a significant impact on the dynamics of the suggested predator–prey model represented by Equation (11). In general, it has an acceleration effect on the model process. It is remarkable that the model has not been previously considered in terms of fractional derivatives. For this reason, making a comparison of it with those existing in the literature is a bit difficult. A possible comparison can be done with the prey–predator model which was constructed by integer-order derivative in [53]. In terms of comparison we notice that the fractional order derivative generates an acceleration effect in the dynamics. These mentioned differences can be seen when looking at the comparisons of Figures 6 and 9; Figures 7 and 10.

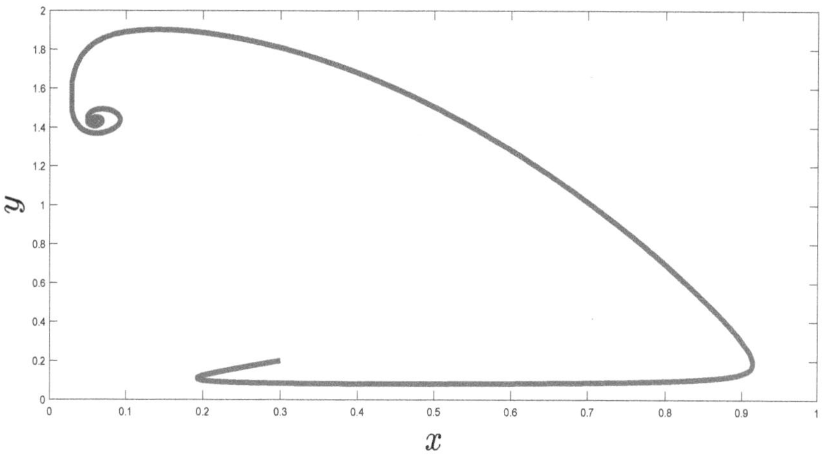

Figure 8. Dynamics of the predator and prey in the model for $\gamma = 0.85$.

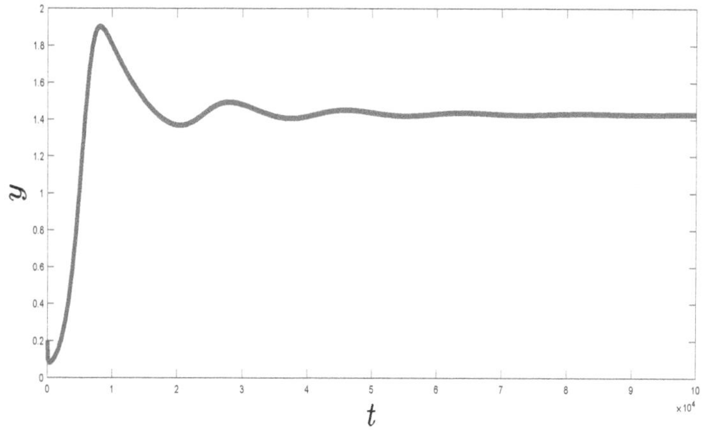

Figure 9. Dynamics of the predator in the model for $\gamma = 0.85$.

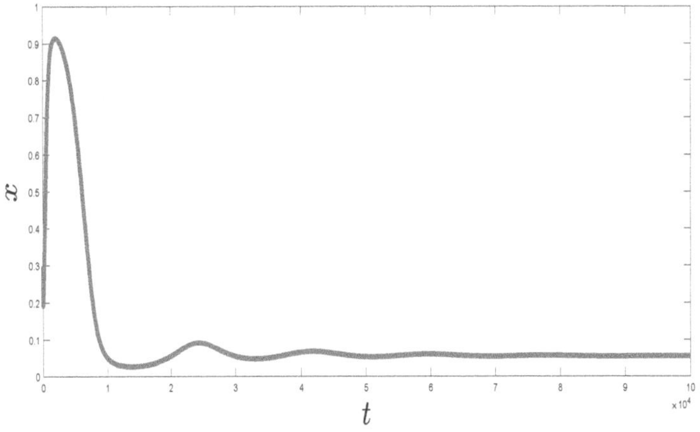

Figure 10. Dynamics of the prey in the model for $\gamma = 0.85$.

8. Concluding Remarks

In this paper, modeling and analysis of the fractional order P–PM which contains the harvesting rate have been provided. Since the harvesting rate has a significant impact on the dynamics of the predator–prey models, we have demonstrated after certain values, the behaviors of the solutions are in contradiction with the real possible phenomena. Moreover, the basic reproduction number $\mathcal{R}_0$ has been computed by the next generation matrix method which performs as a threshold parameter in the disease transmission and determines whether the disease persists or vanishes from the population. The existence and uniqueness of the solutions of the proposed fractional system have been examined. Additionally, the stability conditions of the equilibrium points for the fractional system have been discussed. Meanwhile, the global dynamics of the equilibria have been obtained by the Lyapunov functional approach method. It is well-known that the infection spreads in the population when $\mathcal{R}_0 > 1$. A new numerical algorithm based on the numerical discretization of the Riemann–Liouville integral has been introduced and it has been successfully applied for the corresponding numerical solution of the proposed predator–prey fractional-order model to carry out the numerical simulations for different values of the fractional order γ. The model introduced in the paper is new in the context of fractional order derivatives; therefore, to analyze the dynamics of the predator and prey, we need to get the solutions to the proposed model. Since it is straightforward that the analytical solution to the proposed model is not possible, an alternative way to deal with this issue is to construct the numerical scheme. This is because we used an effective and accurate numerical scheme including the discretization of the Riemann–Liouville integral, and by using this scheme, we have managed to obtain numerical solutions to the aforementioned problem. Finally, it has been demonstrated that physical processes are better described using the derivative of fractional order which is more accurate and reliable in comparison with the classical order case. Hence, we replace the integer order time derivative with the Caputo type fractional order derivative.

Author Contributions: Conceptualization, M.Y. and N.S.; methodology, M.Y. and N.S.; investigation, M.Y. and N.S.; writing—original draft preparation, N.S.; writing—review and editing, M.Y. All authors have read and agreed to the published version of the manuscript.

Funding: This research received no external funding.

Acknowledgments: M. Yavuz was supported by TUBITAK (The Scientific and Technological Research Council of Turkey). The authors would like to thank the reviewers for their thoughtful comments and careful efforts towards improving our manuscript.

Conflicts of Interest: The authors declare no conflict of interest.

References

1. Podlubny, I. Fractional Differential Equations. In *Mathematics in Science and Engineering*; Academic Press: New York, NY, USA, 1999; Volume 198.
2. Samko, S.G.; Kilbas, A.A.; Marichev, O.I. *Fractional Integrals and Derivatives*; Gordon and Breach Science Publishers: Yverdon Yverdon-les-Bains, Switzerland, 1993; Volume 1.
3. Katugampola, U.N. New approach to a generalized fractional integral. *Appl. Math. Comput.* **2011**, *218*, 860–865. [CrossRef]
4. Caputo, M.; Fabrizio, M. A new definition of fractional derivative without singular kernel. *Progr. Fract. Differ. Appl.* **2015**, *1*, 1–15.
5. Atangana, A.; Baleanu, D. New fractional derivatives with non-local and non-singular kernel theory and application to heat transfer model. *arXiv* **2016**, arXiv:1602.03408.
6. Wang, X.; Wang, Z. Dynamic Analysis of a Delayed Fractional-Order SIR Model with Saturated Incidence and Treatment Functio. *Int. J. Bifurc. Chaos* **2018**, *28*, 1850180. [CrossRef]
7. Yavuz, M.; Bonyah, E. New approaches to the fractional dynamics of schistosomiasis disease model. *Phys. A Stat. Mech. Its Appl.* **2019**, *525*, 373–393. [CrossRef]
8. Ucar, S.; Ucar, E.; Ozdemir, N.; Hammouch, Z. Mathematical analysis and numerical simulation for a smoking model with Atangana–Baleanu derivative. *Chaos Solitons Fractals* **2019**, *118*, 300–306. [CrossRef]
9. Jajarmi, A.; Ghanbari, B.; Baleanu, D. A new and efficient numerical method for the fractional modelling and optimal control of diabetes and tuberculosis co-existence. *Chaos* **2019**, *29*, 093111. [CrossRef]
10. Naik, P.A.; Yavuz, M.; Zu, J. The Role of Prostitution on HIV Transmission with Memory: A Modeling Approach. *Alex. Eng. J.* **2020**. [CrossRef]
11. Yavuz, M.; Ozdemir, N. Analysis of an Epidemic Spreading Model with Exponential Decay Law. *Math. Sci. Appl. E Notes* **2020**, *8*, 142–154. [CrossRef]
12. Sene, N. Stokes' first problem for heated flat plate with Atangana–Baleanu fractional derivative. *Chaos Solitons Fractals* **2018**, *117*, 68–75. [CrossRef]
13. Sene, N. Integral Balance Methods for Stokes' First, Equation Described by the Left Generalized Fractional Derivative. *Physics* **2019**, *1*, 15. [CrossRef]
14. Sene, N. Second-grade fluid model with Caputo-Liouville generalized fractional derivative. *Chaos Solitons Fractals* **2020**, *133*, 109631. [CrossRef]
15. Ozarslan, R.; Bas, E.; Baleanu, D.; Acay, B. Fractional physical problems including wind-influenced projectile motion with Mittag-Leffler kernel. *AIMS Math.* **2020**, *5*, 467. [CrossRef]
16. Kumar, D.; Singh, J.; Tanwar, K.; Baleanu, D. A new fractional exothermic reactions model having constant heat source in porous media with power, exponential and Mittag-Leffler laws. *Int. J. Heat Mass Transf.* **2019**, *138*, 1222–1227. [CrossRef]
17. Yavuz, M.; Ozdemir, N. European vanilla option pricing model of fractional order without singular kernel. *Fractal Fract.* **2018**, *2*, 3. [CrossRef]
18. Yavuz, M.; Ozdemir, N. A different approach to the European option pricing model with new fractional operator. *Math. Model. Nat. Phenom.* **2018**, *13*, 12. [CrossRef]
19. Sene, N. Analytical solutions and numerical schemes of certain generalized fractional diffusion models. *Eur. Phys. J. Plus* **2019**, *134*, 199. [CrossRef]
20. Qureshi, S.; Yusuf, A.; Ali Shaikh, A.; Inc, M.; Baleanu, D. Mathematical modeling for adsorption process of dye removal nonlinear equation using power law and exponentially decaying kernels. *Chaos Interdiscip. J. Nonlinear Sci.* **2020**, *30*, 043106. [CrossRef]
21. Owolabi, K.M.; Atangana, A. On the formulation of Adams-Bashforth scheme with Atangana-Baleanu-Caputo fractional derivative to model chaotic problems. *Chaos* **2019**, *29*, 023111. [CrossRef]
22. Bhatter, S.; Mathur, A.; Kumar, D.; Nisar, K.S.; Singh, J. Fractional modified Kawahara equation with Mittag-Leffler law. *Chaos Solitons Fractals* **2020**, *131*, 109508. [CrossRef]
23. Usta, F. A conformable calculus of radial basis functions and its applications. *Int. J. Optim. Control. Theor. Appl. (IJOCTA)* **2018**, *8*, 176–182. [CrossRef]
24. Yavuz, M. Characterization of two different fractional operators without singular kernel. *Math. Model. Nat. Phenom.* **2019**, *14*, 302. [CrossRef]

25. Yildiz, T.A.; Jajarmi, A.; Yıldız, B.; Baleanu, D. New aspects of time fractional optimal control problems within operators with nonsingular kernel. *Discret. Contin. Dyn. Syst. S* **2020**, *13*, 407–428. [CrossRef]
26. Budak, H.; Usta, F.; Sarikaya, M.Z.; Ozdemir, M.E. On generalization of midpoint type inequalities with generalized fractional integral operators. *Revista de la Real Academia de Ciencias Exactas, Físicas y Naturales. Serie A. Matemáticas* **2019**, *113*, 769–790. [CrossRef]
27. Yavuz, M.; Sulaiman, T.A.; Usta, F.; Bulut, H. Analysis and numerical computations of the fractional regularized long-wave equation with damping term. *Math. Methods Appl. Sci.* **2020**. [CrossRef]
28. Özkan, Y.S.; Yaşar, E.; Seadawy, A.R. A third-order nonlinear Schrödinger equation: The exact solutions, group-invariant solutions and conservation laws. *J. Taibah Univ. Sci.* **2020**, *14*, 585–597. [CrossRef]
29. Yavuz, M.; Yaşkıran, B. Conformable Derivative Operator in Modelling Neuronal Dynamics. *Appl. Appl. Math.* **2018**, *13*, 803–817.
30. Jena, R.M.; Chakraverty, S.; Yavuz, M. Two-hybrid techniques coupled with an integral transform for caputo time-fractional Navier-Stokes Equations. *Prog. Fract. Differ. Appl.* **2020**, *6*, 201–213.
31. Ahmad, H.; Seadawy, A.R.; Khan, T.A.; Thounthong, P. Analytic approximate solutions for some nonlinear Parabolic dynamical wave equations. *J. Taibah Univ. Sci.* **2020**, *14*, 346–358. [CrossRef]
32. Yavuz, M. Dynamical behaviors of separated homotopy method defined by conformable operator. *Konuralp J. Math.* **2019**, *7*, 1–6.
33. Avci, D.; Yavuz, M.; Özdemir, N. Fundamental solutions to the Cauchy and Dirichlet problems for a heat conduction equation equipped with the Caputo-Fabrizio differentiation. In *Heat Conduction: Methods, Applications and Research*; Nova Science Publishers: Hauppauge, NY, USA, 2019; pp. 95–107.
34. Arnous, A.H.; Seadawy, A.R.; Alqahtani, R.T.; Biswas, A. Optical solitons with complex Ginzburg–Landau equation by modified simple equation method. *Optik* **2017**, *144*, 475–480. [CrossRef]
35. Yavuz, M.; Yokus, A. Analytical and numerical approaches to nerve impulse model of fractional-order. *Numer. Methods Partial. Differ. Equ.* **2020**. [CrossRef]
36. Selima, E.S.; Seadawy, A.R.; Yao, X. The nonlinear dispersive Davey-Stewartson system for surface waves propagation in shallow water and its stability. *Eur. Phys. J. Plus* **2016**, *131*, 1–16. [CrossRef]
37. Yavuz, M.; Özdemir, N. New numerical techniques for solving fractional partial differential equations in conformable sense. In *Non-Integer Order Calculus and Its Applications*; Springer: Cham, Switzerland, 2019; pp. 49–62.
38. Seadawy, A.R.; Jun, W. Mathematical methods and solitary wave solutions of three-dimensional Zakharov-Kuznetsov-Burgers equation in dusty plasma and its applications. *Results Phys.* **2017**, *7*, 4269–4277.
39. Naik, P.A.; Zu, J.; Ghoreishi, M. Estimating the approximate analytical solution of HIV viral dynamic model by using homotopy analysis method. *Chaos Solitons Fractals* **2020**, *131*, 109500. [CrossRef]
40. Yavuz, M. Novel recursive approximation for fractional nonlinear equations within Caputo-Fabrizio operator. In *ITM Web of Conferences*; EDP Sciences: Jules, France, 2018; Volume 22, p. 01008.
41. Naik, P.A.; Zu, J.; Owolabi, K.M. Modeling the mechanics of viral kinetics under immune control during primary infection of HIV-1 with treatment in fractional order. *Phys. A Stat. Mech. Its Appl.* **2020**, *545*, 123816. [CrossRef]
42. Avci, D.; Ozdemir, N.; Yavuz, M. Fractional Optimal Control of Diffusive Transport Acting on a Spherical Region. In *Methods of Mathematical Modelling: Fractional Differential Equations*; CRC Press: Boca Raton, FL, USA, 2019; p. 63.
43. Seadawy, A.R.; El-Rashidy, K. Dispersive solitary wave solutions of Kadomtsev-Petviashvili and modified Kadomtsev-Petviashvili dynamical equations in unmagnetized dust plasma. *Results Phys.* **2018**, *8*, 1216–1222. [CrossRef]
44. Yavuz, M.; Özdemir, N.; Baskonus, H.M. Solutions of Partial Differential Equations Using the Fractional Operator Involving Mittag-Leffler Kernel. *Eur. Phys. J. Plus* **2018**, *133*, 215. [CrossRef]
45. Tukur, A.S.; Yavuz, M.; Bulut, H.; Baskonus, H.M. Investigation of the Fractional Coupled Viscous Burger's Equation Involving Mittag-Leffler Kernel. *Phys. A Stat. Mech. Its Appl.* **2019**, *527*, 121126.
46. Iqbal, M.; Seadawy, A.R.; Lu, D. Construction of solitary wave solutions to the nonlinear modified Kortewege-de Vries dynamical equation in unmagnetized plasma via mathematical methods. *Mod. Phys. Lett. A* **2018**, *33*, 1850183. [CrossRef]
47. Keten, A.; Yavuz, M.; Baleanu, D. Nonlocal cauchy problem via a fractional operator involving power kernel in Banach spaces. *Fractal Fract.* **2019**, *3*, 27. [CrossRef]

48. Helal, M.A.; Seadawy, A.R.; Zekry, M.H. Stability analysis of solitary wave solutions for the fourth-order nonlinear Boussinesq water wave equation. *Appl. Math. Comput.* **2014**, *232*, 1094–1103. [CrossRef]
49. Sulaiman, T.A.; Bulut, H.; Yokus, A.; Baskonus, H.M. On the exact and numerical solutions to the coupled Boussinesq equation arising in ocean engineering. *Indian J. Phys.* **2019**, *93*, 647–656. [CrossRef]
50. Evirgen, F.; Yavuz, M. An alternative approach for nonlinear optimization problem with Caputo-Fabrizio derivative. In *ITM Web of Conferences*; EDP Sciences: Jules, France, 2018; Volume 22, p. 01009.
51. Fahd, J.; Abdeljawad, T.; Baleanu, D. On the generalized fractional derivatives and their Caputo modification. *J. Nonlinear Sci. Appl.* **2017**, *10*, 2607–2619.
52. Kilbas, A.A.; Srivastava, H.M.; Trujillo, J.J. Theory and Applications of Fractional Differential Equations. In *North-Holland Mathematics Studies*; Elsevier: Amsterdam, The Netherlands, 2006; Volume 204.
53. Li, B.; Liu, S.; Cui, J.; Li, J. A Simple Predator-Prey Population Model with Rich Dynamics. *Appl. Sci.* **2016**, *6*, 151. [CrossRef]
54. Dubey, B. A Prey-Predator Model with a Reserved Area. *Nonlinear Anal. Model. Control* **2007**, *12*, 479–494. [CrossRef]
55. Seo, G.; DeAngelis, D.L. A Predator-Prey Model with a Holling Type I Functional Response Including a Predator Mutual Interference. *J. Nonlinear Sci.* **2013**, *21*, 811–833. [CrossRef]
56. Suryanto, A.; Darti, I.; Panigoro, H.S.; Kilicman, A. A Fractional-Order Predator–Prey Model with Ratio-Dependent Functional Response and Linear Harvesting. *Mathematics* **2019**, *7*, 1100. [CrossRef]
57. Tang, B. Dynamics for a fractional-order predator-prey model with group defense. *Sci. Rep.* **2020**, *10*, 4906. [CrossRef]
58. Elettreby, M.F.; Al-Raezah, A.A.; Nabil, T. Fractional-Order Model of Two-Prey One-Predator System. *Math. Probl. Eng.* **2017**, *2017*, 6714538. [CrossRef]
59. Liu, Y.; Xin, B. Numerical Solutions of a Fractional Predator-Prey System. *Adv. Differ. Equ.* **2011**, *2011*, 1–11. [CrossRef]
60. lv, Y.; Yuan, R.; Pei, Y. A prey-predator model with harvesting for fishery resource with reserve area. *Appl. Math. Model.* **2013**, *37*, 3048–3062. [CrossRef]
61. Heggeru, C.M.; Lan, K. Local stability analysis of ratio-dependent predator–prey models with predator harvesting rates. *Appl. Math. Comput.* **2015**, *270*, 349–357.
62. Kar, T.K. Selective harvesting in a predator-prey fishery with time delay. *Math. Comput. Model.* **2003**, *38*, 449–458. [CrossRef]
63. Javidi, M.; Nyamoradi, N. Dynamic analysis of a fractional order prey-predator interaction with harvesting. *Appl. Math. Model.* **2013**, *37*, 8946–8956. [CrossRef]
64. Huanga, J.; Ruan, S.; Song, J. Bifurcations in a predator-prey system of Leslie type with generalized Holling typeIII functional response. *J. Differ. Equ.* **2014**, *257*, 1721–1752. [CrossRef]
65. Rebaza, J. Dynamics of prey threshold harvesting and refuge. *J. Comput. Appl. Math.* **2012**, *236*, 1743–1752. [CrossRef]
66. Bulai, I.M.; Hilker, F.M. Eco-epidemiological interactions with predator interference and infection. *Theor. Popul. Biol.* **2019**, *130*, 191–202. [CrossRef]
67. Laurie, H.; Venturino, E.; Bulai, I.M. Herding induced by encounter rate, with predator pressure influencing prey response. In *Current Trends in Dynamical Systems in Biology and Natural Sciences*; Springer: Cham, Switzerland, 2020; pp. 63–93.
68. Matignon, D. Stability results on fractional differential equations to control processing. In Proceedings of the Computational Engineering in Syatems and Application Multiconference, Lille, France, 9–12 July 1996; IMACS, IEEE-SMC: Lille, France, 1996; Volume 2, pp. 963–968.
69. Sene, N. Stability analysis of the generalized fractional differential equations with and without exogenous inputs. *J. Nonlinear Sci. Appl.* **2019**, *12*, 562–572. [CrossRef]
70. Seo, G.; Kot, M. A comparison of two predator–prey models with Holling's type I functional response. *Math. Biosci.* **2008**, *212*, 161–179. [CrossRef]
71. Murdoch, W.W.; Briggs, C.J.; Nisbet, R.M. *Consumer-Resource Dynamics*; Princeton University Press: Princeton, NJ, USA, 2003; Volume 36.

72. Lin, W. Global existence theory and chaos control of fractional differential equations. *J. Math. Anal. Appl.* **2007**, *332*, 709–726. [CrossRef]
73. Garrappa, R. Numerical solution of fractional differential equations: A survey and a software tutorial. *Mathematics* **2018**, *6*, 16. [CrossRef]

fractal and fractional

MDPI

Article

Laplace Transform Method for Economic Models with Constant Proportional Caputo Derivative

Esra Karatas Akgül [1,*], Ali Akgül [1] and Dumitru Baleanu [2,3,4]

1 Art and Science Faculty, Department of Mathematics, Siirt University, TR-56100 Siirt, Turkey; aliakgul@siirt.edu.tr
2 Department of Mathematics, Cankaya University, Balgat, 06530 Ankara, Turkey; dumitru@cankaya.edu.tr
3 Institute of Space Sciences, R76900 Magurele-Bucharest, Romania
4 Department of Medical Research, China Medical University, Taichung 40402, Taiwan
* Correspondence: esrakaratas@siirt.edu.tr

Received: 30 May 2020; Accepted: 25 June 2020; Published: 3 July 2020

Abstract: In this study, we solved the economic models based on market equilibrium with constant proportional Caputo derivative using the Laplace transform. We proved the accuracy and efficiency of the method. We constructed the relations between the solutions of the problems and bivariate Mittag–Leffler functions.

Keywords: Laplace transforms; constant proportional Caputo derivative; modeling

MSC: 44A10; 26A33

---

1. Introduction

Fractional differential equations have taken much interest in the recent years. Ghanbari et al. [1,2] investigated the new application of fractional Atangana–Baleanu derivatives and abundant new analytical and approximate solutions to the generalized Schamel equation. Allahviranloo et al. [3] worked the fuzzy fractional differential equation with Atangana–Baleanu fractional derivative approach. Salari et al. [4] searched existence and multiplicity for some boundary value problems involving Caputo and Atangana–Baleanu fractional derivatives. Akgül et al. [5–7] investigated the solutions of new type fractional differential equations occurring in the electrohydrodynamic flow, analysis and dynamical behavior of fractional-order cancer model with vaccine strategy, and the solutions of fractional order telegraph partial differential equation by Crank–Nicholson finite difference method.

We consider the following economic models:

$$q_d(x) = d_0 - d_1 h(x), \quad q_s(x) = -s_0 + s_1 h(x), \tag{1}$$

where h the price of goods, d_0, s_0, d_1, s_1 are positive constants. For $q_d(x) = q_s(x)$, when the demanded quantity and the supplied quantity are equal, the equilibrium price is found as; $h^* = \frac{d_0+s_0}{d_1+s_1}$. Then, the price is disposed to stay stable. Now, considering [8]:

$$h'(x) = k(q_d - q_s). \tag{2}$$

where $k > 0$. Then, we get

$$h'(x) + k(d_1 + s_1)h(x) = k(d_0 + s_0). \tag{3}$$

When we solved the first order ordinary differential equation, the solution can be found:

$$h(x) = \frac{d_0 + s_0}{d_1 + s_1} - \left[h(0) + \frac{d_0 + s_0}{d_1 + s_1}\right] \exp\left(-k(d_1 + s_1)x\right), \tag{4}$$

where $h(0)$ is the price at the time $x = 0$ and in here we do not interest to the expectation of agents in market.

In the above equation, we define the $h(0)$ as the expense at the time $x = 0$. If we take into consideration the prospects of agents, the request and provision functions containing supplement elements q_d and q_d alters as:

$$q_d(x) = d_0 - d_1 h(x) + d_2 h'(x), \quad q_s(x) = -s_0 + s_1 h(x) - s_2 h'(x). \tag{5}$$

We equalize $q_d(x)$, $q_s(x)$ and obtain:

$$h'(x) - \frac{d_1 + s_1}{d_2 + s_2} h(x) = -\frac{d_0 + s_0}{d_2 + s_2}. \tag{6}$$

and when the linear differential Equation (6) is solved, the solution is acquired as:

$$h(x) = \frac{d_0 + s_0}{d_1 + s_1} - \left[h(0) + \frac{d_0 + s_0}{d_1 + s_1}\right] \exp\left(\frac{d_1 + s_1}{d_2 + s_2} x\right). \tag{7}$$

We consider the above economic models with constant proportional Caputo derivative that has been presented very recently in [9]. We construct the Laplace transform method (LTM) to solve the economic models. The Laplace transform is one of the best integral transform used by many researchers.

Gupta et al. [10] investigated analytical solutions of convection–diffusion problems by combining Laplace transform method and homotopy perturbation method. Anjum et al. [11] worked Laplace transform making the variational iteration method easier. Convergence of iterative Laplace transform methods for a system of fractional partial differential equations and partial integro-ifferential equations arising in option pricing has been searched by Zhou [12]. Bashir et al. [13] studied solution of non-homogeneous differential equations using Faddeev–Leverrier method together with Laplace transform. Convergence analysis of iterative Laplace transform methods for the coupled partial differential equations from regime-switching option pricing was investigated by Jingtang [14]. Eljaoui et al. [15] researched Aumann fuzzy improper integral and its application to solve fuzzy integro-differential equations by LTM. Zhou et al. [16] have worked fast LTM for free-boundary problems of fractional diffusion equations. The transform method for the ulam stability of linear fractional differential equations with constant coefficient was studied by Yonghong [17]. Fatoorehchi et al. [18] investigated series solution of nonlinear differential equations by a novel extension of the LTM. Jacobs [19] searched high-order compact finite difference and Laplace transform method for the solution of time-fractional heat equations with Dirichlet and Neumann boundary conditions. See these reference for more details [20,21].

Mittag–Leffler functions are very important in the fractional calculus. There are many useful works related to the Mittag–Leffler functions in the literature. Özarslan et al. [22,23] studied on a singular integral equation including a set of multivariate polynomials suggested by Laguerre polynomials and on a certain bivariate Mittag–Leffler function analyzed from a fractional-calculus point of view. For more details [24–29].

Acay et al. [30] found the solutions of these models with three different derivatives which are Caputo, Caputo–Fabrizio and Atangana–Baleanu. They presented the efficiency of the Laplace transform method for these models. For more details see [31–33].

We organize the paper as follows: we give the main definitions and lemmas related to the constant proportional Caputo derivative in Section 2. We present the applications of the economic models by Laplace transform method in Section 3. We give some conclusions remarks in the last section.

2. Preliminaries

Definition 1. *The Caputo fractional derivative is defined as [34]:*

$$ {}_{a}^{C}D^{\sigma}h(x) = \frac{1}{\Gamma(1-\sigma)} \int_a^x (x-\tau)^{-\sigma} h'(\tau) d\tau, \tag{8} $$

where $0 < \sigma \leq 1$.

Definition 2. *The Riemann–Liouville integral is given as [34];*

$$ {}_{a}^{RL}I^{\sigma}h(x) = \frac{1}{\Gamma(\sigma)} \int_a^x (x-\tau)^{\sigma-1} h(\tau) d\tau. \tag{9} $$

in here h is an integrable function and $\sigma > 0$.

From above definitons,

$$ {}_{a}^{C}D^{\sigma}h(x) = {}_{a}^{RL} I^{1-\sigma} h'(x). \tag{10} $$

is written.

Definition 3. *The constant proportional Caputo (CPC) derivative is defined by [9]*

$$ {}_{0}^{CPC}D_x^{\alpha}h(x) = \frac{1}{\Gamma(1-\alpha)} \int_0^x \left[k_1(\alpha)h(\tau) + k_0(\alpha)h'(\tau) \right] (x-\tau)^{-\alpha} d\tau. \tag{11} $$

Definition 4. *Let* $\xi, \eta : [0,\infty) \to \Re$, *then the convolution of* ξ, η *is*

$$ (\xi * \eta) = \int_0^x \xi(x-u)\eta(u) du. \tag{12} $$

and assume that $\xi, \eta : [0,\infty) \to \Re$, *then we write:*

$$ L\{(\xi * \eta)(x)\} = L\{\xi(x)\} L\{\eta(x)\}. \tag{13} $$

Definition 5. *We define* $E_{\alpha}(v)$ *by:*

$$ E_{\alpha}(v) = \sum_{l=0}^{\infty} \frac{v^l}{\Gamma(\alpha l + 1)} \quad (v \in \mathbb{C}, Re(\alpha) > 0). \tag{14} $$

The Mittag–Leffler function which has two parameters is given as:

$$ E_{\alpha,\beta}(v) = \sum_{l=0}^{\infty} \frac{v^l}{\Gamma(\alpha l + \beta)} \quad (v, \beta \in \mathbb{C}, Re(\alpha) > 0), \tag{15} $$

it is worth, $E_{\alpha,\beta}(v)$ *corresponds to the Mittag–Leffler function* (14) *when* $\beta = 1$.

Lemma 1. *The Laplace transform of constant proportional Caputo (CPC) derivative is found as [9], for Laplace transform of the derivatives see Table 1:*

$$ L\{{}_{0}^{CPC}D_x^{\alpha}h(x)\} = \left[\frac{k_1(\alpha)}{s} + k_0(\alpha) \right] s^{\alpha} L\{h(x)\} - k_0(\alpha) s^{\alpha-1} h(0). \tag{16} $$

Table 1. Laplace transform of the Caputo (C), constant proportional Caputo (CPC) derivatives and the Riemann–Liouville (RL) integral.

C, CPC and RL	Convolution	Laplace Transform
${}_{0}^{C}D_{t}^{\alpha}f(t)$	$\frac{df(t)}{dt}*\frac{t^{-\alpha}}{\Gamma(1-\alpha)}$	$(sL\{f(t)\}-f(0))\,s^{\alpha-1}$
${}_{0}^{RL}I_{t}^{\alpha}f(t)$	$f(t)*\frac{t^{\alpha-1}}{\Gamma(\alpha)}$	$s^{-\alpha}L\{f(t)\}$
${}_{0}^{CPC}D_{t}^{\alpha}f(t)$	$f(t)*\frac{k_1(\alpha)t^{-\alpha}}{\Gamma(1-\alpha)}+\frac{df(t)}{dt}*\frac{k_0(\alpha)t^{-\alpha}}{\Gamma(1-\alpha)}$	$k_1(\alpha)s^{\alpha-1}L\{f(t)\}+(sL\{f(t)\}-f(0))\,s^{\alpha-1}k_0(\alpha)$

3. Applications of the Economic Model

Let us take into consideration the first model with the constant proportional Caputo derivative as:

$$ {}_{0}^{CPC}D_{x}^{\alpha}h(x)+k(d_1+s_1)h(x)=k(d_0+s_0). \tag{17}$$

Applying the Laplace transform to the equation, we acquire

$$ L\{{}_{0}^{CPC}D_{x}^{\alpha}h(x)\}+k(d_1+s_1)L\{h(x)\}=L\{k(d_0+s_0)\}. \tag{18}$$

Using the expression Lemma 1, then we obtain:

$$ \left[\frac{k_1(\alpha)}{s}+k_0(\alpha)\right]s^{\alpha}L\{h(x)\}-k_0(\alpha)s^{\alpha-1}h(0)+k(d_1+s_1)L\{h(x)\}=\frac{k(d_0+s_0)}{s}, \tag{19}$$

and

$$\begin{aligned}
L\{h(x)\} &= \frac{k(d_0+s_0)}{k_1(\alpha)s^{\alpha}+k_0(\alpha)s^{\alpha+1}+k(d_1+s_1)s} \\
&\quad+\frac{k_0(\alpha)h(0)s^{\alpha}}{k_1(\alpha)s^{\alpha}+k_0(\alpha)s^{\alpha+1}+k(d_1+s_1)s} \\
&= \frac{d_0+s_0}{d_1+s_1}s^{-1}\left[1-\frac{-k_1(\alpha)s^{\alpha-1}-k_0\alpha s^{\alpha}}{k(d_0+s_0)}\right]^{-1} \\
&\quad+h(0)s^{-1}\left[1-\frac{-k_1(\alpha)s^{-1}-k(d_1+s_1)s^{-\alpha}}{k_0(\alpha)}\right]^{-1} \\
&= \frac{d_0+s_0}{d_1+s_1}s^{-1}\sum_{j=0}^{\infty}\left[\frac{-k_1(\alpha)s^{\alpha-1}-k_0(\alpha)s^{\alpha}}{k(d_0+s_0)}\right]^{j} \\
&\quad+h(0)s^{-1}\sum_{j=0}^{\infty}\left[\frac{-k_1(\alpha)s^{-1}-k(d_1+s_1)s^{-\alpha}}{k_0(\alpha)}\right]^{j} \\
&= \frac{d_0+s_0}{d_1+s_1}s^{-1}\sum_{j=0}^{\infty}\frac{1}{k^j(d_0+s_0)^j}\sum_{r=0}^{j}\binom{j}{r}[-k_1(\alpha)s^{\alpha-1}]^{j-r}[-k_0(\alpha)s^{\alpha}]^{r} \\
&\quad+h(0)s^{-1}\sum_{j=0}^{\infty}\frac{1}{k_0(\alpha)^j}\sum_{r=0}^{j}\binom{j}{r}[-k_1(\alpha)s^{-1}]^{j-r}[-k(d_1+s_1)s^{-\alpha}]^{r} \\
&= \frac{d_0+s_0}{d_1+s_1}\sum_{j=0}^{\infty}\sum_{r=0}^{j}(-1)^j\frac{k_1(\alpha)^{j-r}k_0(\alpha)^r}{k^j(d_0+s_0)^j}\binom{j}{r}s^{(\alpha-1)(j-r)+\alpha r-1} \\
&\quad+h(0)\sum_{j=0}^{\infty}\sum_{r=0}^{j}(-1)^j\frac{k_1(\alpha)^{j-r}k^r(d_1+s_1)^r}{k_0(\alpha)^j}\binom{j}{r}s^{j-r-\alpha r-1}.
\end{aligned}$$

Then, implementing the inverse LTM gives:

$$
\begin{aligned}
h(x) &= \frac{d_0+s_0}{d_1+s_1}\sum_{j=0}^{\infty}\sum_{r=0}^{j}(-1)^j\frac{k_1(\alpha)^{j-r}k_0(\alpha)^r}{k^j(d_0+s_0)^j}\binom{j}{r}\frac{x^{(1-\alpha)j-r}}{\Gamma((1-\alpha)j-r+1)}\\
&+h(0)\sum_{j=0}^{\infty}\sum_{r=0}^{j}(-1)^j\frac{k_1(\alpha)^{j-r}k^r(d_1+s_1)^r}{k_0(\alpha)^j}\binom{j}{r}\frac{x^{j+(\alpha-1)r}}{\Gamma(j+(\alpha-1)r+1)},
\end{aligned}
$$

When we take $p = j - r$, we will get:

$$
\begin{aligned}
h(x) &= \frac{d_0+s_0}{d_1+s_1}\sum_{r=0}^{\infty}\sum_{p=0}^{\infty}\frac{(r+p)!}{r!p!}\frac{(-k_1(\alpha))^p(-k_0(\alpha))^r}{k^{p+r}(d_0+s_0)^{p+r}}\frac{x^{(1-\alpha)p-\alpha r}}{\Gamma((1-\alpha)p-\alpha r+1)}\\
&+h(0)\sum_{r=0}^{\infty}\sum_{p=0}^{\infty}\frac{(r+p)!}{r!p!}\frac{(-k_1(\alpha))^p(-k(d_1+s_1))^r}{k_0(\alpha)^{p+r}}\frac{x^{p+\alpha r}}{\Gamma(p+\alpha r+1)},
\end{aligned}
$$

$$
\begin{aligned}
h(x) &= \frac{d_0+s_0}{d_1+s_1}\sum_{r=0}^{\infty}\sum_{p=0}^{\infty}\frac{(r+p)!}{r!p!}\left[\frac{-k_0(\alpha)}{k(d_0+s_0)}x^{-\alpha}\right]^r\left[\frac{-k_1(\alpha)}{k(d_0+s_0)}x^{1-\alpha}\right]^p\frac{1}{\Gamma((1-\alpha)p-\alpha r+1)}\\
&+h(0)\sum_{r=0}^{\infty}\sum_{p=0}^{\infty}\frac{(r+p)!}{r!p!}\left[\frac{-k(d_1+s_1)}{k_0(\alpha)}x^{\alpha}\right]^r\left[\frac{-k_1(\alpha)}{k_0(\alpha)}x\right]^p\frac{1}{\Gamma(p+\alpha r+1)}.
\end{aligned}
$$

We can write geometric series as [35]:

$$
\begin{aligned}
h(x) &= \frac{d_0+s_0}{d_1+s_1}E^1_{1-\alpha,-\alpha,1}\left(\frac{-k_1(\alpha)}{k(d_0+s_0)}x^{1-\alpha},\frac{-k_0(\alpha)}{k(d_0+s_0)}x^{-\alpha}\right)\\
&+h(0)E^1_{1,\alpha,1}\left(\frac{-k_1(\alpha)}{k_0(\alpha)}x,\frac{-k(d_1+s_1)}{k_0(\alpha)}x^{\alpha}\right).
\end{aligned}
$$

Let us take into consideration the second model with the constant proportional Caputo derivative as:

$$
{}_0^{CPC}D_x^{\alpha}h(x)-\frac{d_1+s_1}{d_2+s_2}h(x)=-\frac{d_0+s_0}{d_2+s_2}. \tag{20}
$$

If we implement the LTM, we will get

$$
L\{{}_0^{CPC}D_x^{\alpha}h(x)\}+k(d_1+s_1)L\{h(x)\}=L\{k(d_0+s_0)\}. \tag{21}
$$

Using the expression Lemma 1, then we obtain:

$$
\left[\frac{k_1(\alpha)}{s}+k_0(\alpha)\right]s^{\alpha}L\{h(x)\}-k_0(\alpha)s^{\alpha-1}h(0)-\frac{d_1+s_1}{d_2+s_2}L\{h(x)\}=-\frac{d_0+s_0}{d_2+s_2s}, \tag{22}
$$

and

$$
\begin{aligned}
L\{h(x)\} &= -\frac{d_0+s_0}{d_2+s_2k_1(\alpha)s^{\alpha}+k_0(\alpha)(d_2+s_2)s^{\alpha+1}-(d_1+s_1)s} \\
&+\frac{k_0(\alpha)h(0)s^{\alpha}(d_2+s_2)}{(d_2+s_2)k_1(\alpha)s^{\alpha}+k_0(\alpha)(d_2+s_2)s^{\alpha+1}-(d_1+s_1)s} \\
&= \frac{d_0+s_0}{d_1+s_1}s^{-1}\left[1-\frac{(d_2+s_2)s^{\alpha-1}+k_0\alpha s^{\alpha}}{(d_1+s_1)}\right]^{-1} \\
&+h(0)s^{-1}\left[1-\frac{-k_1(\alpha)(d_2+s_2)s^{-1}+(d_1+s_1)s^{-\alpha}}{k_0(\alpha)(d_2+s_2)}\right]^{-1} \\
&= \frac{d_0+s_0}{d_1+s_1}s^{-1}\sum_{j=0}^{\infty}\left[\frac{(d_2+s_2)s^{\alpha-1}+k_0(\alpha)(d_2+s_2)s^{\alpha}}{(d_1+s_1)}\right]^{j} \\
&+h(0)s^{-1}\sum_{j=0}^{\infty}\left[\frac{-k_1(\alpha)(d_2+s_2)s^{-1}+(d_1+s_1)s^{-\alpha}}{k_0(\alpha)(d_2+s_2)}\right]^{j} \\
&= \frac{d_0+s_0}{d_1+s_1}s^{-1}\sum_{j=0}^{\infty}\frac{1}{(d_1+s_1)^j}\sum_{r=0}^{j}\binom{j}{r}[(d_2+s_2)s^{\alpha-1}]^{j-r}[k_0(\alpha)(d_2+s_2)s^{\alpha}]^{r} \\
&+h(0)s^{-1}\sum_{j=0}^{\infty}\frac{1}{k_0(\alpha)^j(d_2+s_2)^j}\sum_{r=0}^{j}\binom{j}{r}[-k_1(\alpha)(d_2+s_2)s^{-1}]^{j-r}[(d_1+s_1)s^{-\alpha}]^{r} \\
&= \frac{d_0+s_0}{d_1+s_1}\sum_{j=0}^{\infty}\sum_{r=0}^{j}\frac{(d_2+s_2)^{j-r}k_0(\alpha)^r(d_2+s_2)^r}{(d_1+s_1)^j}\binom{j}{r}s^{(\alpha-1)(j-r)+\alpha r-1} \\
&+h(0)\sum_{j=0}^{\infty}\sum_{r=0}^{j}\frac{(-k_1(\alpha))^{j-r}(d_2+s_2)^{j-r}(d_1+s_1)^r}{k_0(\alpha)^j(d_2+s_2)^j}\binom{j}{r}s^{r-j-\alpha r-1}.
\end{aligned}
$$

Applying the inverse Laplace transform, we have:

$$
\begin{aligned}
h(x) &= \frac{d_0+s_0}{d_1+s_1}\sum_{j=0}^{\infty}\sum_{r=0}^{j}\frac{(d_2+s_2)^{j-r}k_0(\alpha)^r(d_2+s_2)^r}{(d_1+s_1)^j}\binom{j}{r}\frac{x^{(1-\alpha)(j-r)-\alpha r}}{\Gamma((1-\alpha)(j-r)-\alpha r+1)} \\
&+h(0)\sum_{j=0}^{\infty}\sum_{r=0}^{j}\frac{(-k_1(\alpha))^{j-r}(d_2+s_2)^{j-r}(d_1+s_1)^r}{k_0(\alpha)^j(d_2+s_2)^j}\binom{j}{r}\frac{x^{j-r+\alpha r}}{\Gamma((j-r+\alpha r+1)}.
\end{aligned}
$$

When we take $p=j-r$, we will get:

$$
\begin{aligned}
h(x) &= \frac{d_0+s_0}{d_1+s_1}\sum_{r=0}^{\infty}\sum_{p=0}^{\infty}\frac{(r+p)!}{r!p!}\frac{((d_2+s_2))^{p+m}(k_0(\alpha))^r}{(d_1+s_1)^{p+r}}\frac{x^{(1-\alpha)p-\alpha r}}{\Gamma((1-\alpha)p-\alpha r+1)} \\
&+h(0)\sum_{r=0}^{\infty}\sum_{p=0}^{\infty}\frac{(r+p)!}{r!p!}\frac{(-k_1(\alpha))^p((d_1+s_1))^r}{k_0(\alpha)^{p+r}}(d_2+s_2)^r\frac{x^{p+\alpha r}}{\Gamma(p+\alpha r+1)},
\end{aligned}
$$

$$
\begin{aligned}
h(x) &= \frac{d_0+s_0}{d_1+s_1}\sum_{r=0}^{\infty}\sum_{p=0}^{\infty}\frac{(r+p)!}{r!p!}\left[\frac{(d_2+s_2)k_0(\alpha)}{(d_1+s_1)}x^{-\alpha}\right]^r\left[\frac{d_2+s_2}{d_1+s_1}x^{1-\alpha}\right]^p\frac{1}{\Gamma((1-\alpha)p-\alpha r+1)} \\
&+h(0)\sum_{r=0}^{\infty}\sum_{p=0}^{\infty}\frac{(r+p)!}{r!p!}\left[\frac{(d_1+s_1)}{k_0(\alpha)(d_2+s_2)}x^{\alpha}\right]^r\left[\frac{-k_1(\alpha)}{k_0(\alpha)}x\right]^p\frac{1}{\Gamma(p+\alpha r+1)}.
\end{aligned}
$$

We can write geometric series as [35]:

$$
\begin{aligned}
h(x) &= \frac{d_0+s_0}{d_1+s_1}E^1_{1-\alpha,-\alpha,1}\left(\frac{d_2+s_2}{d_1+s_1}x^{1-\alpha}, \frac{(d_2+s_2)k_0(\alpha)}{(d_1+s_1)}x^{-\alpha}\right)\\
&\quad +h(0)E^1_{1,\alpha,1}\left(\frac{-k_1(\alpha)}{k_0(\alpha)}x, \frac{(d_1+s_1)}{k_0(\alpha)(d_2+s_2)}x^{\alpha}\right).
\end{aligned}
$$

4. Comparison

In this section, we give the results that were found for the first economic model with Caputo fractional derivative [30], Caputo–Fabrizio derivative in Caputo sense [30], Atangana–Baleanu derivative [30] and constant proportional Caputo derivative.

$$
h(x) = \frac{(d_0+s_0)}{(d_1+s_1)}[1-E_\alpha(-k(d_1+s_1)x^\alpha)] + h(0)E_\alpha(-k(d_1+s_1)x^\alpha),
$$

$$
\begin{aligned}
h(x) &= \frac{M(\alpha)h(0)\exp\left(\frac{\alpha k(d_1+s_1)x}{-M(\alpha)+(\alpha-1)k(d_1+s_1)}\right)}{M(\alpha)-(\alpha-1)k(d_1+s_1)}\\
&\quad -\frac{M(\alpha)(d_0+s_0)(-1+\exp\left(\frac{\alpha k(d_1+s_1)x}{-M(\alpha)+(\alpha-1)k(d_1+s_1)}\right)) + (\alpha-1)k(d_1+s_1)}{(d_1+s_1)(-M(\alpha)+(\alpha-1)k(d_1+s_1))}
\end{aligned}
$$

$$
\begin{aligned}
h(x) &= \frac{AB(\alpha)h(0)}{AB(\alpha)+(1-\alpha)k(d_1+s_1)}E_\alpha\left(-\frac{\alpha k(d_1+s_1)x^\alpha}{AB(\alpha)+(1-\alpha)k(d_1+s_1)}\right)\\
&\quad +\frac{(1-\alpha)k(d_0+s_0)}{AB(\alpha)+(1-\alpha)k(d_1+s_1)}E_\alpha\left(-\frac{\alpha k(d_1+s_1)x^\alpha}{AB(\alpha)+(1-\alpha)k(d_1+s_1)}\right)\\
&\quad +\frac{(d_0+s_0)}{(d_1+s_1)}\left[1-E_\alpha\left(-\frac{\alpha k(d_1+s_1)x^\alpha}{AB(\alpha)+(1-\alpha)k(d_1+s_1)}\right)\right]
\end{aligned}
$$

$$
\begin{aligned}
h(x) &= \frac{(d_0+s_0)}{(d_1+s_1)}E^1_{1-\alpha,-\alpha,1}\left(\frac{-k_1(\alpha)}{k(d_0+s_0)}x^{1-\alpha}, \frac{-k_0(\alpha)}{k(d_0+s_0)}x^{-\alpha}\right)\\
&\quad +h(0)E^1_{1,\alpha,1}\left(\frac{-k_1(\alpha)}{k_0(\alpha)}x, \frac{-k(d_1+s_1)}{k_0(\alpha)}x^{\alpha}\right).
\end{aligned}
$$

We give the results that were found for the second economic model with Caputo fractional derivative [30], Caputo–Fabrizio derivative in Caputo sense [30], Atangana–Baleanu derivative [30] and constant proportional Caputo derivative respectively as:

$$
h(x) = -\frac{(d_0+s_0)}{(d_1+s_1)}\left[1-E_\alpha\left(\frac{(d_1+s_1)}{(d_2+s_2)}x^\alpha\right)\right] + h(0)E_\alpha\left(\frac{(d_1+s_1)}{(d_2+s_2)}x^\alpha\right),
$$

$$
\begin{aligned}
h(x) &= \frac{M(\alpha)h(0)(d_2+s_2)}{M(\alpha)(d_2+s_2)+(\alpha-1)d_1+(\alpha-1)s_1}\exp\left(\frac{\alpha(d_1+s_1)x}{M(\alpha)(d_2+s_2)+(\alpha-1)d_1+(\alpha-1)s_1}\right)\\
&\quad +\frac{(d_0+s_0)((\alpha-1)d_1+(\alpha-1)s_1-M(\alpha)(-1+\exp\left(\frac{\alpha k(d_1+s_1)x}{M(\alpha)(d_2+s_2)+(\alpha-1)d_1+(\alpha-1)s_1}\right)(d_2+s_2)))}{(d_1+s_1)(M(\alpha)(d_2+s_2)+(\alpha-1)d_1+(\alpha-1)s_1}
\end{aligned}
$$

$$h(x) = \frac{AB(\alpha)h(0)(d_2+s_2)}{AB(\alpha)(d_2+s_2)+(\alpha-1)d_1+(\alpha-1)s_1}E_\alpha\left(\frac{\alpha(d_1+s_1)x^\alpha}{AB(\alpha)(d_2+s_2)+(\alpha-1)d_1+(\alpha-1)s_1}\right)$$
$$-\frac{(\alpha-1)(d_0+s_0)}{AB(\alpha)(d_2+s_2)+(\alpha-1)d_1+(\alpha-1)s_1}E_\alpha\left(\frac{\alpha(d_1+s_1)x^\alpha}{AB(\alpha)(d_2+s_2)+(\alpha-1)d_1+(\alpha-1)s_1}\right)$$
$$+\frac{(\alpha-1)(d_0+s_0)}{\alpha(d_1+s_1)}\left[1-E_\alpha\left(\frac{\alpha(d_1+s_1)x^\alpha}{AB(\alpha)(d_2+s_2)+(\alpha-1)d_1+(\alpha-1)s_1}\right)\right]$$

$$h(x) = \frac{(d_0+s_0)}{(d_1+s_1)}E^1_{1-\alpha,-\alpha,1}\left(\frac{(d_2+s_2)}{(d_1+s_1)}x^{1-\alpha}, \frac{(d_2+s_2)k_0(\alpha)}{(d_1+s_1)}x^{-\alpha}\right)$$
$$+h(0)E^1_{1,\alpha,1}\left(\frac{-k_1(\alpha)}{k_0(\alpha)}x, \frac{(d_1+s_1)}{k_0(\alpha)(d_2+s_2)}x^\alpha\right).$$

5. Conclusions

In this study, we gave some details of the Laplace transform. Then, we constructed the economic models and we solved these models by the Laplace transform. We concluded that the Laplace transform is very effective for solving such problems. We presented an application of the economic models by using the newly introduced constant proportional Caputo derivative. The obtained results will be useful for researchers who interest the economic models and the integral transforms.

Author Contributions: Conceptualization, A.A. and E.K.A.; methodology, D.B.; software, A.A.; validation, A.A., E.K.A. and D.B.; formal analysis, E.K.A.; investigation, A.A.; resources, E.K.A.; data curation, D.B.; writing—original draft preparation, E.K.A.; writing—review and editing, A.A.; visualization, E.K.A.; supervision, D.B.; project administration, E.K.A.; funding acquisition, A.A. All authors have read and agreed to the published version of the manuscript.

Funding: This research received no external funding.

Conflicts of Interest: The authors declare that they do not have any conflict of interest.

References

1. Ghanbari, B.; Atangana, A. A new application of fractional Atangana–Baleanu derivatives: Designing ABC-fractional masks in image processing. *Phys. Stat. Mech. Its Appl.* **2020**, *542*, 123516, [CrossRef]
2. Ghanbari, B.; Akgül, A. Abundant new analytical and approximate solutions to the generalized Schamel equation. *Phys. Scr.* **2020**, *95*, 075201. [CrossRef]
3. Allahviranloo, T.; Ghanbari, B. On the fuzzy fractional differential equation with interval Atangana-Baleanu fractional derivative approach. *Chaos Solitons Fractals* **2020**, *128*, 109397. [CrossRef]
4. Salari, A.; Ghanbari, B. Existence and multiplicity for some boundary value problems involving Caputo and Atangana–Baleanu fractional derivatives: A variational approach. *Chaos Solitons Fractals* **2019**, *127*, 312–317. [CrossRef]
5. Akgül, A.; Akgül, E.K. On solutions of new type fractional differential equations occurring in the electrohydrodynamic flow. *Electron. Res. Arch.* **2020**, *28*, 537.
6. Farman, M.; Akgül, A.; Ahmad, A.; Imtiaz, S. Analysis and dynamical behavior of fractional-order cancer model with vaccine strategy. *Math. Methods Appl. Sci.* **2020**, *43*, 4871–4882. [CrossRef]
7. Modanli, M.; Akgül, A. On Solutions of Fractional order Telegraph partial differential equation by Crank-Nicholson finite difference method. *Appl. Math. Nonlinear Sci.* **2020**, *5*, 163–170. [CrossRef]
8. Nagle, R.K.; Staff, E.B.; Snider, A.D. *Fundamentals Dfferential Equations*; Pearson: Upper Saddle River, NJ, USA, 2008.
9. Baleanu, D.; Fernandez, A.; Akgül, A. On a fractional operator combining proportional and classical differintegrals. *Mathematics* **2020**, *8*, 360. [CrossRef]
10. Gupta, S.; Kumar, D.; Singh, J. Analytical solutions of convection–diffusion problems by combining Laplace transform method and homotopy perturbation method. *Alexasandria Eng. J.* **2015**, *54*, 645–651. [CrossRef]
11. Anjum, N.; He, J.H. Laplace transform, making the variational iteration method easier. *Appl. Math. Lett.* **2019**, *92*, 134–138. [CrossRef]

12. Zhou, Z.; Ma, J.; Gao, X. Convergence of iterative Laplace transform methods for a system of fractional PDEs and PIDEs arising in option pricing. *East Asian J. Appl. Math.* **2018**, *8*, 782–808. [CrossRef]
13. Bashir, T.; Kalim, M. Solution of non-homogeneous differential equations using faddeev-leverrier method together with Laplace transform. *Adv. Differ. Equations Control. Process.* **2018**, *19*, 343–357. [CrossRef]
14. Jingtang, M.; Zhiqiang, Z. Convergence analysis of iterative Laplace transform methods for the coupled PDEs from regime-switching option pricing. *J. Sci. Comput.* **2018**, *75*, 1656–1674.
15. Eljaoui, E.; Melliani, S.; Chadli, L.S. Aumann fuzzy improper integral and its application to solve fuzzy integro-differential equations by Laplace transform method. *Adv. Fuzzy Syst.* **2018**, *2018*, 9730502. [CrossRef]
16. Zhou, Z.; Ma, J.; Sun, H.W. Fast Laplace transform methods for free-boundary problems of fractional diffusion equations. *J. Sci. Comput.* **2018**, *74*, 49–69. [CrossRef]
17. Yonghong, S.; Wei, C. Laplace Transform method for the ulam stability of linear fractional differential equations with constant coefficient. *Mediterr. J. Math.* **2017**, *14*, UNSP 25.
18. Fatoorehchi, H.; Abolghasemi, H. Series solution of nonlinear differential equations by a novel extension of the Laplace transform method. *Int. J. Comput. Math.* **2016**, *93*, 1299–1319. [CrossRef]
19. Jacobs, A.B. High-order compact finite difference and Laplace transform method for the solution of time-fractional heat equations with Dirichlet and Neumann boundary conditions. *Numer. Methods Partial. Differ. Equ.* **2016**, *32*, 1184–1199. [CrossRef]
20. Gao, W.; Veeresha, P.; Prakasha, D.G.; Baskonus, H.M. Novel dynamical structures of 2019-nCoV with nonlocal operator via powerful computational technique. *Biology* **2020**, *9*, 107. [CrossRef]
21. Sulaiman, T.A.; Bulut, H.; Atas, S.S. Optical solitons to the fractional Schrödinger-Hirota equation. *Appl. Math. Nonlinear Sci.* **2019**, 4, 535–542. [CrossRef]
22. Özarslan, M.A. On a singular integral equation including a set of multivariate polynomials suggested by Laguerre polynomials. *Appl. Math. Comput.* **2014**, *229*, 350–358. [CrossRef]
23. Kürt, C.; Özarslan, M.A.; Fernandez, A. On a certain bivariate Mittag-Leffler function analysed from a fractional-calculus point of view. *Math. Meth. Appl. Sci.* **2020**. [CrossRef]
24. Logeswari, K.; Ravichandran, C. A new exploration on existence of fractional neutral integro- differential equations in the concept of Atangana–Baleanu derivative. *Phys. A Stat. Mech. Its Appl.* **2020**, *544*, 123454. [CrossRef]
25. Ravichandran, C.; Logeswaria, K.; Jarad, F. New results on existence in the framework of Atangana–Baleanu derivative for fractional integro-differential equations. *Chaos Solitons Fractals* **2019**, *125*, 194–200. [CrossRef]
26. Kumar, S.; Nisar, K.S.; Kumar, R.; Cattani, C.; Samet, B. A new Rabotnov fractional-exponential function-based fractional derivative for diffusion equation under external force. *Math. Methods Appl. Sci.* **2020**, *43*, 4460–4471. [CrossRef]
27. Kumar, S.; Kumar, A.; Odibat, Z.; Aldhaifallah, M. Kottakkaran Sooppy Nisar, A comparison study of two modified analytical approach for the solution of nonlinear fractional shallow water equations in fluid flow. *AIMS Math.* **2020**, *5*, 3035–3055. [CrossRef]
28. Manafianheris, J. Solving the integro-differential equations using the modified Laplace Adomian decomposition method. *J. Math. Ext.* **2012**, *6*, 1–15.
29. Manafianheris, J.; Lakestani, M. New Improvement of the Expansion Methods for Solving the Generalized Fitzhugh-Nagumo Equation with Time-Dependent Coefficients. *Int. J. Eng. Math.* **2015**, *2015*, 107978.
30. Acay, B.; Baş, E.; Abdeljawad, T. Fractional economic models based on market equilibrium in the frame of different type kernels. *Chaos Solitons Fractals* **2020**, *130*, 109438. [CrossRef]
31. Gao, W.; Veeresha, P.; Baskonus, H.M.; Prakasha, D.G.; Kumar, P. A New Study of Unreported Cases of 2019-nCOV Epidemic Outbreaks. *Chaos Solitons Fractals* **2020**, *138*, 1–6. [CrossRef]
32. Cattani, C. A review on Harmonic Wavelets and their fractional extension. *J. Adv. Eng. Comput.* **2018**, 2, 224–238. [CrossRef]
33. Cattani, C.; Rushchitskii, Y.Y. Cubically nonlinear elastic waves: Wave equations and methods of analysis. *Int. Appl. Mech.* **2003**, *39*, 1115–1145. [CrossRef]

34. Podlubny, I. *Fractional Differential Equations*; Academic Press: San Diego, CA, USA, 1999.
35. Fernandez, A.; Kürt, C.; Özarslan, M.A. A naturally emerging bivariate Mittag-Leffler function and associated fractional-calculus operators. *arXiv* **2020**, arXiv:2002.12171.

fractal and fractional

MDPI

Article

Extraction Complex Properties of the Nonlinear Modified Alpha Equation

Haci Mehmet Baskonus [1,*] and Muzaffer Ercan [2]

1 Department of Mathematics and Science Education, Faculty of Education, Harran University, Sanliurfa 63510, Turkey
2 Faculty of Arts and Sciences, Harran University, Sanliurfa 63510, Turkey; muzaffercan6347@gmail.com
* Correspondence: hmbaskonus@gmail.com

Abstract: This paper applies one of the special cases of auxiliary method, which is named as the Bernoulli sub-equation function method, to the nonlinear modified alpha equation. The characteristic properties of these solutions, such as complex and soliton solutions, are extracted. Moreover, the strain conditions of solutions are also reported in detail. Observing the figures plotted by considering various values of parameters of these solutions confirms the effectiveness of the approximation method used for the governing model.

Keywords: modified alpha equation; Bernoulli sub-equation function method; rational function solution; complex solution; contour surface

Citation: Baskonus, H.M.; Ercan, M. Extraction Complex Properties of the Nonlinear Modified Alpha Equation. *Fractal Fract.* **2021**, *5*, 6. https://doi.org10.3390/fractalfract5010006

Received: 13 November 2020
Accepted: 31 December 2020
Published: 7 January 2021

1. Introduction

In the last three decades, we have seen an enthralling research topic on the real world problems expressed by using mathematical models. Qi et al. have investigated some important models used to describe the certain waves in physics [1,2]. In this sense, an interesting model for investigating numerically the nonlinear weakly singular models has been presented by Ray et al. [3]. Syam has worked on the Bernoulli sub-equation method [4]. He has also obtained a lot of different interesting results for the governing model. A few years ago, Mendo has studied the series of wave forces connected with Bernoulli structures [5]. He has also produced a different Bernoulli variable algorithm. Rani et al. have studied on a special matrix that could be solved by Bernoulli polynomials [6]. Jeon et al. have investigated the generalized hypergeometric differential [7]. In 2019, Arqub et al. have studied the Riccati and Bernoulli properties to find new and different solutions for the governing model [8]. Ordokhani et al. have observed some important properties the Bernoulli wavelets with their special cases [9]. Yang has proved a new form of high order Bernoulli polynomials in 2008 [10], which obtained many new special cases about the Bernoulli model. In 2016, Dilcher has searched for identities of the Bernoulli polynomial properties in a physical aspect [11,12]. Furthermore, they have given more detailed information regarding these special functions. Ordokhani et al. have defined an original rational relation based on the Bernoulli wavelet [13]. Tian et al. have worked on the solution of beam problem by using an ansatz method based on the Bernoulli polinomials [14], and so on [15–27].

More general properties of auxiliary and sub-equation function methods have been comprehensively introduced in the literature [28,29]. Moreover, there are many published methods for solving similar equations using different techniques and methods [30–49].

In the organization of this paper, in Section 2, we give some preliminaries about the method. In Section 3, we discuss the application of projected method to the nonlinear modified alpha equation (MAE) defined as [21]

$$u_t - u_{xxt} + (\alpha+1)u^2u_x - \alpha u_x u_{xx} - u u_{xxx} = 0, \tag{1}$$

in which α is real constant and non-zero. Islam et al., have applied the modified simple equation method to Equation (1) for getting some important properties [21]. Wazwaz investigated the physical meaning of Equation (1) in a previous study [22].

Comparison and discussion related to the solutions obtained in this paper are presented in Section 4. After the graphical simulations, a conclusion completes the paper.

2. Fundamental Facts of BSEFM

This section presents the general properties of BSEFM [23] based on the four steps defined as follows:

Step 1. We consider the following nonlinear partial differential equation (NLPDE) given as

$$P\left(u, u_x, u_{xt}, u_{xx}, u^2, \ldots\right) = 0, \tag{2}$$

which is taking into account the travelling wave transformation

$$u(x,t) = U(\eta),\ \eta = kx - ct, \tag{3}$$

where $k \neq 0, c \neq 0$. Substituting Equation (3) into Equation (2) yields the following ordinary differential equation:

$$N\left(U, U', U'', U^2, \ldots\right) = 0, \tag{4}$$

$$\text{where } U = U(\eta), U' = \frac{dU}{d\eta}, U'' = \frac{d^2U}{d\eta^2}, \ldots.$$

Step 2. In this step, we take the following trial solution equation to the Equation (4):

$$U(\eta) = \sum_{i=0}^{n} a_i F^i = a_0 + a_1 F + a_2 F^2 + \ldots + a_n F^n, \tag{5}$$

and

$$F' = bF + dF^M,\ b \neq 0,\ d \neq 0,\ M \in R - \{0,1,2\}, \tag{6}$$

where $F(\eta)$ is Bernoulli differential polynomial. Substituting Equation (5) along with Equation (6) into Equation (4), it produces an algebraic equation of polynomial $\Omega(F)$ as follows:

$$\Omega(F) = \rho_s F^s + \ldots + \rho_1 F + \rho_0 = 0. \tag{7}$$

We can find more than one solution by obtaining a relation between M and n via the balancing principle and then using this relation.

Step 3. If we take into account that all the coefficients of $\Omega(F)$ are zero:

$$\rho_i = 0,\ i = 0, \ldots, s.$$

If we solve this system, we will find and control the values of

$$a_0, a_1, a_2, \ldots, a_n \tag{8}$$

Step 4. Solving Equation (6), we find the following according to b and d:

$$F(\eta) = \left[\frac{-d}{b} + \frac{\varepsilon}{e^{b(M-1)\eta}}\right]^{\frac{1}{1-M}},\ b \neq d, \tag{9}$$

$$F(\eta) = \left[\frac{(\varepsilon - 1) + (\varepsilon + 1)\tanh\left(\frac{b(1-M)\eta}{2}\right)}{1 - \tanh\left(\frac{b(1-M)\eta}{2}\right)}\right]^{\frac{1}{1-M}},\ b = d,\ \varepsilon \in R.$$

Using a complete discrimination system for polynomial parameters, we find the solutions to Equation (4), using some computational programs, and organize the exact solutions to Equation (4). In order to better understand the results obtained in this way, we can draw the two and three dimensional surfaces of the solutions by considering the appropriate parameter values.

3. Implementation of the BSEFM

This section of the manuscript applies the BSEFM to the MAE to obtain new complex and exponential solutions. Using

$$u(x,t) = U(\eta), \eta = kx - ct$$

where c, k are real constants and non-zero, we obtain the nonlinear ordinary equation as follows:

$$6ck^2U'' - 6k^3UU'' + 3k^3(1-\alpha)\left(U'\right)^2 - 6cU + 2k(\alpha+1)U^3 = 0. \tag{10}$$

With the help of the balance principle, it is obtained a relationship between n and M as follows:

$$2M = n + 2. \tag{11}$$

This gives some new analytical solutions for the governing model being Equation (1).

Case 1: Considering as $n = 4$ and $M = 3$ produce the following trial solution for Equation (10):

$$U = a_0 + a_1F + a_2F^2 + a_3F^3 + a_4F^4, \tag{12}$$

$$U' = a_1bF + a_1dF^3 + 2a_2bF^2 + 2a_2dF^4 + 3a_3bF^3 + 3a_3dF^5 + 4a_4bF^4 + 4a_4dF^6, \tag{13}$$

and

$$\begin{aligned} U'' &= a_1d^2F + 4a_1bdF^3 + 3a_1b^2F^5 + 4a_2d^2F^2 + 12a_2bdF^4 + 8a_2b^2F^6 + 9a_3d^2F^3 \\ &\quad + 24a_3bdF^5 + 15a_3b^2F^7 + 16a_4d^2F^4 + 40a_4bdF^6 + 24a_4b^2F^8. \end{aligned} \tag{14}$$

where $a_4 \neq 0,\ b \neq 0,\ d \neq 0$. Putting Equations (12)–(14) into Equation (10), it gives a system of algebraic equations of F. With the help of powerful computational programs, we get the following coefficients and solutions.

Case 1.1. If it is selected follows:

$$\begin{aligned} a_0 &= -\frac{3d^2\alpha + \sqrt{3}\sqrt{-d^4(-4+\alpha^2)}}{2d^2(1+\alpha)}, a_1 = a_3 = 0, \\ k &= -\frac{1}{2}\sqrt{-\frac{d^2(2+a)(-1+2\alpha) + \sqrt{3}\sqrt{-d^4(-4+\alpha^2)}}{d^4(1+\alpha)(2+\alpha)}}, \\ a_2 &= -\frac{6b}{d^3(1+\alpha)^2}\left(d^2(2+a)(-1+2\alpha) + \sqrt{3}\sqrt{-d^4(-4+\alpha^2)}\right), \\ a_4 &= -\frac{6b^2}{d^4(1+\alpha)^2}\left(d^2(2+a)(-1+2\alpha) + \sqrt{3}\sqrt{-d^4(-4+\alpha^2)}\right), \\ c &= -\frac{1}{4d^2(1+\alpha)}\sqrt{-\frac{d^2(2+a)(-1+2\alpha) + \sqrt{3}\sqrt{-d^4(-4+\alpha^2)}}{d^4(1+\alpha)(2+\alpha)}} \\ &\quad \times\left(\alpha\sqrt{3}\sqrt{-d^4(-4+\alpha^2)} + d^2\left(2+\alpha^2\right)\right), \end{aligned} \tag{15}$$

we find the following new singular soliton solution for the governing model being Equation (1):

$$u_1(x,t) = \sigma - \frac{\omega}{d^4(1+\alpha)^2\left(-\frac{b}{d} + e^{-2d(-\frac{1}{2}x\tau + t\tau\varpi)}\varepsilon\right)^2} - \frac{\omega}{bd^3(1+\alpha)^2\left(-\frac{b}{d} + e^{-2d(-\frac{1}{2}x\tau + t\tau\varpi)}\varepsilon\right)}, \tag{16}$$

in which

$$\tau=\sqrt{-\frac{d^2(2+\alpha)(-1+2\alpha)+\sqrt{3}\sqrt{-d^4(-4+\alpha^2)}}{d^4(1+\alpha)(2+\alpha)}},\omega=6b^2\left(d^2(2+\alpha)(-1+2\alpha)+\sqrt{3}\sqrt{-d^4(-4+\alpha^2)}\right),$$
$$\varpi=\frac{\left(\sqrt{3}\alpha\sqrt{-d^4(-4+\alpha^2)}+d^2(2+\alpha^2)\right)}{4d^2(1+\alpha)},\sigma=-\frac{3d^2\alpha+\sqrt{3}\sqrt{-d^4(-4+\alpha^2)}}{2d^2(1+\alpha)},-2<\alpha<-1$$

for validity of Equation (16). Choosing the suitable values of parameters in Equation (16), we plot various figures as follows as being in Figures 1 and 2.

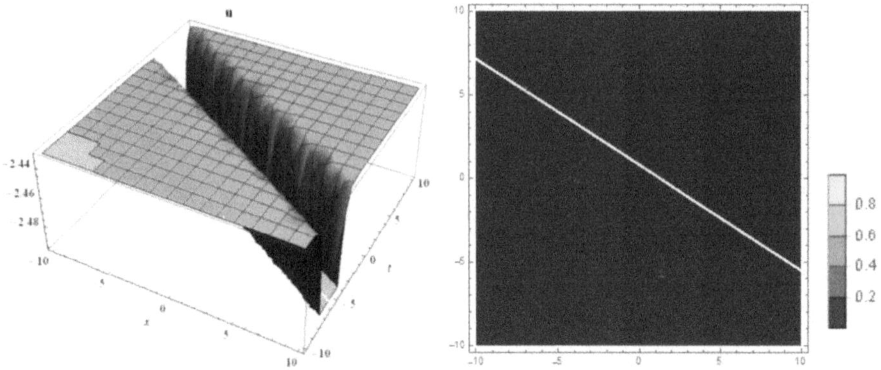

Figure 1. The 3D and contour surfaces of Equation (16) under the values of $d=0.1,\alpha=-1.8,b=0.5,\varepsilon=0.4$.

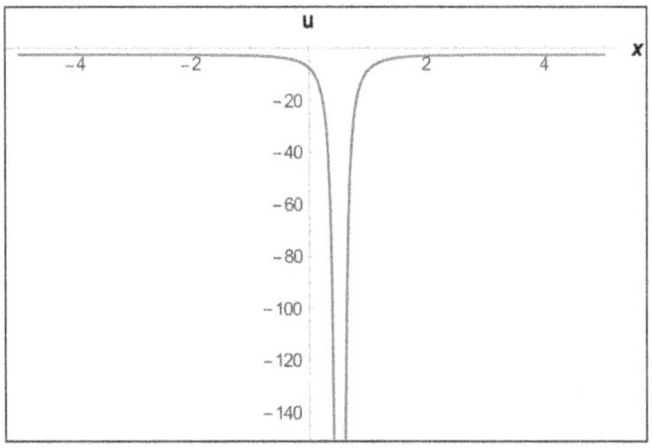

Figure 2. The 2D graph of Equation (16) under the values of $d=0.1,\alpha=-1.8,b=0.5,\varepsilon=0.4$, $t=0.5,-5<x<5$.

Case 1.2. For $b\neq d$, when they are considered as follows:

$$a_0=a_1=a_3=0,a_2=\frac{-24bc}{1+\alpha},a_4=\frac{96b^2c^2}{2+3a+\alpha^2},k=\frac{2c}{2+\alpha},d=-\frac{2+\alpha}{4c}, \tag{17}$$

This produces a new singular soliton solution for the governing model as:

$$u_2(x,t)=-\tfrac{24bc}{1+a}\left(\tfrac{4bc}{2+a}+\varepsilon e^{\frac{2+a}{2c}(-ct+\frac{2c}{2+a}x)}\right)^{-1}+\tfrac{96b^2c^2}{\alpha^2+3a+2}\left(\tfrac{4bc}{2+a}+\varepsilon e^{\frac{2+a}{2c}(-ct+\frac{2c}{2+a}x)}\right)^{-2}. \tag{18}$$

The strain condition is also given as $\alpha\neq-1,\alpha\neq-2$. We can observe the wave surfaces of Equation (18) as being in Figures 3 and 4.

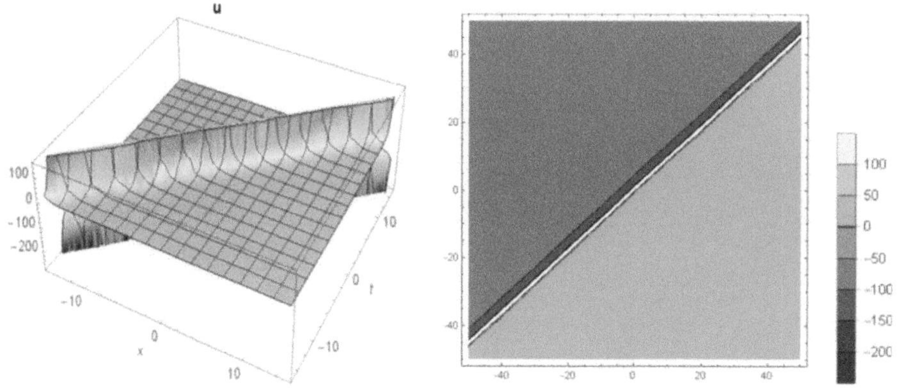

Figure 3. 3D and contour graphs of Equation (18) for $\alpha = 0.2, b = 0.3, c = -0.5, \varepsilon = 0.4, d = 0.1, -15 < x < 15, -15 < t < 15$.

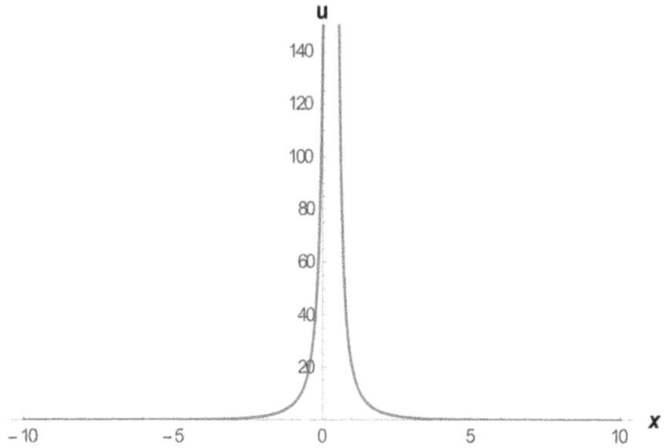

Figure 4. 2D graph of Equation (18) for $\alpha = 0.2, b = 0.3, c = -0.5, \varepsilon = 0.4, d = 0.1, t = 0.6$, $-10 < x < 10$.

Case 1.3. If we select the following complex coefficient together with $b \neq d$,

$$\begin{aligned} &a_4 = 4, k = 1, a_0 = i, a_1 = a_3 = 0, a_2 = 4\sqrt{-1+3i}, b = -\tfrac{1}{10}\sqrt{11-2i}, c = \tfrac{-7}{13} + \tfrac{4i}{13}, \\ &d = -\tfrac{1}{2}\sqrt{\tfrac{-1}{5} + \tfrac{7i}{5}}, \alpha = \tfrac{8}{13} - \tfrac{12i}{13}, \end{aligned} \tag{19}$$

it produces a complex soliton solution for the governing model as:

$$\begin{aligned} u_3(x,t) = i + 4&\left(-\tfrac{1}{\sqrt{-1+7i}}\sqrt{\tfrac{11}{5} - \tfrac{2i}{5}} + \varepsilon e^{\sqrt{\frac{-1}{5}+\frac{7i}{5}}\left(x+\left(\frac{7}{13}-\frac{4i}{13}\right)t\right)}\right)^{-2} \\ +4\sqrt{-1+3i}&\left(-\tfrac{1}{\sqrt{-1+7i}}\sqrt{\tfrac{11}{5} - \tfrac{2i}{5}} + \varepsilon e^{\sqrt{\frac{-1}{5}+\frac{7i}{5}}\left(x+\left(\frac{7}{13}-\frac{4i}{13}\right)t\right)}\right)^{-1}. \end{aligned} \tag{20}$$

Wave surfaces of Equation (20) can be observed in Figures 5–7.

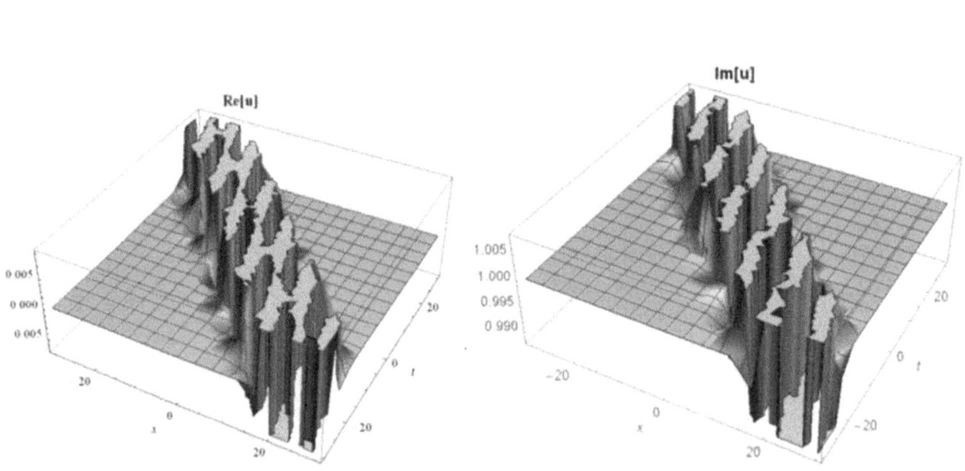

Figure 5. The 3D surfaces of Equation (20) under the values of $\varepsilon = 0.4, -30 < x < 30, -30 < t < 30$.

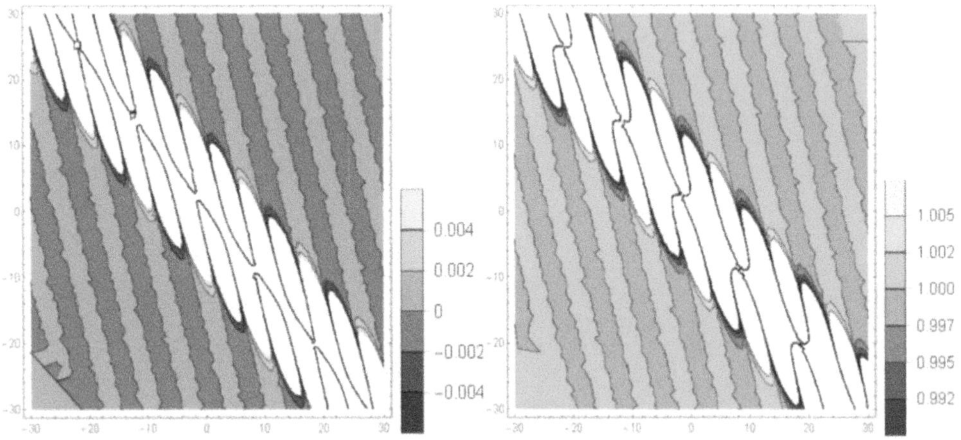

Figure 6. The contour surfaces of Equation (20) under the values of $\varepsilon = 0.4, -30 < x < 30, -30 < t < 30$.

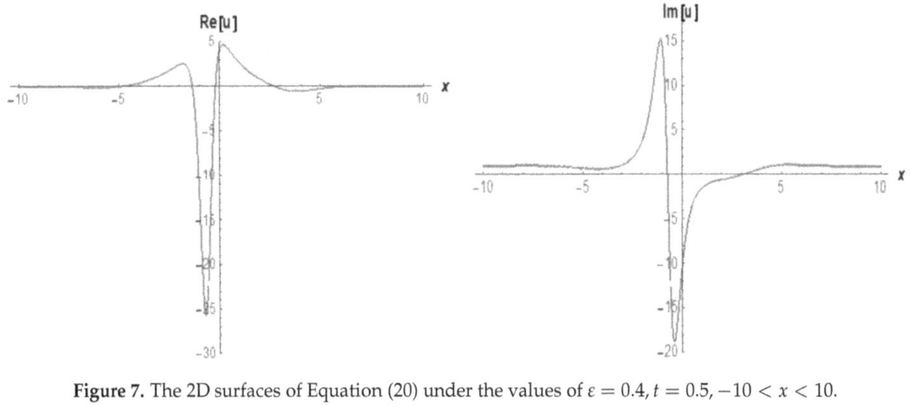

Figure 7. The 2D surfaces of Equation (20) under the values of $\varepsilon = 0.4, t = 0.5, -10 < x < 10$.

Case 1.4. When choosing the following other complex coefficients and also $b \neq d$,

$$a_4 = 4, k = 1, a_0 = i, a_1 = a_3 = 0, a_2 = -4\sqrt{-1+3i}, b = -\frac{1}{10}\sqrt{11-2i},$$
$$d = \frac{1}{2}\sqrt{\frac{-1}{5} + \frac{7i}{5}}, \alpha = \frac{8}{13} - \frac{12i}{13}, c = \frac{-7}{13} + \frac{4i}{13}, \tag{21}$$

it produces another complex soliton solution to the governing model as:

$$u_4(x,t) = i + 4\left(\frac{1}{\sqrt{-1+7i}}\sqrt{\frac{11}{5} - \frac{2i}{5}} + \varepsilon e^{-\sqrt{\frac{-1}{5}+\frac{7i}{5}}\left(x+\left(\frac{7}{13}-\frac{4i}{13}\right)t\right)}\right)^{-2}$$
$$-4\sqrt{-1+3i}\left(\frac{1}{\sqrt{-1+7i}}\sqrt{\frac{11}{5} - \frac{2i}{5}} + \varepsilon e^{-\sqrt{\frac{-1}{5}+\frac{7i}{5}}\left(x+\left(\frac{7}{13}-\frac{4i}{13}\right)t\right)}\right)^{-1}. \tag{22}$$

Under the suitable choosing of the values of these parameters, we plot various graphs as being Figures 8–10.

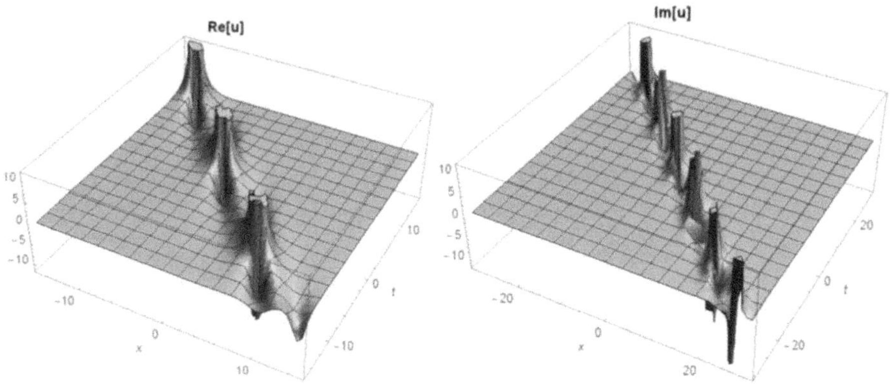

Figure 8. The 3D surfaces of Equation (22) under the values of $\varepsilon = 0.4, -15 < x < 15, -15 < t < 15$.

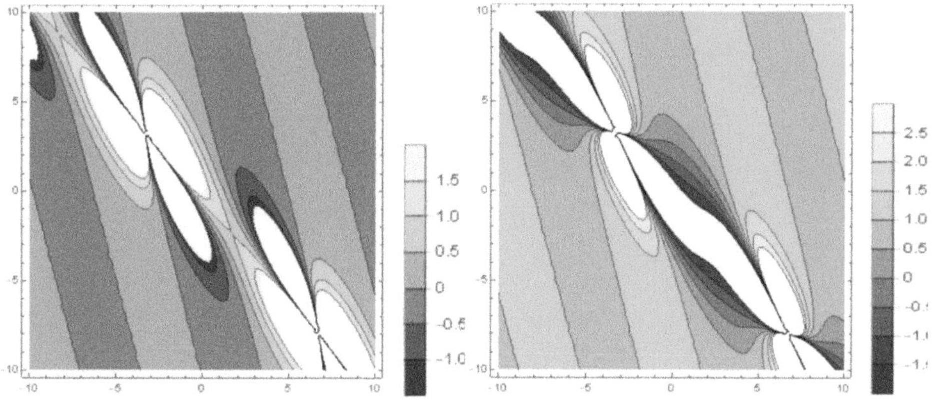

Figure 9. The contour surfaces of Equation (22) under the values of $\varepsilon = 0.4, -15 < x < 15, -15 < t < 15$.

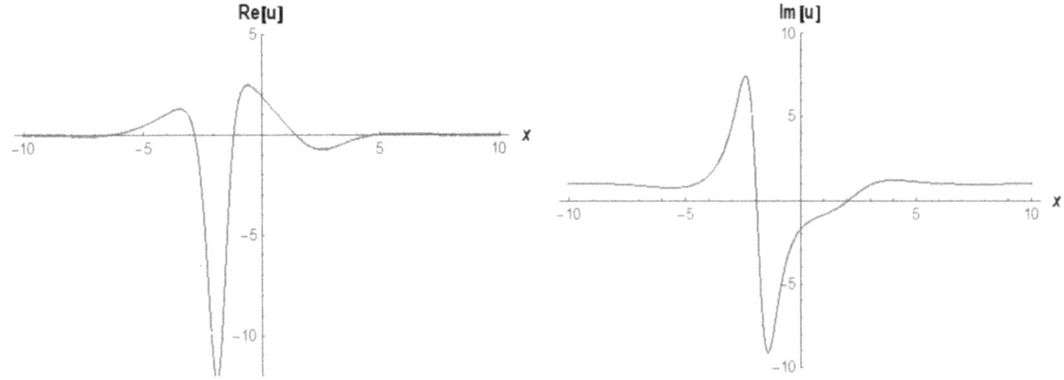

Figure 10. The 2D surfaces of Equation (22) under the values of $\varepsilon = 0.4, t = 0.5, -15 < x < 15$.

Case 1.5. Choosing the following other complex coefficients by considering $b \neq d$,

$$\begin{aligned} &a_4 = -i, k = 1, a_0 = 2, a_1 = 0, a_2 = (-2+2i)\sqrt{5}, a_3 = 0, b = \tfrac{1}{10} - \tfrac{i}{10}, d = \tfrac{-2}{\sqrt{5}}, \\ &\alpha = \tfrac{-1}{13}, c = \tfrac{16}{13}, \end{aligned} \tag{23}$$

gives another complex exponential function solution as:

$$u_5(x,t) = 2 - i\left(\frac{1-i}{4\sqrt{5}} + \varepsilon e^{\frac{4}{\sqrt{5}}(x - \frac{16}{13}t)}\right)^{-2} - (2-2i)\sqrt{5}\left(\frac{1-i}{4\sqrt{5}} + \varepsilon e^{\frac{4}{\sqrt{5}}(x - \frac{16}{13}t)}\right)^{-1}. \tag{24}$$

Choosing the suitable values of these parameters, we present several simulations as Figures 11–13.

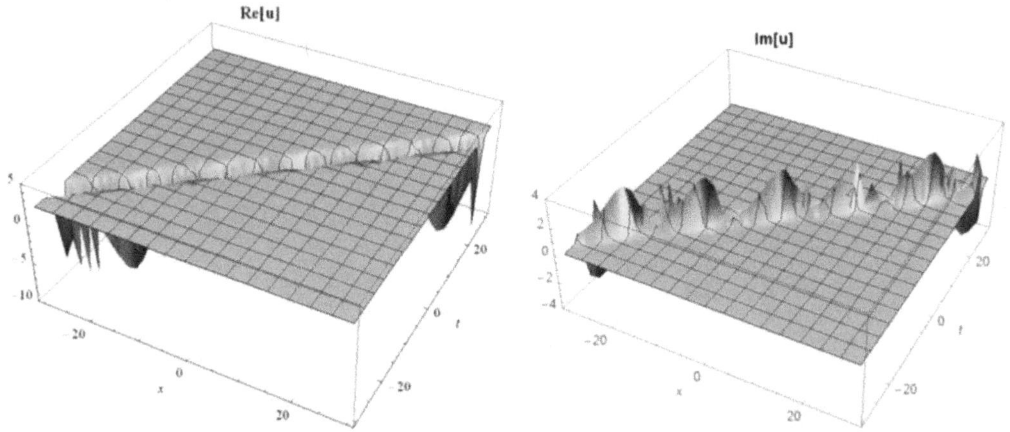

Figure 11. The 3D simulations of Equation (24) under the values of $\varepsilon = 0.4, -30 < x < 30, -30 < t < 30$.

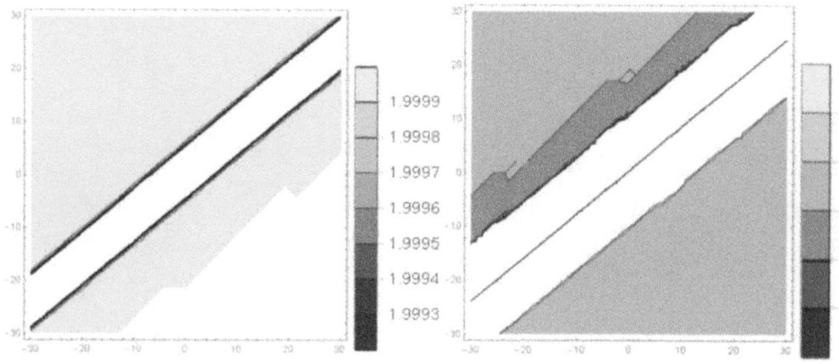

Figure 12. The contour graphs of Equation (24) under the values of $\varepsilon = 0.4, -30 < x < 30, -30 < t < 30$.

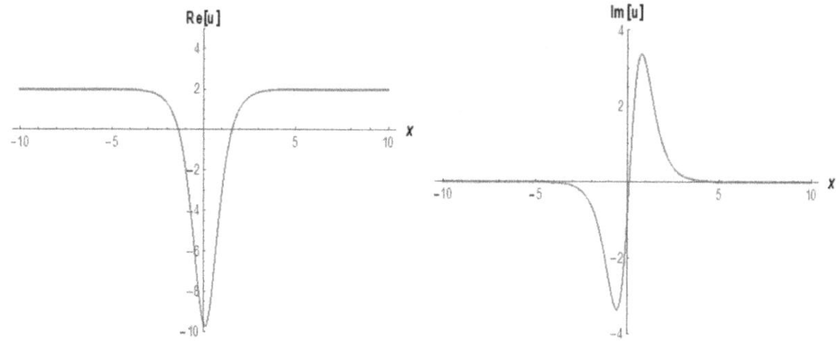

Figure 13. The 2D graphs of Equation (24) under the values of $\varepsilon = 0.4, t = 0.5, -10 < x < 10$.

Case 1.6. Taking the following other complex coefficients with $b \neq d$,

$$a_4 = -i, k = 1, a_0 = 2, a_1 = 0, a_2 = (2-2i)\sqrt{5}, a_3 = 0, b = -\frac{1}{10} + \frac{i}{10}, d = \frac{-2}{\sqrt{5}}, \\ \alpha = \frac{-1}{13}, c = \frac{16}{13}, \tag{25}$$

gives another complex exponential function solution as:

$$u_6(x,t) = 2 - i\left(\frac{-1+i}{4\sqrt{5}} + \varepsilon e^{\frac{4}{\sqrt{5}}(x - \frac{16}{13}t)}\right)^{-2} + (2-2i)\sqrt{5}\left(\frac{-1+i}{4\sqrt{5}} + \varepsilon e^{\frac{4}{\sqrt{5}}(x - \frac{16}{13}t)}\right)^{-1}. \tag{26}$$

Various simulations of Equation (26) may be observed in Figures 14–16.

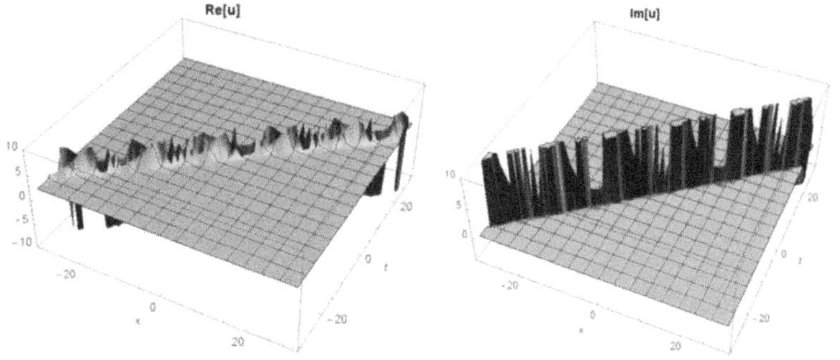

Figure 14. The 3D simulations of Equation (26) under the values of $\varepsilon = 0.4, -30 < x < 30, -30 < t < 30$.

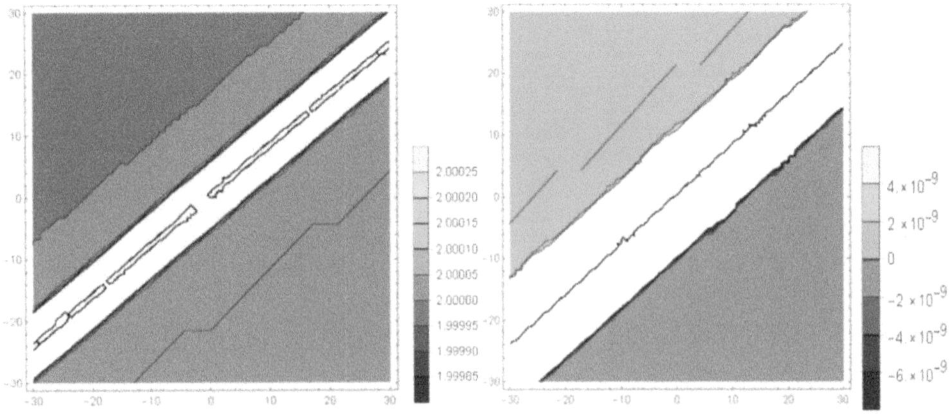

Figure 15. The contour graphs of Equation (26) under the values of $\varepsilon = 0.4, -30 < x < 30, -30 < t < 30$.

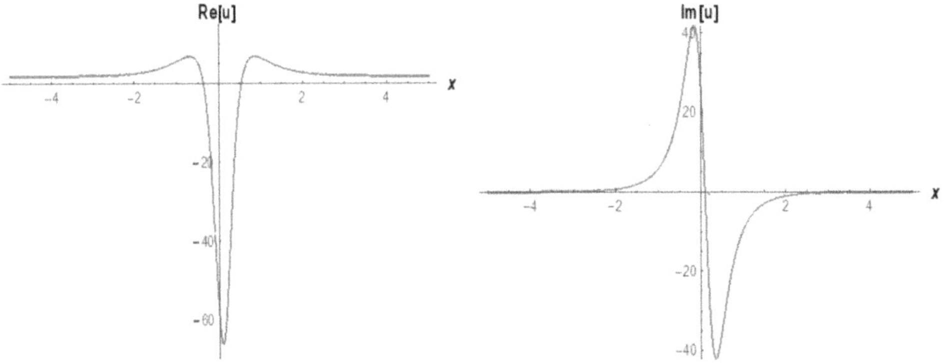

Figure 16. The 2D graphs of Equation (26) under the values of $\varepsilon = 0.4, t = 0.5, -5 < x < 5$.

Case 2. Taking $n = 6$ and $M = 4$, we can write as follows:

$$U = a_0 + a_1F + a_2F^2 + a_3F^3 + a_4F^4 + a_5F^5 + a_6F^6, \tag{27}$$

and

$$\begin{aligned} U' &= a_1F' + 2a_2FF' + 3a_3F^2F' + 4a_4F^3F' + 5a_5F^4F' + 6a_6F^5F', \\ U'' &= \ldots. \end{aligned} \tag{28}$$

where $a_6 \neq 0,\ b \neq 0,\ d \neq 0$. Putting Equations (27) and (28) into Equation (10) produces some entirely new analytical solutions for the governing model as follows.

Case 2.1: When

$$\begin{aligned} &d = 2, a_0 = a_1 = a_2 = a_4 = a_5 = 0, a_3 = (-1+i)\sqrt{3/5}, a_6 = i, b = (1-i)\sqrt{5/3}, \\ &k = 1/6, \alpha = -11/6, c = 1/72, \end{aligned} \tag{29}$$

another new complex soliton solution is extracted as:

$$u_7(x,t) = i\left(\frac{i\sqrt{5}-\sqrt{5}}{2\sqrt{3}} + \varepsilon e^{-x+\frac{t}{12}}\right)^{-2} + (i-1)\frac{\sqrt{3}}{\sqrt{5}}\left(\frac{i\sqrt{5}-\sqrt{5}}{2\sqrt{3}} + \varepsilon e^{-x+\frac{t}{12}}\right)^{-1}, \tag{30}$$

in which ε is a real constant with non-zero. Under the suitable chosen of parameters, we can presents various graphs as in Figures 17–19.

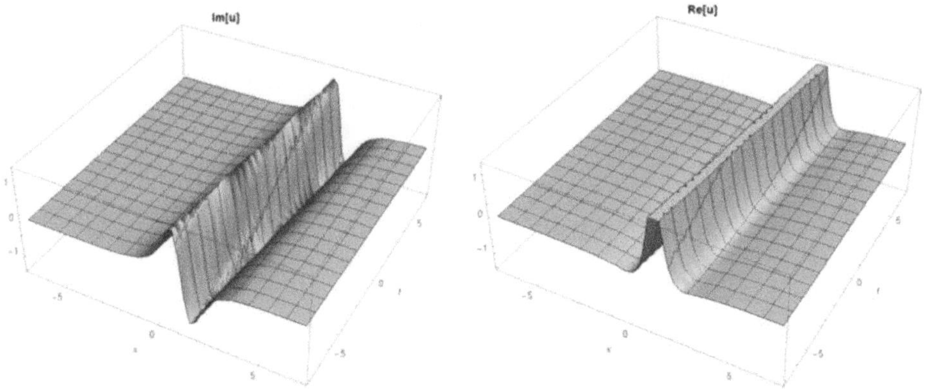

Figure 17. The 3D surfaces of Equation (30) under the values of $\varepsilon = 5, -7 < x < 7, -7 < t < 7$.

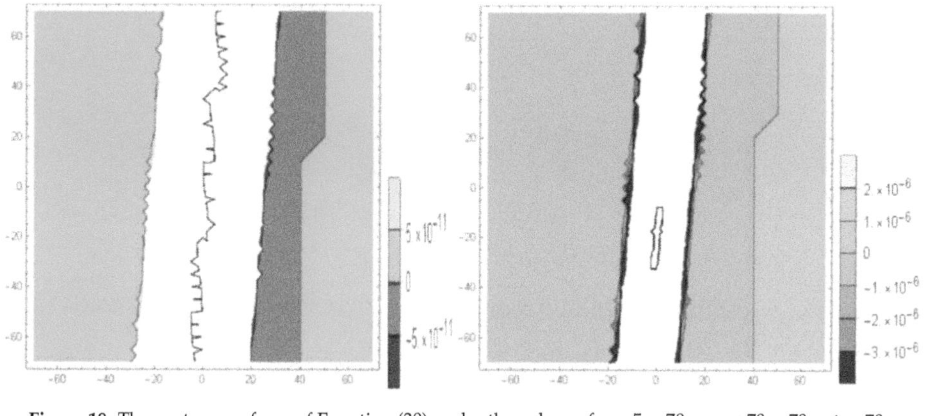

Figure 18. The contour surfaces of Equation (30) under the values of $\varepsilon = 5, -70 < x < 70, -70 < t < 70$.

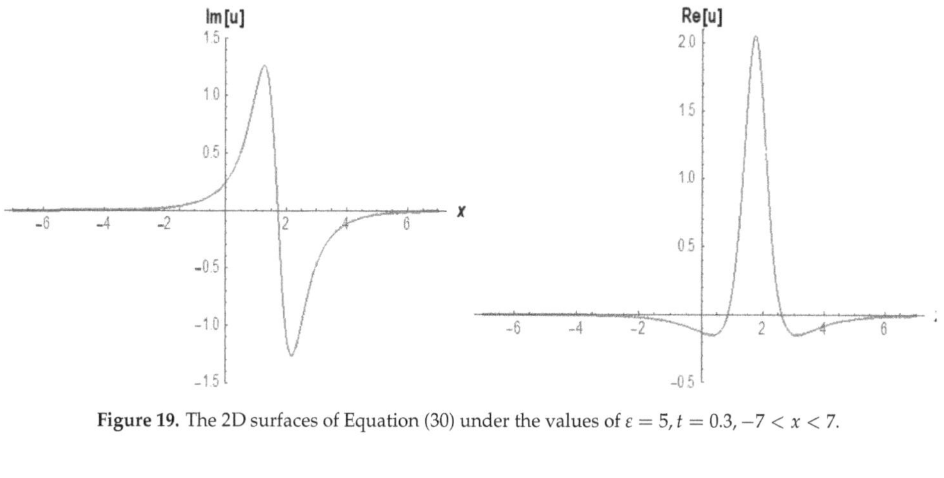

Figure 19. The 2D surfaces of Equation (30) under the values of $\varepsilon = 5, t = 0.3, -7 < x < 7$.

Case 2.2. Considering the following:

$$d = 2, a_0 = a_1 = a_2 = a_4 = a_5 = 0, a_3 = \left(\sqrt{6}(1+\alpha)\sqrt{2+\alpha}\right)/(i(1+\alpha))^{3/2}, a_6 = i, \\ k = 1/6, b = \left(-\sqrt{2/3}\sqrt{i(1+\alpha)}\right)/\sqrt{2+\alpha}, c = (2+\alpha)/12, \tag{31}$$

another new complex mixed dark soliton solution is extracted as:

$$u_8(x,t) = i\left(\frac{1 - Tanh(f(x,t))}{\varpi + \varepsilon + (\varepsilon - \varpi)Tanh(f(x,t))}\right)^2 + \frac{1 - Tanh(f(x,t))}{\varpi + \varepsilon + (\varepsilon - \varpi)Tanh(f(x,t))}, \tag{32}$$

in which ε, α are real constants and non-zero and also

$$\varpi = \frac{\sqrt{i(1+\alpha)}}{\sqrt{12+6\alpha}}, \sigma = \frac{\sqrt{6}(1+\alpha)\sqrt{2+\alpha}}{(i(1+\alpha))^{3/2}}, \\ f(x,t) = \frac{2+\alpha}{4}t - \frac{x}{2}.$$

We plot its surfaces in Figures 20–22.

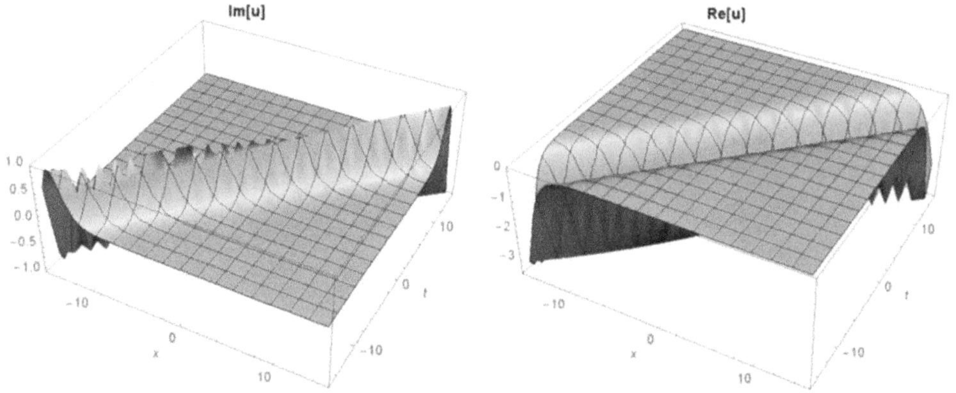

Figure 20. The 3D surfaces of Equation (32) for $\varepsilon = 0.4, \alpha = 0.1, -15 < x < 15, -15 < t < 15$.

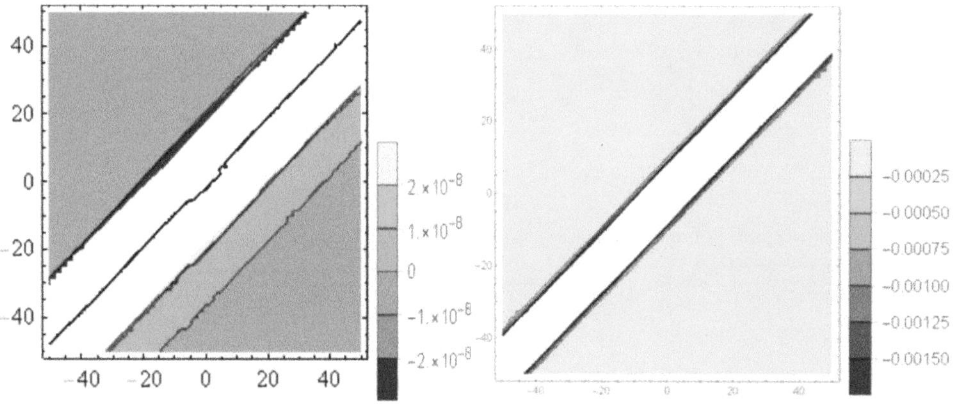

Figure 21. The contour surfaces of Equation (32) for $\varepsilon = 0.4, \alpha = 0.1, -50 < x < 50, -50 < t < 50$.

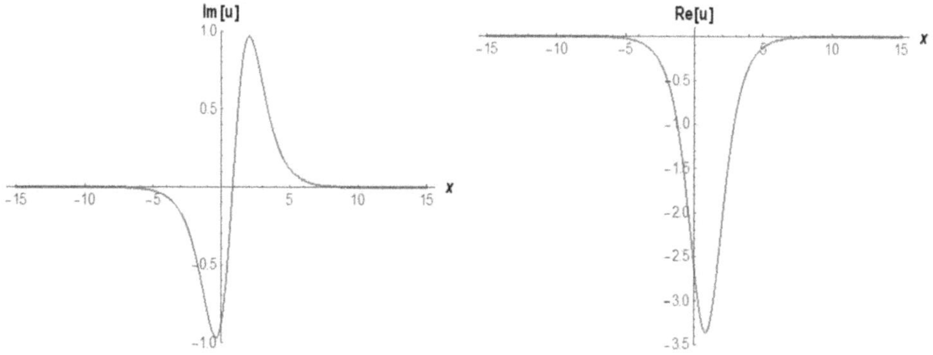

Figure 22. The 2D surfaces of Equation (32) for $\varepsilon = 0.4, \alpha = 0.1, t = 0.5, -15 < x < 15$.

4. Comparison and Discussion

In a previous research [21], Asaduzzman et al., have studied the special cases of Equation (1) by considering $\alpha = 2$. In this paper, we have extracted the general solutions of MAE according to α as being in the solutions of Equations (16), (18), and (32). Moreover, we have also investigated other values of α such as complex and rations in the coefficients of Equations (19), (21), (23), (25) and (29). When we compare these solutions with the solutions presented in the previous study [21], it may be observed that they are an entirely new solution for the governing model of MAE.

Moreover, if we consider more values of n, M as $n = 8$ and $M = 5$, we obtain another new solution for the governing model as:

$$U = a_0 + a_1 F + a_2 F^2 + a_3 F^3 + a_4 F^4 + a_5 F^5 + a_6 F^6 + a_7 F^7 + a_8 F^8, \tag{33}$$

in which $a_8 \neq 0,\ b \neq 0,\ d \neq 0$. By getting the necessary derivations of Equation (33) for Equation (10), we report more new complex and rational wave solutions to the MAE, which these solutions produced by BSEFM. In this regard, this projected technique is a powerful tool for obtaining new analytical solutions for the nonlinear partial differential equations.

In the physical sense, if we consider the solution of $u_8(x,t)$ being Equation (32), this is a complex mixed dark soliton solution for the governing model. Such reported results in this manuscript have some important properties. To illustrate this, the hyperbolic tangent (dark soliton) arises in the calculation of magnetic moment and rapidity of special relativity [50]. In this regard, it is estimated that this solution may help to better understanding of the meaning of MAE physically.

5. Conclusions

In this article, we have successfully applied BSEFM to the MAE. We obtained many entirely new complex and exponential characteristic properties of MAE. We observed that the results obtained with the help of the projected algorithm are new deeper investigations and a generalized version according to α. Moreover, we have reported the strain conditions for the validity of solutions. Various wave behaviors in many simulations from Figures 1–22 have been also presented to observe wave distributions of solutions. All figures are clearly commented, which give the idea of effectiveness of the proposed schemes. The method proposed in this paper can be used to seek more travelling wave solutions of such governing models, because the method has some advantages such as easily calculations, writing programme for obtaining coefficients, and many others.

Author Contributions: The first Author has majorly contributed to the paper. Formal analysis, H.M.B.; Writing—original draft, M.E. All authors have read and agreed to the published version of the manuscript.

Funding: This research received no external funding.

Institutional Review Board Statement: Not applicable.

Informed Consent Statement: Not applicable.

Data Availability Statement: Data available in a publicly accessible repository.

Acknowledgments: This paper belongs to the Master's thesis of the second author.

Conflicts of Interest: The authors declare no conflict of interest.

References

1. Qi, F.-H.; Huang, Y.-H.; Wang, P. Solitary-wave and new exact solutions for an extended (3+1)-dimensional Jimbo–Miwa-like equation. *Appl. Math. Lett.* **2020**, *100*, 106004. [CrossRef]
2. Cao, B. Solutions of Jimbo-Miwa Equation and Konopelchenko-Dubrovsky Equations. *arXiv* **2009**, arXiv:0902.3308.
3. Behera, S.; Ray, S.S. An operational matrix based scheme for numerical solutions of nonlinear weakly singular partial integro-differential equations. *Appl. Math. Comput.* **2020**, *367*, 124771. [CrossRef]
4. Syam, M.I. The solution of Cahn-Allen equation based on Bernoulli sub-equation method. *Results Phys.* **2019**, *14*, 102413. [CrossRef]
5. Mendo, L. An asymptotically optimal Bernoulli factory for certain functions that can be expressed as power series. *Stoch. Process. Their Appl.* **2019**, *129*, 4366–4384. [CrossRef]
6. Rani, D.; Mishra, V. Numerical inverse Laplace transform based on Bernoulli polynomials operational matrix for solving nonlinear differential equations. *Results Phys.* **2020**, *16*, 102836. [CrossRef]
7. Lee, J.Y.; Jeon, W. Exact solution of Euler-Bernoulli equation for acoustic black holes via generalized hypergeometric differential equation. *J. Sound Vib.* **2019**, *452*, 191–204. [CrossRef]
8. Arqub, O.A.; Maayah, B. Modulation of reproducing kernel Hilbert space method for numerical solutions of Riccati and Bernoulli equations in the Atangana-Baleanu fractional sense. *Chaos Solitons Fractals* **2019**, *125*, 163–170.
9. Rahimkhani, P.; Ordokhani, Y.; Babolian, E. Numerical solution of fractional pantograph differential equations by using generalized fractional-order Bernoulli wavelet. *J. Comput. Appl. Math.* **2017**, *309*, 493–510. [CrossRef]
10. Yang, S.L. An identity of symmetry for the Bernoulli polynomials. *Discret. Math.* **2008**, *308*, 550–554.
11. Dilcher, K.; Vignat, C. General convolution identities for Bernoulli and Euler polynomials. *J. Math. Anal. Appl.* **2016**, *435*, 1478–1498.
12. Dilcher, K.; Straub, A.; Vignat, C. Identities for Bernoulli polynomials related to multiple Tornheim zeta functions. *J. Math. Anal. Appl.* **2019**, *476*, 569–584. [CrossRef]
13. Rahimkhani, P.; Ordokhani, Y.; Babolian, E. Fractional-order Bernoulli wavelets and their applications. *Appl. Math. Model.* **2016**, *40*, 8087–8107. [CrossRef]
14. Ren, Q.; Tian, H. Numerical solution of the static beam problem by Bernoulli collocation method. *Appl. Math. Model.* **2016**, *40*, 8886–8897. [CrossRef]
15. Jamei, M.M.; Beyki, M.R.; Koepf, W. An extension of the Euler-Maclaurin quadrature formula using a parametric type of Bernoulli polynomials. *Bull. Des. Sci. Mathématiques* **2019**, *156*, 102798.
16. Rahimkhani, P.; Ordokhani, Y.; Babolian, E. Fractional-order Bernoulli functions and their applications in solving fractional Fredholem–Volterra integro-differential equations. *Appl. Numer. Math.* **2017**, *122*, 66–81. [CrossRef]
17. Biswas, A.; Mirzazade, M.; Triki, H.; Zhou, Q.; Ullah, M.Z.; Moshokoa, S.P.; Belic, M. Perturbed resonant 1-soliton solution with an-ti-cubic nonlinearity by Riccati-Bernoulli sub-ODE method. *Optik* **2018**, *156*, 346–350.
18. Keshavarz, E.; Ordokhani, Y.; Razzaghi, M. The Bernoulli wavelets operational matrix of integration and its applications for the solution of linear and nonlinear problems in calculus of variations. *Appl. Math. Comput.* **2019**, *351*, 83–98. [CrossRef]
19. Zeghdane, R. Numerical solution of stochastic integral equations by using Bernoulli operational matrix. *Math. Comput. Simul.* **2019**, *165*, 238–254.
20. Marinov, T.T.; Vatsala, A.S. Inverse problem for coefficient identification in the Euler–Bernoulli equation. *Comput. Math. Appl.* **2008**, *56*, 400–410. [CrossRef]
21. Islam, N.; Asaduzzaman, M.; Ali, S. Exact wave solutions to the simplified modified Camassa-Holm equation in mathematical physics. *AIMS Math.* **2020**, *5*, 26–41. [CrossRef]
22. Wazwaz, A.M. Solitary wave solutions for modified forms of Degasperis–Procesi and Camassa–Holm equations. *Phys. Lett. A* **2006**, *352*, 500–504. [CrossRef]
23. Baskonus, H.M.; Bulut, H. On the complex structures of Kundu-Eckhaus equation via improved Bernoulli sub-equation function method. *Waves Random Complex Media* **2015**, *25*. [CrossRef]

24. Ihan, E.; Kiymaz, I.O. A generalization of truncated M-fractional derivative and applications to fractional differential equations. *Appl. Math. Nonlinear Sci.* **2020**, *5*, 171–188.
25. Pandey, P.K.; Jaboob, S.S.A. A finite difference method for a numerical solution of elliptic boundary value problems. *Appl. Math. Nonlinear Sci.* **2018**, *3*, 311–320. [CrossRef]
26. Durur, H.; Ilhan, E.; Bulut, H. Novel Complex Wave Solutions of the (2+1)-Dimensional Hyperbolic Nonlinear Schrödinger Equation. *Fractal Fract.* **2020**, *4*, 41. [CrossRef]
27. Eskitascioglu, E.I.; Aktas, M.B.; Baskonus, H.M. New Complex and Hyperbolic Forms for Ablowitz-Kaup-Newell-Segur Wave Equation with Fourth Order. *Appl. Math. Nonlinear Sci.* **2019**, *4*, 105–112.
28. Conte, R.; Musette, M. Elliptic General Analytic Solutions. *Stud. Appl. Math.* **2009**, *123*, 63–81. [CrossRef]
29. Contel, R.; Ng, T.W. Meromorphic solutions of a third order nonlinear differential equation. *J. Math. Phys.* **2010**, *51*, 033518. [CrossRef]
30. Gao, W.; Yel, G.; Baskonus, H.M.; Cattani, C. Complex solitons in the conformable (2+1)-dimensional Ablowitz-Kaup-Newell-Segur equation. *AIMS Math.* **2020**, *5*, 507–521. [CrossRef]
31. Ismael, H.F.; Bulut, H.; Baskonus, H.M.; Gao, W. Newly modified method and its application to the coupled Boussinesq equation in ocean engineering with its linear stability analysis. *Commun. Theor. Phys.* **2020**, *72*, 115002. [CrossRef]
32. Liu, J.-G.; Yang, X.-J.; Feng, Y.-Y. Analytical solutions of some integral fractional differential–difference equations. *Mod. Phys. Lett. B* **2020**, *34*, 2050009. [CrossRef]
33. Silambarasan, R.; Baskonus, H.M.; Rajasekaran, V.A.; Dinakaran, M.; Balusamy, B.; Gao, W. Longitudinal strain waves propagating in an infinitely long cylindrical rod composed of generally incompressible materials and it's Jacobi elliptic function solutions. *Math. Comput. Simul.* **2020**, *182*, 566–602. [CrossRef]
34. Ghanbari, B.; Günerhan, H.; Ilhan, O.A.; Baskonus, H.M. Some new families of exact solutions to a new extension of nonlinear Schrödinger equation. *Phys. Scr.* **2020**, *95*, 075208. [CrossRef]
35. Berna, F.B. Analysis of fractional Klein–Gordon–Zakharov equations using efficient method. *Num. Method. Partial Dif. Eq.* **2020**. [CrossRef]
36. Houwe, A.; Sabi'U, J.; Hammouch, Z.; Doka, S.Y. Solitary pulses of a conformable nonlinear differential equation governing wave propagation in low-pass electrical transmission line. *Phys. Scr.* **2020**, *95*, 045203. [CrossRef]
37. Cordero, A.; Jaiswal, J.P.; Torregrosa, J.R. Stability analysis of fourth-order iterative method for finding multiple roots of non-linear equations. *Appl. Math. Nonlinear Sci.* **2019**, *4*, 43–56. [CrossRef]
38. Liu, J.-G.; Yang, X.-J.; Feng, Y.-Y. Characteristic of the algebraic traveling wave solutions for two extended (2 + 1)-dimensional Kadomtsev–Petviashvili equations. *Mod. Phys. Lett. A* **2019**, *35*, 2050028. [CrossRef]
39. Ozer, O. Fundamental units for real quadratic fields determined by continued fraction conditions. *AIMS Math.* **2020**, *5*, 2899–2908. [CrossRef]
40. Gao, W.; Senel, M.; Yel, G.; Baskonus, H.M.; Senel, B. New complex wave patterns to the electrical transmission line model arising in network system. *AIMS Math.* **2020**, *5*, 1881–1892. [CrossRef]
41. Yang, X.-J.; Gao, F. A new technology for solving diffusion and heat equations. *Therm. Sci.* **2017**, *21*, 133–140. [CrossRef]
42. Hosseini, K.; Samavat, M.; Mirzazadeh, M.; Ma, W.X.; Hammouch, Z. A New $$(3+ 1) $$-dimensional Hirota Bilinear Equation: Its Bäcklund Transformation and Rational-type Solutions. *Regul. Chaotic Dyn.* **2020**, *25*, 383–391. [CrossRef]
43. Gao, W.; Ismael, H.F.; Husien, A.M.; Bulut, H.; Baskonus, H. Optical Soliton solutions of the Nonlinear Schrödinger and Resonant Nonlinear Schrödinger Equation with Parabolic Law. *Appl. Sci.* **2020**, *10*, 219. [CrossRef]
44. Uddin, M.F.; Hafez, M.G.; Hammouch, Z.; Baleanu, D. Periodic and rogue waves for Heisenberg models of ferromag-netic spin chains with fractional beta derivative evolution and obliqueness. *Waves Random Complex Media* **2020**. [CrossRef]
45. Cattani, C.; Sulaiman, T.A.; Baskonus, H.M.; Bulut, H. On the soliton solutions to the Nizhnik-Novikov-Veselov and the Drinfel'd-Sokolov systems. *Opt. Quantum Electron.* **2018**, *50*, 138. [CrossRef]
46. Khader, M.M.; Saad, K.M.; Hammouch, Z.; Baleanu, D. A spectral collocation method for solving fractional KdV and KdV-Burger's equations with non-singular kernel derivatives. *Appl. Numer. Math.* **2020**. [CrossRef]
47. Yokus, A.; Sulaiman, T.A.; Baskonus, H.M.; Atmaca, S.P. On the exact and numerical solutions to a nonlinear model aris-ing in mathematical biology. *ITM Web Conf.* **2018**, *22*, 8815363. [CrossRef]
48. Sulaiman, T.A.; Yokus, A.; Gulluoglu, N.; Baskonus, H.M.; Bulut, H. Regarding the Numerical and Stability Analysis of the Sharma-Tosso-Olver Equation. *ITM Web Conf.* **2018**, *22*, 102555. [CrossRef]
49. Baskonus, H.M.; Cattani, C.; Ciancio, A. Periodic, Complex and Kink-type Solitons for the Nonlinear Model in Microtu-bules. *J. Appl. Sci.* **2019**, *21*, 34–45.
50. Weisstein, E.W. *Concise Encyclopedia of Mathematics*; CRC Press: New York, NY, USA, 2002.

fractal and fractional

MDPI

Article

Numerical Solution of Fractional Order Burgers' Equation with Dirichlet and Neumann Boundary Conditions by Reproducing Kernel Method

Onur Saldır *, Mehmet Giyas Sakar and Fevzi Erdogan

Faculty of Sciences, Department of Mathematics, Van Yuzuncu Yıl University, 65080 Van, Turkey; giyassakar@yyu.edu.tr (M.G.S.); ferdogan@yyu.edu.tr (F.E.)

* Correspondence: onursaldir@yyu.edu.tr

Received: 22 April 2020; Accepted: 16 June 2020; Published: 19 June 2020

Abstract: In this research, obtaining of approximate solution for fractional-order Burgers' equation will be presented in reproducing kernel Hilbert space (RKHS). Some special reproducing kernel spaces are identified according to inner products and norms. Then an iterative approach is constructed by using kernel functions. The convergence of this approach and its error estimates are given. The numerical algorithm of the method is presented. Furthermore, numerical outcomes are shown with tables and graphics for some examples. These outcomes demonstrate that the proposed method is convenient and effective.

Keywords: Burgers' equation; reproducing kernel method; error estimate; Dirichlet and Neumann boundary conditions; Caputo derivative

1. Introduction

In this article, produced from a part of PhD thesis number 519846 from the Council of Higher Education, an iterative approach of reproducing kernel method (RKM) is considered for obtaining an approximate solution of the Burgers' equation with fractional order as follows:

$$\begin{gathered} {}^cD_\xi^\alpha u(z,\xi) + c_1(z,\xi)u_{zz}(z,\xi) + c_2(z,\xi)u(z,\xi) + c_3(z,\xi)u_z(z,\xi) + c_4(z,\xi)u(z,\xi)u_z(z,\xi) = f(z,\xi) \\ 0 \le z \le 1,\ 0 \le \xi \le 1,\ 0 < \alpha \le 1, \end{gathered} \tag{1}$$

Here, ${}^cD_\xi^\alpha$ is fractional differential operator in Caputo sense with respect to time variable ξ and also $f(z,\xi)$, $c_1(z,\xi)$, $c_2(z,\xi)$, $c_3(z,\xi)$, $c_4(z,\xi)$ are continuous functions. For this model problem, initial-Neumann boundary conditions:

$$\begin{cases} u(z,0) = 0 \\ u_z(0,\xi) = u_z(1,\xi) = 0 \end{cases} \tag{2a}$$

and initial-Dirichlet boundary conditions:

$$\begin{cases} u(z,0) = 0 \\ u(0,\xi) = u(1,\xi) = 0 \end{cases} \tag{2b}$$

will be taken as above.

The Burgers' equation is a simplified version of the Navier–Stokes equation. It was obtained by use of removing the pressure term from the Navier–Stokes equation by Burgers [1] in 1939. In other words, the Burgers' equation can be expressed as a result of combining nonlinear wave motion with linear diffusion. Lately, many scientists have focused on Burgers' equation by using several methods and different approaches. For instance, existence and uniqueness of local and global solution for Burgers' equation was presented in [2] by Guesmia and Daili. Lombard and Matignon used a diffusive approximation for fractional-order Burgers' equation in [3]. The averaging principle was proposed by Dong et al. for stochastic Burgers' equation in [4]. Nojavan et al. obtained a numerical solution of Burgers' equation by using discretization in reproducing kernel Hilbert space [5]. The Chebyshev wavelet method was developed by Oruc et al. for the numerical solution of time-fractional Burgers' equation [6]. Pei et al. presented the local discontinuous Galerkin method for modified Burgers' equation in [7]. The Petrov–Galerkin method was used by Roshan and Bhamra for modified Burgers' equation in [8]. The collocation method was presented by Ramadan and Danaf for modified Burgers' equation in [9]. Bahadir and Saglam constructed a mixed method for one dimensional Burgers' equation [10]. Dag et al. used the cubic B-splines method [11]. Caldwell et al. proposed a finite element approximation for Burgers' equation [12]. A finite difference method was used by Kutluay et al. for one-dimensional Burgers' equation [13]. An approximate solution obtained by using the reproducing kernel method for Burgers' equation [14]. A hybrid technique for the unsteady flow of a Burgers' fluid is given by Raza et al. [15]. Laplace and finite Hankel transformations were proposed by Safdar et al. for generalized Burgers' fluid with fractional derivative [16]. Time-fractional coupled Burgers' equations were solved with generalized differential transform method by Liu and Hou [17]. Zhang et al proposed an analytical and numerical approach for multi-term time-fractional Burgers' fluid model [18]. The Adomian decomposition method was applied to space-and time-fractional Burgers' equation by Momani [19]. A generalized Taylor series technique was proposed by Ajou et al. for fractional nonlinear KdV-Burgers' equation [20]. Mittal and Arora presented a numerical approach by using cubic B-spline functions for coupled viscous Burgers' equation [21]. Jiwari used a hybrid numerical scheme for Burgers' equation [22]. Kutluay et al. proposed a B-spline finite element method for Burgers' equation [23].

Reproducing kernel concept is introduced by Zaremba [24]. In his study, Zaremba focused on the boundary value problem, which includes the Dirichlet boundary condition. Furthermore, the theoretical concept of reproducing kernel is developed in [25,26]. Reproducing kernel spaces of polynomial and trigonometric functions are constructed in [27]. Many studies have been conducted by using reproducing kernel method. For instance, eighth order boundary value problems [28], fractional advection-dispersion equation [29], fractional order systems of Dirichlet function types [30], fractional order Bagley–Torvik equation [31], time fractional telegraph equation [32], a local reproducing kernel method for Burgers' equation [33], time-fractional partial integro differential equations [34], Riccati differential equations [35], nonlinear hyperbolic telegraph equation [36], time-fractional Tricomi and Keldysh equations [37], one-dimensional sine–Gordon equation [38], reaction-diffusion equations [39], integro differential equations of Fredholm operator type [40], fredholm integro-differential equations [41], nonlinear system of PDEs [42], class of fractional partial differential equation [43], Bagley–Torvik and Painlevé equations [44], nonlinear coupled Burgers equations [45] and so on [46–59].

This research is organized as: Specific definitions and Hilbert spaces are demonstrated in Section 2. Reproducing kernel solution is identified by RKM in Section 3. Convergence analysis of the approximate solution is proved in Section 4. Error estimation of the method is presented in Section 5. Two examples of fractional order Burgers' equation are examined by the RKM and the algorithm of the process is given in Section 6. Finally, a short conclusion is given in Section 7.

The notation table Table 1 is given as follow:

Table 1. Notation table.

Symbol	Explanation
${}^{c}D_{\xi}^{\alpha}$	Caputo derivative operator with arbitrary real order
Θ	Region of $[0,1] \times [0,1]$
$W_2^3[0,1]$	Hilbert space with one variable function
$W_2^{(3,2)}(\Theta)$	Hilbert Space with two variable function
$K_{(\tau,\beta)}(z,\xi)$	Reproducing kernel function of $W_2^{(3,2)}(\Theta)$
$u(z,\xi)$	Exact solution
$u_n(z,\xi)$	Reproducing kernel solution
L	Linear operator
$\langle .,. \rangle$	Inner (scalar) product

2. Some Specific Definitions and Hilbert Spaces

In this section, some basic definitions and significant reproducing kernel spaces will be given.

Definition 1. *([58,59]) Fractional α order Caputo derivative is defined as:*

$$ {}^{c}D_{\xi}^{\alpha}u(z,\xi) = \frac{1}{\Gamma(n-\alpha)} \int_0^{\xi} \frac{\partial_r u(z,r)}{(\xi - r)^{1+\alpha-n}} dr, \;\; n-1 < \alpha \leq n, \;\; \xi > 0. $$

Definition 2. *Let H be Hilbert space and $T \neq \emptyset$ an abstract set. If following conditions are provide, then $S : T \times T \to \mathbb{C}$ is is called as reproducing kernel function:*

$$ i. S(.,\tau) \in H, \;\; \forall \tau \in T, $$
$$ ii. \langle \mu(.), S(.,\tau) \rangle = \mu(\tau), \;\; \forall \tau \in T, \; \forall \mu \in H. $$

2.1. Reproducing Kernel Spaces with One Variable

In this subsection, reproducing kernel functions will be presented for some special Hilbert spaces. Definitions and kernel functions of these spaces will be given for z and ξ variables. $W_2^n[a,b]$ shows the general reproducing kernel space for one variable. Equations (1) and (2a,b) has second order derivative for z and first order derivative for ξ. Therefore, the kernel function of $W_2^3[0,1]$ will be given for u_{zz} and the kernel function of $W_2^2[0,1]$ will be given for u_{ξ}. Furthermore, $W_2^1[0,1]$ space will be given for general function (without derivative). For the obtaining procedure of reproducing kernel functions, please see [47].

$\mathbf{W_2^1[0,1]}$ Hilbert space

$$ W_2^1[0,1] = \{ g(z) | g \text{ is absolutely continuous function}, \; g' \in L^2[0,1] \}. $$

1. The inner product of $W_2^1\,[0,\,1]$ can be taken as follows:

$$ \langle g(z), f(z) \rangle_{W_2^1} = g(0) f(0) + \int_0^1 g'(z) f'(z) dz. \tag{3} $$

2. The norm of $W_2^1\,[0,\,1]$ can be taken as follows:

$$ \|g\|_{W_2^1}^2 = \langle g, g \rangle_{W_2^1}, \;\; g, f \in W_2^1\,[0,\,1]. $$

3. The kernel function of $W_2^1[0,1]$ is as follows:

$$R_{\tau}^{\{1\}}(z) = \begin{cases} 1+z, & z \le \tau, \\ 1+\tau, & \tau > z. \end{cases} \quad (4)$$

$\mathbf{W_2^2[0,1]}$ Hilbert Space

$$W_2^2[0,1] = \{g(\xi) | g, g' \text{ are absolutely continuous functions, } g'' \in L^2[0,1], g(0) = 0\}.$$

Here, $L^2[0,1] = \{g \,|\, \int_0^1 g^2(\xi)\, d\xi < \infty\}$.

1. The inner product of $W_2^2[0,1]$ can be taken as follows:

$$\langle g(\xi), f(\xi) \rangle_{W_2^2} = g(0) f(0) + g'(0) f'(0) + \int_0^1 g''(\xi) f''(\xi)\, d\xi. \quad (5)$$

2. The norm of $W_2^2[0,1]$ can be taken as follows:

$$\|g\|_{W_2^2}^2 = \langle g, g \rangle_{W_2^2}, \quad f, g \in W_2^2[0,1].$$

3. The kernel function of $W_2^2[0,1]$ is as follows:

$$R_{\beta}^{\{2\}}(\xi) = \begin{cases} \xi\beta + \frac{1}{2}\beta\xi^2 - \frac{1}{6}\xi^3, & \xi \le \beta, \\ -\frac{1}{6}\beta^3 + \frac{1}{2}\xi\beta^2 + \beta\xi, & \xi > \beta. \end{cases} \quad (6)$$

$\mathbf{W_2^3[0,1]}$ Hilbert Space

$W_2^3[0,1]$ space with Dirichlet boundary condition:

$$W_2^3[0,1] = \{g(z) | g, g', g'' \text{ are absolutely continuous functions, } g^{(3)} \in L^2[0,1], g(0) = g(1) = 0\}.$$

1. The inner product of $W_2^3[0,1]$ can be taken as follows:

$$\langle g(z), f(z) \rangle_{W_2^3} = g(0) f(0) + g'(0) f'(0) + g(1) f(1) + \int_0^1 g^{(3)}(z) f^{(3)}(z)\, dz. \quad (7)$$

2. The norm of $W_2^3[0,1]$ can be taken as follows:

$$\|g\|_{W_2^3}^2 = \langle g, g \rangle_{W_2^3}, \quad f, g \in W_2^3[0,1].$$

3. The kernel function of $W_2^3[0,1]$ is as follows:

$$R_{\tau}^{\{3\}}(z) = \begin{cases} \frac{-1}{120}(\tau - 1)z(z\tau^4 - 4z\tau^3 + 6z\tau^2 + \tau z^4 - 5\tau z^3 - 120\tau z + 120\tau + z^4), & z \le \tau, \\ \frac{-1}{120}(z - 1)\tau(\tau z^4 - 4\tau z^3 + 6\tau z^2 + z\tau^4 - 5z\tau^3 - 120z\tau + 120z + \tau^4), & z > \tau. \end{cases} \quad (8)$$

$W_2^3[0,1]$ space with Neumann boundary condition:

1. The inner product of $W_2^3[0,1]$ can be taken as follows:

$$\langle g(z), f(z)\rangle_{W_2^3} = g(0) f(0) + g'(0) f'(0) + g''(0) f''(0) + \int_0^1 g^{(3)}(z) f^{(3)}(z)\, dz. \tag{9}$$

2. The norm of $W_2^3[0,1]$ can be taken as follows:

$$\|g\|^2_{W_2^3} = \langle g, g\rangle_{W_2^3}, \ f, g \in W_2^3[0,1].$$

3. The kernel function of $W_2^3[0,1]$ is as follows:
For $z \le \tau$, the kernel function:

$$\begin{aligned} R_\tau^{\{3\}}(z) &= z(\tfrac{1}{56}\tau^4 - \tfrac{1}{14}\tau^3 - \tfrac{3}{14}\tau^2 + \tfrac{4}{7}\tau) + z^2(\tfrac{1}{7}\tau^2 - \tfrac{1}{112}\tau^4 - \tfrac{1}{28}\tau^3 + \tfrac{3}{14}\tau) \\ &+ z^3(\tfrac{1}{21}\tau^2 + \tfrac{1}{336}\tau^4 - \tfrac{1}{84}\tau^3 - \tfrac{1}{14}\tau) + z^4(\tfrac{-1}{1344}\tau^4 + \tfrac{1}{36}\tau^3 + \tfrac{1}{112}\tau^2 - \tfrac{1}{42}\tau) + \tfrac{1}{120}z, \end{aligned} \tag{10}$$

and for $z > \tau$ the kernel function:

$$\begin{aligned} R_\tau^{\{3\}}(z) &= \tau(\tfrac{1}{56}z^4 - \tfrac{1}{14}z^3 - \tfrac{3}{14}z^2 + \tfrac{4}{7}z) + \tau^2(\tfrac{1}{7}z^2 - \tfrac{1}{112}z^4 - \tfrac{1}{28}z^3 + \tfrac{3}{14}z) \\ &+ \tau^3(\tfrac{1}{21}z^2 + \tfrac{1}{336}z^4 - \tfrac{1}{84}z^3 - \tfrac{1}{14}z) + \tau^4(\tfrac{-1}{1344}z^4 + \tfrac{1}{36}z^3 + \tfrac{1}{112}z^2 - \tfrac{1}{42}z) + \tfrac{1}{120}\tau \end{aligned} \tag{11}$$

2.2. Reproducing Kernel Spaces for Two Variable

The problem (1) and (2a,b) has two variables z and ξ. For this reason, we should give the spaces, inner products, and kernel functions according to these variables. Because the highest order derivatives z and ξ to be considered, reproducing kernel spaces will be given for both z and ξ variables. The region which we consider is $\Theta = [0,1] \times [0,1]$. In this part, $W_2^{(3,2)}(\Theta)$ space is given for Dirichlet boundary conditions. These reproducing kernel spaces are also determined in the same way for Neumann boundary conditions.

$\mathbf{W_2^{(3,2)}(\Theta)}$ Hilbert Space

$$\begin{aligned} W_2^{(3,2)}(\Theta) = \{u(z,\xi) \mid \tfrac{\partial^3 u}{\partial z^2 \partial \xi} \text{ is completely continuous in } \Theta, \\ \tfrac{\partial^5 u}{\partial z^3 \partial \xi^2} \in L^2(\Theta), u(z,0) = u(0,\xi) = u(1,\xi) = 0\}. \end{aligned} \tag{12}$$

1. The inner product of $W_2^{(3,2)}(\Theta)$ can be taken as follows:

$$\begin{aligned} \langle u(z,\xi), v(z,\xi)\rangle_{W_2^{(3,2)}} &= \sum_{i=0}^{1} \int_0^1 [\tfrac{\partial^2}{\partial \xi^2} \tfrac{\partial^i}{\partial z^i} u(0,\xi) \tfrac{\partial^2}{\partial \xi^2} \tfrac{\partial^i}{\partial z^i} v(0,\xi)] d\xi + \int_0^1 \tfrac{\partial^2}{\partial \xi^2} u(1,\xi) \tfrac{\partial^2}{\partial \xi^2} v(1,\xi) d\xi \\ &+ \Sigma_{j=0}^1 \langle \tfrac{\partial^j}{\partial \xi^j} u(z,0), \tfrac{\partial^j}{\partial \xi^j} v(z,0)\rangle_{W_2^3} \\ &+ \int_0^1 \int_0^1 [\tfrac{\partial^3}{\partial z^3} \tfrac{\partial^2}{\partial \xi^2} u(z,\xi) \tfrac{\partial^3}{\partial z^3} \tfrac{\partial^2}{\partial \xi^2} v(z,\xi)] dz d\xi. \end{aligned} \tag{13}$$

2. The norm of $W_2^{(3,2)}(\Theta)$ can be taken as follows:

$$\|u\|^2_{W_2^{(3,2)}} = \langle u, u\rangle_{W_2^{(3,2)}}, \ u, v \in W_2^{(3,2)}(\Theta).$$

Theorem 1. *$K_{(\tau,\beta)}(z,\xi)$ is the kernel function of $W_2^{(3,2)}(\Theta)$ and also it is obtained by multiplying kernel functions of $W_2^3[0,1]$ and $W_2^2[0,1]$, respectively. So, it can be written that*

$$K_{(\tau,\beta)}(z,\xi) = R_\tau^{\{3\}}(z) R_\beta^{\{2\}}(\xi).$$

For any $u(z,\xi) \in W_2^{(3,2)}(\Theta)$

$$u(\tau,\beta) = \langle u(z,\xi), K_{(\tau,\beta)}(z,\xi)\rangle_{W_2^{(3,2)}}$$

and

$$K_{(z,\xi)}(\tau,\beta) = K_{(\tau,\beta)}(z,\xi). \tag{14}$$

Proof. Inner product of $W_2^{(3,2)}$ space (Equation (13)) will be used to prove the theorem.

$$\begin{aligned}
&\langle u(z,\xi), R_\tau^{\{3\}}(z)R_\beta^{\{2\}}(\xi)\rangle_{W_2^{(3,2)}} \\
= &\sum_{j=0}^{1}\langle\frac{\partial^j}{\partial\xi^j}u(z,0), R_\tau^{\{3\}}(z)\frac{\partial^j}{\partial\xi^j}R_\beta^{\{2\}}(0)\rangle_{W_2^3} + \sum_{i=0}^{1}\int_0^1\Big[\frac{\partial^2}{\partial\xi^2}\frac{\partial^i}{\partial z^i}u(0,\xi)\frac{\partial^2}{\partial\xi^2}R_\beta^{\{2\}}(\ xi)\frac{\partial^i}{\partial z^i}R_\tau^{\{3\}}(0)\Big]d\xi \\
+ &\int_0^1\frac{\partial^2}{\partial\xi^2}u(1,\xi)R_\tau^{\{3\}}(1)\frac{\partial^2}{\partial\xi^2}R_\beta^{\{2\}}(\xi)d\xi + \int_0^1\int_0^1\Big[\frac{\partial^3}{\partial z^3}\frac{\partial^2}{\partial\xi^2}u(z,\xi)\frac{\partial^3}{\partial z^3}R_\tau^{\{3\}}(z)\frac{\partial^2}{\partial\xi^2}R_\beta^{\{2\}}(\xi)\Big]dzd\xi \\
= &\int_0^1\frac{\partial^2}{\partial\xi^2}R_\beta^{\{2\}}(\xi)\frac{\partial^2}{\partial\xi^2}\Big[\int_0^1\frac{\partial^3}{\partial z^3}u(z,\xi)\frac{\partial^3}{\partial z^3}R_\tau^{\{3\}}(z)dz + \sum_{i=0}^{1}\frac{\partial^i}{\partial z^i}u(0,\xi)\frac{\partial^i}{\partial z^i}R_\tau^{\{3\}}(0) + u(1,\xi)R_\tau^{\{3\}}(1)\Big]d\xi \\
+ &\sum_{j=0}^{1}\frac{\partial^j}{\partial\xi^j}u(\tau,0)\frac{\partial^j}{\partial\xi^j}R_\beta^{\{2\}}(0) \\
= &\sum_{j=0}^{1}\frac{\partial^j}{\partial\xi^j}u(\tau,0)\frac{\partial^j}{\partial\xi^j}R_\beta^{\{2\}}(0) + \int_0^1\frac{\partial^2}{\partial\xi^2}R_\beta^{\{2\}}(\xi)\frac{\partial^2}{\partial\xi^2}\langle u(z,\xi), R_\tau^{\{3\}}(z)\rangle_{W_2^3}d\xi \\
= &\sum_{j=0}^{1}\frac{\partial^j}{\partial\xi^j}u(\tau,0)\frac{\partial^j}{\partial\xi^j}R_\beta^{\{2\}}(0) + \int_0^1\frac{\partial^2}{\partial\xi^2}R_\beta^{\{2\}}(\xi)\frac{\partial^2}{\partial\xi^2}u(\tau,\xi)d\xi \\
= &\langle u(\tau,\xi), R_\beta^{\{2\}}(\xi)\rangle_{W_2^2} = u(\tau,\beta).
\end{aligned}$$

So, $\langle u(\tau,\xi), R_\beta^{\{2\}}(\xi)\rangle = u(\tau,\beta)$, and

$$K_{(\tau,\beta)}(z,\xi) = \langle K_{(\tau,\beta)}(x,y), K_{(z,\xi)}(x,y)\rangle_{W_2^{(3,2)}} = \langle K_{(z,\xi)}(x,y), K_{(\tau,\beta)}(x,y)\rangle_{W_2^{(3,2)}} = K_{(z,\xi)}(\tau,\beta).$$

Therefore, the proof is completed. □

$\mathbf{W_2^{(1,1)}(\Theta)}$ Hilbert Space

$$W_2^{(1,1)}(\Theta) = \{u(z,\xi)|\ u \text{ is completely continuous in } \Theta, \frac{\partial^2 u}{\partial z\partial\xi} \in L^2(\Theta)\}.$$

1. The inner product of $W_2^{(1,1)}(\Theta)$ can be taken as follows:

$$\begin{aligned}
\langle u(z,\xi), v(z,\xi)\rangle_{W_2^{(1,1)}} &= \int_0^1[\frac{\partial}{\partial\xi}u(0,\xi)\frac{\partial}{\partial\xi}v(0,\xi)]d\xi + \langle u(z,0), v(z,0)\rangle_{W_2^1} \\
&+ \int_0^1\int_0^1[\frac{\partial}{\partial z}\frac{\partial}{\partial\xi}u(z,\xi)\frac{\partial}{\partial z}\frac{\partial}{\partial\xi}v(z,\xi)]dzd\xi
\end{aligned}$$

2. The norm of $W_2^{(1,1)}(\Theta)$ can be taken as follows:

$$\|u\|^2_{W_2^{(1,1)}} = \langle u, u\rangle_{W_2^{(1,1)}}, \quad u, v \in W_2^{(1,1)}(\Theta).$$

3. The kernel function of $W_2^{(1,1)}(\Theta)$ is as follows:

$$\tilde{K}_{(\tau,\beta)}(z,\xi) = R_\tau^{\{1\}}(z) R_\beta^{\{1\}}(\xi).$$

Remark 1. *In the next sections all analysis will be given for the Dirichlet boundary conditions. A similar analysis can be made for Neumann boundary conditions.*

3. Obtaining of Reproducing Kernel Solution for Equations (1) and (2a,b) in $W_2^{(3,2)}(\Theta)$

In the reproducing kernel method, an approximate solution will be obtained with the help of kernel function and linear operator L. The choosing of L is arbitrary. One can choose the whole linear part of the model problem or any linear part of it. Here, the whole linear part of the model problem is chosen as follow:

$$L : W_2^{(3,2)}(\Theta) \to W_2^{(1,1)}(\Theta)$$

$$Lu(z,\xi) = {}^cD_\xi^\alpha u + c_1(z,\xi)u_{zz} + c_2(z,\xi)u + c_3(z,\xi)u_z. \tag{15}$$

The new statement of Equations (1)-(2a-2b) can be expressed as:

$$Lu(z,\xi) = F(z,\xi,u(z,\xi),u_z(z,\xi)), \quad \xi, z \in [0,1] \tag{16}$$

and $F(z,\xi,u(z,\xi),u_z(z,\xi)) = f(z,\xi) - c_4(z,\xi)u(z,\xi)u_z(z,\xi)$.

Let $\{(z_i,\xi_i)\}_{i=1}^\infty$ be a countable dense subset in Θ. Now, $\psi_i(z,\xi)$ basis function will be defined by applying the kernel function to the operator L.

$$\begin{aligned}
\psi_i(z,\xi) &= L_{(\tau,\beta)} K_{(\tau,\beta)}(z,\xi)|_{(\tau,\beta)=(z_i,\xi_i)} \\
&= \{ {}^cD_t^\alpha K_{(\tau,\beta)}(z,\xi) + c_1(\tau,\beta)\tfrac{\partial^2}{\partial x^2} K_{(\tau,\beta)}(z,\xi) + c_2(\tau,\beta) K_{(\tau,\beta)}(z,\xi) \\
&+ c_3(\tau,\beta)\tfrac{\partial}{\partial x} K_{(\tau,\beta)}(z,\xi)\}|_{(\tau,\beta)=(z_i,\xi_i)} \\
&= \tfrac{1}{\Gamma(1-\alpha)} \int_0^{\xi_i} \tfrac{\partial_r K_{(z,r)}(z,\xi)}{(\xi_i - r)^\alpha} dr + c_1(z_i,\xi_i)\tfrac{\partial^2}{\partial x^2} K_{(z_i,\xi_i)}(z,\xi) + c_2(z_i,\xi_i) K_{(z_i,\xi_i)}(z,\xi) \\
&+ c_3(z_i,\xi_i)\tfrac{\partial}{\partial x} K_{(z_i,\xi_i)}(z,\xi), i = 1, 2, \ldots
\end{aligned} \tag{17}$$

Now, it will be shown that $\psi_i(z,\xi)$ basis function belong to $W_2^{(3,2)}(\Theta)$ space and $\psi_i(z,\xi)$ satisfies the initial-boundary condition of $W_2^{(3,2)}(\Theta)$ space. For this purpose, the following theorem will be given.

Theorem 2. *The basis function $\psi_i(z,\xi)$ is belong to $W_2^{(3,2)}(\Theta)$ reproducing space for $i = 1, 2, \ldots$.*

Proof. To prove the theorem, we must show that the following conditions are provided.

1. It should be shown that $\frac{\partial^5 \psi_i(z,\xi)}{\partial z^3 \partial \xi^2} \in L^2(\Theta)$.
2. $\frac{\partial^3 \psi_i(z,\xi)}{\partial z^2 \partial \xi}$ is completely continuous function.
3. $\psi_i(z,\xi)$ basis function satisfies the initial and boundary conditions.

One can see that any elements of $W_2^{(3,2)}(\Theta)$ satisfy the above conditions. Now, the following equation can be written using the property of the kernel function $K_{(\tau,\beta)}(z,\xi)$

$$\partial^7_{\tau^2 z^3 \xi^2} K_{(\tau,\beta)}(z,\xi) = \partial^5_{\tau^2 z^3} R^{\{3\}}_\tau(z) \partial^2_{\xi^2} R^{\{2\}}_\beta(\xi).$$

Here, both $\partial^5_{\tau^2 z^3} R^{\{3\}}_\tau(z)$ and $\partial^2_{\xi^2} R^{\{2\}}_\beta(\xi)$ are continuous in $[0,1]$. These functions are bounded because they are continuous in $[0,1]$. So, it can be written

$$|\partial^7_{\tau^2 z^3 \xi^2} K_{(\tau,\beta)}(z,\xi)| \leq M_1.$$

In the same way, one can write that

$$\begin{aligned} |\partial^6_{\beta z^3 \xi^2} K_{(\tau,\beta)}(z,\xi)| &\leq M_2 \\ |\partial^5_{z^3 \xi^2} K_{(\tau,\beta)}(z,\xi)| &\leq M_3 \\ |\partial^6_{\tau z^3 \xi^2} K_{(\tau,\beta)}(z,\xi)| &\leq M_4. \end{aligned}$$

Here, M_1, M_2, M_3 and M_4 are positive constants. From (17),

$$\begin{aligned} \left|\frac{\partial^5 \psi_i(z,\xi)}{\partial z^3 \partial \xi^2}\right| &\leq \left|\frac{1}{\Gamma(1-\alpha)} \int_0^{\xi_i} \frac{M_2}{(\xi_i - r)^\alpha} dr + c_1(z_i,\xi_i) M_1 \right. \\ &+ \left. c_2(z_i,\xi_i) M_3 + c_3(z_i,\xi_i) M_4 \right| \\ &\leq \frac{M_2}{\Gamma(2-\alpha)} \xi_i^{1-\alpha} + |c_1(z_i,\xi_i)| M_1 + |c_2(z_i,\xi_i)| M_3 + |c_3(z_i,\xi_i)| M_4. \end{aligned}$$

Therefore, $\frac{\partial^5 \psi_i(z,\xi)}{\partial z^3 \partial \xi^2} \in L^2(\Theta)$. Furthermore, $\frac{\partial^3 \psi_i(z,\xi)}{\partial z^2 \partial \xi}$ is completely continuous in Θ since Θ is closed region. Finally, basis function $\psi_i(z,\xi)$ satisfies initial-boundary conditions such that $K_{(\tau,\beta)}(z,0) = 0$ and $K_{(\tau,\beta)}(0,\xi) = K_{(\tau,\beta)}(1,\xi) = 0$. Therefore, $\psi_i(z,\xi) \in W_2^{(3,2)}(\Theta)$. □

Theorem 3. *$\{\psi_i(z,\xi)\}_{i=1}^\infty$ is a complete system in $W_2^{(3,2)}(\Theta)$.*

Proof. It is known that

$$\begin{aligned} \psi_i(z,\xi) &= (L^*\varphi_i)(z,\xi) = \langle (L^*\varphi_i)(\tau,\beta), K_{(z,\xi)}(\tau,\beta) \rangle_{W_2^{(3,2)}} \\ &= \langle \varphi_i(\tau,\beta), L_{(\tau,\beta)} K_{(z,\xi)}(\tau,\beta) \rangle_{W_2^{(1,1)}} = L_{(\tau,\beta)} K_{(z,\xi)}(\tau,\beta)|_{(\tau,\beta)=(z_i,\xi_i)} \\ &= L_{(\tau,\beta)} K_{(\tau,\beta)}(z,\xi)|_{(\tau,\beta)=(z_i,\xi_i)}. \end{aligned} \tag{18}$$

Clearly, for each fixed $u(z,\xi) \in W_2^{(3,2)}(\Theta)$, if $\langle u(z,\xi), \psi_i(z,\xi) \rangle_{W_2^{(3,2)}} = 0$ then $\psi_i(z,\xi) \in W_2^{(3,2)}(\Theta)$, $i = 1,2,....$ Therefore,

$$\langle u(z,\xi), (L^*\varphi_i)(z,\xi) \rangle_{W_2^{(3,2)}} = \langle Lu(z,\xi), \varphi_i(z,\xi) \rangle_{W_2^{(1,1)}} = (Lu)(z_i,\xi_i) = 0, \;\; i = 1,2,... \tag{19}$$

$\{(z_i,\xi_i)\}_{i=1}^\infty$ is dense in Θ. Hence, $(Lu)(z,\xi) = 0$. By using of inverse operator L^{-1}, it can be seen that $u = 0$. So, theorem is proven. □

The orthonormal basis system $\{\overline{\psi_i}(z,\xi)\}_{i=1}^\infty$ of $W_2^{(3,2)}(\Theta)$ can be obtained by the way of Gram–Schmidt orthogonalization process of $\{\psi_i(z,\xi)\}_{i=1}^\infty$ as follow:

$$\overline{\psi_i}(z,\xi) = \sum_{k=1}^{i} \eta_{ik} \psi_k(z,\xi), \;\; i = 1,2,... \tag{20}$$

In Equation (20), $\eta_{ii} > 0$ and η_{ik} are orthogonalization coefficients.

Theorem 4. *If $\{(z_i, \xi_i)\}_{i=1}^{\infty}$ is dense in Θ, then the solution (16) is*

$$u(z,\xi) = \sum_{i=1}^{\infty}\sum_{k=1}^{i} \eta_{ik} F(z_k, \xi_k, u(z_k, \xi_k), \partial_z u(z_k, \xi_k)) \overline{\psi}_i(z,\xi). \tag{21}$$

Proof. It is known that $\{\psi_i(z,\xi)\}_{i=1}^{\infty}$ system is complete in $W_2^{(3,2)}(\Theta)$ from the previous theorem. So, it can be written

$$\begin{aligned} u(z,\xi) &= \sum_{i=1}^{\infty} \langle u(z,\xi), \overline{\psi}_i(z,\xi) \rangle_{W_2^{(3,2)}} \overline{\psi}_i(z,\xi) = \sum_{i=1}^{\infty}\sum_{k=1}^{i} \eta_{ik} \langle u(z,\xi), \psi_k(z,\xi) \rangle_{W_2^{(3,2)}} \overline{\psi}_i(z,\xi) \\ &= \sum_{i=1}^{\infty}\sum_{k=1}^{i} \eta_{ik} \langle u(z,\xi), L^* \varphi_k(z,\xi) \rangle_{W_2^{(3,2)}} \overline{\psi}_i(z,\xi) = \sum_{i=1}^{\infty}\sum_{k=1}^{i} \eta_{ik} \langle Lu(z,\xi), \varphi_k(z,\xi) \rangle_{W_2^{(1,1)}} \overline{\psi}_i(z,\xi) \\ &= \sum_{i=1}^{\infty}\sum_{k=1}^{i} \eta_{ik} \langle Lu(z,\xi), \tilde{K}_{(z_k,\xi_k)}(z,\xi) \rangle_{W_2^{(1,1)}} \overline{\psi}_i(z,\xi) = \sum_{i=1}^{\infty}\sum_{k=1}^{i} \eta_{ik} Lu(z_k,\xi_k) \overline{\psi}_i(z,\xi) \\ &= \sum_{i=1}^{\infty}\sum_{k=1}^{i} \eta_{ik} F(z_k, \xi_k, u(z_k, \xi_k), \partial_z u(z_k, \xi_k)) \overline{\psi}_i(z,\xi). \end{aligned} \tag{22}$$

So, theorem is proven. □

In Equation (21), $u(z,\xi)$ is described as infinite term sum. In the next equation, finitely n-terms solution will be given as $u_n(z,\xi)$:

$$u_n(z,\xi) = \sum_{i=1}^{n}\sum_{k=1}^{i} \eta_{ik} F(z_k, \xi_k, u(z_k, \xi_k), \partial_z u(z_k, \xi_k)) \overline{\psi}_i(z,\xi). \tag{23}$$

4. Convergence of Reproducing Kernel Solution

In this section, it will be shown that

$$\|u(z,\xi) - u_n(z,\xi)\| \to 0 \text{ as } n \to \infty. \tag{24}$$

If we take

$$A_i = \sum_{k=1}^{i} \eta_{ik} F(z_k, \xi_k, u(z_k, \xi_k), \partial_z u(z_k, \xi_k)), \tag{25}$$

then (21) can be described as

$$u(z,\xi) = \sum_{i=1}^{\infty} A_i \overline{\psi}_i(z,\xi). \tag{26}$$

Now, $u(z_1, \xi_1)$ is found by taking $(z_1, \xi_1) = 0$ from the initial conditions of problem. Furthermore, by choosing $u_0(z_1, \xi_1) = u(z_1, \xi_1)$, the n-term approximation to $u(z,\xi)$ is expressed as follows:

$$u_n(z,\xi) = \sum_{i=1}^{n} B_i \overline{\psi}_i(z,\xi), \tag{27}$$

here

$$B_i = \sum_{k=1}^{i} \eta_{ik} F(z_k, \xi_k, u_{k-1}(z_k, \xi_k), \partial_z u_{k-1}(z_k, \xi_k)). \tag{28}$$

Now, some theoretical results will be given for convergence of $F(z_n,\xi_n,u_{n-1}(z_n,\xi_n),\partial_z u_{n-1}(z_n,\xi_n))$ and $u_n(z,\xi)$, respectively.

Lemma 1. *If $F(z,\xi,u(z,\xi),u_z(z,\xi))$ is continuous and $u_n \to \hat{u}$ for $(z_n,\xi_n) \to (\tau,\beta)$, then*

$$F(z_n,\xi_n,u_{n-1}(z_n,\xi_n),\partial_z u_{n-1}(z_n,\xi_n)) \to F(\tau,\beta,\hat{u}(\tau,\beta),\partial_z \hat{u}(\tau,\beta)). \tag{29}$$

Proof. Since

$$\begin{aligned} |u_{n-1}(z_n,\xi_n) - \hat{u}(\tau,\beta)| &= |u_{n-1}(z_n,\xi_n) - u_{n-1}(\tau,\beta) + u_{n-1}(\tau,\beta) - \hat{u}(\tau,\beta)| \\ &\leq |u_{n-1}(z_n,\xi_n) - u_{n-1}(\tau,\beta)| + |u_{n-1}(\tau,\beta) - \hat{u}(\tau,\beta)|. \end{aligned} \tag{30}$$

Using reproducing kernel feature, it can be written that

$$u_{n-1}(z_n,\xi_n) = \langle u_{n-1}(z,\xi), K_{(z_n,\xi_n)}(z,\xi)\rangle_{W_2^{(3,2)}}, \quad u_{n-1}(\tau,\beta) = \langle u_{n-1}(z,\xi), K_{(\tau,\beta)}(z,\xi)\rangle_{W_2^{(3,2)}}. \tag{31}$$

It follows that

$$|u_{n-1}(z_n,\xi_n) - u_{n-1}(\tau,\beta)| = |\langle u_{n-1}(z,\xi), K_{(z_n,\xi_n)}(z,\xi) - K_{(\tau,\beta)}(z,\xi)\rangle|. \tag{32}$$

It can be said that there exists $M > 0$ from the convergence of $u_{n-1}(z,\xi)$ such that

$$\|u_{n-1}(z,\xi)\|_{W_2^{(3,2)}} \leq M\|\hat{u}(\tau,\beta)\|_{W_2^{(3,2)}}, \text{ as } n \geq M. \tag{33}$$

In a similar way, it can be proven

$$\|K_{(z_n,\xi_n)}(z,\xi) - K_{(\tau,\beta)}(z,\xi)\|_{W_2^{(3,2)}} \to 0, \text{ for } n \to \infty \tag{34}$$

by using Equation (14). So,

$$u_{n-1}(z_n,\xi_n) \to \hat{u}(\tau,\beta), \text{ as } (z_n,\xi_n) \to (\tau,\beta). \tag{35}$$

In a similar way it can be shown that

$$\partial_z u_{n-1}(z_n,\xi_n) \to \partial_z \hat{u}(\tau,\beta), \text{ as } (z_n,\xi_n) \to (\tau,\beta). \tag{36}$$

Therefore,

$$F(z_n,\xi_n,u_{n-1}(z_n,\xi_n),\partial_z u_{n-1}(z_n,\xi_n)) \to F(\tau,\beta,\hat{u}(\tau,\beta),\partial_z \hat{u}(\tau,\beta)). \tag{37}$$

So, lemma is proven. □

Theorem 5. *Assume that (16) has a unique solution, $\|u_n\|$ is a bounded and $\{(z_i,\xi_i)\}_{i=1}^{\infty}$ is dense in Θ. Then, $u_n(z,\xi)$ converges to $u(z,\xi)$ and*

$$u(z,\xi) = \sum_{i=1}^{\infty} B_i \overline{\psi}_i(z,\xi). \tag{38}$$

Proof. Firstly, we aim to show that $u_n(z,\xi)$ is convergence. Following equality can be written

$$u_{n+1}(z,\xi) = u_n(z,\xi) + B_{n+1}\overline{\psi}_{n+1}(z,\xi). \tag{39}$$

from the Equation (27). Using the orthonormality of $\{\overline{\psi}_i\}_{i=1}^{\infty}$, we have

$$\|u_{n+1}\|^2 = \|u_n\|^2 + B_{n+1}^2 = \sum_{i=1}^{n+1} B_i^2. \tag{40}$$

Therefore, $\|u_{n+1}\| > \|u_n\|$ satisfies from (40). Here, it seems that $\|u_n\|$ is bounded. So, one can know that $\|u_n\|$ is convergent. Therefore, there exists a constant b so that

$$\sum_{i=1}^{\infty} B_i^2 = b. \tag{41}$$

So, above equation shows that $\{B_i\}_{i=1}^{\infty} \in l^2$. If $m > n$, then

$$\begin{aligned} \|u_m - u_n\|^2 &= \|u_m - u_{m-1} + u_{m-1} - u_{m-2} + \cdots + u_{n+1} - u_n\|^2 \\ &= \|u_m - u_{m-1}\|^2 + \|u_{m-1} - u_{m-2}\|^2 + \cdots + \|u_{n+1} - u_n\|^2. \end{aligned} \tag{42}$$

The following equation is obtained

$$\|u_m - u_{m-1}\|^2 = B_m^2, \tag{43}$$

and consequently

$$\|u_m - u_n\|^2 = \sum_{l=n+1}^{m} B_l^2 \to 0, \text{ as } n \to \infty. \tag{44}$$

The completeness of $W_2^{(3,2)}(\Theta)$ shows that $u_n \to \hat{u}$ for $n \to \infty$. Next, it will be shown that $\hat{u}$ is the representation solution of (16). If the limit is taken both sides of Equation (27), the following equation can be written:

$$\hat{u}(z,\xi) = \sum_{i=1}^{\infty} B_i \overline{\psi}_i(z,\xi). \tag{45}$$

Note that

$$(L\hat{u})(z,\xi) = \sum_{i=1}^{\infty} B_i L\overline{\psi}_i(z,\xi), \tag{46}$$

$$\begin{aligned} (L\hat{u})(z_l,\xi_l) &= \sum_{i=1}^{\infty} B_i L\overline{\psi}_i(z_l,\xi_l) = \sum_{i=1}^{\infty} B_i \langle L\overline{\psi}_i(z,\xi), \varphi_l(z,\xi)\rangle_{W_2^{(1,1)}} \\ &= \sum_{i=1}^{\infty} B_i \langle \overline{\psi}_i(z,\xi), L^*\varphi_l(z,\xi)\rangle_{W_2^{(3,2)}} = \sum_{i=1}^{\infty} B_i \langle \overline{\psi}_i(z,\xi), \psi_l(z,\xi)\rangle_{W_2^{(3,2)}}. \end{aligned} \tag{47}$$

Therefore,

$$\sum_{l=1}^{i} \eta_{il}(L\hat{u})(z_l,\xi_l) = \sum_{i=1}^{\infty} B_i \langle \overline{\psi}_i(z,\xi), \sum_{l=1}^{i} \eta_{il}\psi_l(z,\xi)\rangle_{W_2^{(3,2)}} \tag{48}$$

$$= \sum_{i=1}^{\infty} B_i \langle \overline{\psi}_i(z,\xi), \overline{\psi}_l(z,\xi)\rangle_{W_2^{(3,2)}} = B_l. \tag{49}$$

From (28), the following equation can be expressed

$$L\hat{u}(z_l,\xi_l) = F(z_l,\xi_l,u_{l-1}(z_l,\xi_l),\partial_z u_{l-1}(z_l,\xi_l)). \tag{50}$$

For each $(\tau, \beta) \in \Theta$, $\{(z_i, \xi_i)\}_{i=1}^{\infty}$ is dense in Θ. Therefore, there exists a subsequence $\{(z_{n_j}, \xi_{n_j})\}_{j=1}^{\infty}$ such that $(z_{n_j}, \xi_{n_j}) \to (\tau, \beta), j \to \infty$. It is known that

$$L\hat{u}(z_{n_j}, \xi_{n_j}) = F(z_{n_j}, \xi_{n_j}, u_{n_{j-1}}(z_{n_j}, \xi_{n_j}), \partial_z u_{n_{j-1}}(z_{n_j}, \xi_{n_j})). \tag{51}$$

By using Lemma 1 and continuity of F, it can be seen that

$$(L\hat{u})(\tau, \beta) = F(\tau, \beta, \hat{u}(\tau, \beta), \partial_z \hat{u}(\tau, \beta)), \text{ for } j \to \infty. \tag{52}$$

Equation (52) implies that $\hat{u}(z, \xi)$ satisfies Equation (16). So, proof is completed. □

Theorem 6. *$\partial^i_{z^i} \partial^j_{\xi^j} u_n(z, \xi)$ uniformly converges to $\partial^i_{z^i} \partial^j_{\xi^j} u(z, \xi)$ for $j = 0, 1$ and $i = 0, 1, 2$.*

Proof. The convergence of u_n is given in the previous theorem. Now,

$$\begin{aligned} |\partial^i_{z^i} \partial^j_{\xi^j} u(z, \xi) - \partial^i_{z^i} \partial^j_{\xi^j} u_n(z, \xi)| &= |\langle u(y, s) - u_n(y, s), \partial^i_{z^i} \partial^j_{\xi^j} LK_{(z,\xi)}(y, s) \rangle| \\ &\leq \|u - u_n\| \|\partial^i_{z^i} \partial^j_{\xi^j} LK_{(z,\xi)}(y, s)\| \\ &\leq C_{i,j} \|u - u_n\|. \end{aligned}$$

So,

$$|\partial^i_{z^i} \partial^j_{\xi^j} u_n(z, \xi) - \partial^i_{z^i} \partial^j_{\xi^j} u(z, \xi)| \to 0 \text{ as } n \to \infty.$$

□

5. Error Estimation of Method

In this section, error analysis for the presented method will be given . In this analysis, one can understand that the error estimation varies depending on the selected step size. Now, the step size, chosen of points, and norm will be taken as follow:

$$z_i = ih_z, \ h_z = 1/n, \ \xi_j = jh_\xi, \ h_\xi = 1/n, \ i, j = 1, ..., n.$$

$$\|u(z, \xi)\|_\infty = \max |u(z, \xi)| \text{ for } (z, \xi) \in \Theta$$

Furthermore, $u(z, \xi) - u_n(z, \xi)$ can be written in two ways for each variable as follow:

$$u(z, \xi) - u_n(z, \xi) = u(z_i, \xi) - u_n(z_i, \xi) + \int_{z_i}^{z} (\partial_\tau u(\tau, \xi) - \partial_\tau u_n(\tau, \xi)) d\tau$$

and

$$u(z, \xi) - u_n(z, \xi) = u(z, \xi_i) - u_n(z, \xi_i) + \int_{\xi_i}^{\xi} (\partial_\beta u(z, \beta) - \partial_\beta u_n(z, \beta)) d\beta.$$

The following two theorems will be given for error estimation considering the two equations above.

Theorem 7. *Let $u(z, \xi) - u_n(z, \xi)$ be error in $W_2^{(6,2)}(\Theta)$. Therefore, there exist a $C > 0$ so that*

$$\|u(z, \xi) - u_n(z, \xi)\|_\infty \leq C(h_z^2 + h_z h_\xi).$$

Proof. For $[z_i, z_{i+1}] \times [\xi_j, \xi_{j+1}] \subset \Theta$, the following equality can be written:

$$\partial_z u(z,\xi) - \partial_z u_n(z,\xi) = \partial_z u(z,\xi) - \partial_z u(z_i,\xi_j) + \partial_z u_n(z_i,\xi_j) - \partial_z u_n(z,\xi) + \partial_z u(z_i,\xi_j) - \partial_z u_n(z_i,\xi_j)$$

Here, Taylor expansion will be used to show error estimate for the function $\partial_z u(z,\xi)$ around the point (z_i, ξ_j). This equality will be analyzed in three cases. It is known that

$$\partial_z u(z,\xi) = \partial_z u(z_i,\xi_j) + (h_z\partial_z + h_\xi\partial_\xi)\partial_z u(z_i + \epsilon h_z, \xi_j + \epsilon h_\xi), \ \epsilon \in [0,1].$$

Firstly, the continuity of $\partial^2_{z^2} u(z,\xi)$ and $\partial^2_{z\xi} u(z,\xi)$ on Θ is considered. So, one can write that

$$\|\partial_z u(z,\xi) - \partial_z u(z_i,\xi_j)\|_\infty = O(h_z + h_\xi).$$

Secondly, one know that

$$|\partial_z u_n(z_i,\xi_j) - \partial_z u_n(z,\xi)| \le \int_{z_i}^{z} |\partial^2_{y^2} u_n(y,\xi_j)| dy + \int_{\xi_j}^{\xi} |\partial^2_{zs} u_n(z,s)| ds. \tag{53}$$

The next equation can be stated by using of maximum norm

$$\|\partial_z u_n(z_i,\xi_j) - \partial_z u_n(z,\xi)\|_\infty = O(h_z + h_\xi).$$

Finally, for sufficiently large n, any $\varepsilon > 0$ and using Theorem 6 such that

$$\|\partial_z u(z_i,\xi_j) - \partial_z u_n(z_i,\xi_j)\|_\infty < \varepsilon. \tag{54}$$

From Equation (54), it is known that ε is arbitrary constant and the chosen of n, the following equality can be expressed

$$\|\partial_z u(z_i,\xi_j) - \partial_z u_n(z_i,\xi_j)\|_\infty = O(h_z + h_\xi).$$

In light of the information given above, error estimation will be given as follows:

$$u(z,\xi) - u_n(z,\xi) = u(z_i,\xi) - u_n(z_i,\xi) + \int_{z_i}^{z} (\partial_y u(y,\xi) - \partial_y u_n(y,\xi)) dy$$

$$\begin{aligned} \|u(z,\xi) - u_n(z,\xi)\|_\infty &\le \|u(z_i,\xi) - u_n(z_i,\xi)\|_\infty + \int_{z_i}^{z} \|\partial_y u(y,\xi) - \partial_y u_n(y,\xi)\|_\infty dy \\ &\le C(h_z^2 + h_\xi h_z). \end{aligned}$$

□

So far, error estimation analysis is done for z variable. The error estimation analysis for variable ξ will be given by the next theorem.

Theorem 8. *Assume that $\partial^3_{z^3}\partial_\xi u(z,\xi)$ and $\partial^2_{z^2}\partial^2_{\xi^2} u(z,\xi)$ are continuous and also, $\|\partial^3_{z^3}\partial_\xi u(z,\xi)\|_\infty$ and $\|\partial^2_{z^2}\partial^2_{\xi^2} u(z,\xi)\|_\infty$ are bounded. So, there exist a $C > 0$ such that the error estimate can be expressed as:*

$$\|u_n(z,\xi) - u(z,\xi)\|_\infty \le C(h_\xi h_z^3 + h_\xi^2 h_z^2).$$

Proof. For $[z_i, z_{i+1}] \times [\xi_i, \xi_{i+1}] \in \Theta$, it can be written

$$\begin{aligned}\partial^2_{z^2}\partial_\xi u(z,\xi) - \partial^2_{z^2}\partial_\xi u_n(z,\xi) &= \partial^2_{z^2}\partial_\xi u(z,\xi) - \partial^2_{z^2}\partial_\xi u(z_i,\xi_j) + \partial^2_{z^2}\partial_\xi u_n(z_i,\xi_j) \\ &- \partial^2_{z^2}\partial_\xi u_n(z,\xi) + \partial^2_{z^2}\partial_\xi u(z_i,\xi_j) - \partial^2_{z^2}\partial_\xi u_n(z_i,\xi_j).\end{aligned}$$

Taylor series expansion for $\partial^2_{z^2}\partial_\xi u(z,\xi)$ function around the point (z_i, ξ_j) as follow:

$$\partial^2_{z^2}\partial_\xi u(z,\xi) = \partial^2_{z^2}\partial_\xi u(z_i,\xi_j) + (h_z\partial_z + h_\xi\partial_\xi)\partial^2_{z^2}\partial_\xi u(z_i + h_z\epsilon, \xi_j + h_\xi\epsilon) + ..., \ \epsilon \in [0,1].$$

Firstly, the following expression can be written by considering the continuation of $\partial^3_{z^3}\partial_\xi u(z,\xi)$ and $\partial^2_{z^2}\partial^2_{\xi^2} u(z,\xi)$ on Θ,

$$\|\partial^2_{z^2}\partial_\xi u(z,\xi) - \partial^2_{z^2}\partial_\xi u(z_i,\xi_j)\|_\infty = O(h_z + h_\xi).$$

Secondly, one knows that

$$|\partial^2_{z^2}\partial_\xi u_n(z_i,\xi_j) - \partial^2_{z^2}\partial_\xi u_n(z,\xi)| \le \int_{z_i}^{z} |\partial^3_{y^3}\partial_\xi u_n(y,\xi_j)|dy + \int_{\xi_i}^{\xi} |\partial^2_{z^2}\partial^2_{s^2} u_n(z,s)|ds.$$

The follow equality can be written by using of maximum norm:

$$\|\partial^2_{z^2}\partial_\xi u_n(z_i,\xi_j) - \partial^2_{z^2}\partial_\xi u_n(z,\xi)\|_\infty = O(h_z + h_\xi).$$

The following statement can be written using Theorem 6 and for any arbitrary $\varepsilon > 0$, and sufficiently large n:

$$\|\partial^2_{z^2}\partial_\xi u(z_i,\xi_j) - \partial^2_{z^2}\partial_\xi u_n(z_i,\xi_j)\|_\infty < \varepsilon. \tag{55}$$

The following equation can be written from Equation (55) by choosing of n and using arbitrary constant ε. So, we have

$$\|\partial^2_{z^2}\partial_\xi u(z,\xi) - \partial^2_{z^2}\partial_\xi u_n(z,\xi)\|_\infty = O(h_z + h_\xi). \tag{56}$$

One can know that the following equations can be written from the integral property for differentiable functions:

$$\partial_z\partial_\xi u(z,\xi) - \partial_z\partial_\xi u_n(z,\xi) = \partial_z\partial_\xi u(z_i,\xi) - \partial_z\partial_\xi u_n(z,\xi) + \int_{z_i}^{z} (\partial^2_{y^2}\partial_\xi u(y,\xi) - \partial^2_{y^2}\partial_\xi u_n(y,\xi))dy \tag{57}$$

$$\partial_\xi u(z,\xi) - \partial_\xi u_n(z,\xi) = \partial_\xi u(z_i,\xi) - \partial_\xi u_n(z_i,\xi) + \int_{z_i}^{z} (\partial_y\partial_\xi u(y,\xi) - \partial_y\partial_\xi u_n(y,\xi))dy \tag{58}$$

$$u(z,\xi) - u_n(z,\xi) = u(z,\xi_i) - u_n(z,\xi_i) + \int_{\xi_i}^{\xi} (\partial_s u(z,s) - \partial_s u_n(z,s))ds \tag{59}$$

The following inequality can be written from Equations (56)–(59) and Theorem 6:

$$\|u(z,\xi) - u_n(z,\xi)\|_\infty \le C(h_\xi h_z^3 + h_\xi^2 h_z^2).$$

□

6. Numerical Applications and Algorithm of Method

In this section, two fractional Burgers' problems with variable and constant coefficient are considered. Exact solutions of problems include the fractional parameter α. Reproducing kernel method will be applied for these problems and outcomes will be presented with tables and graphics.

6.1. Algorithm Process of RKM

The algorithm process of RKM is given as follow:
Case 1. Choosing of iteration number as $n = a \times b$.
Case 2. Start $\psi_i(z,\xi) = L_{(\tau,\beta)}K_{(\tau,\beta)}(z,\xi)|_{(\tau,\beta)=(z_i,\xi_i)}$.
Case 3. Obtaining of η_{ik} coefficients.
Case 4. Set $\overline{\psi}_i(z,\xi) = \sum\limits_{k=1}^{i} \eta_{ik}\psi_k(z,\xi)$ for $i = 1,2,...,n$.
Case 5. Start initial approximation $u_0(z_i,\xi_i)$.
Case 6. Calculate $B_i = \sum\limits_{k=1}^{i} \eta_{ik}F(z_k,\xi_k,u_{k-1}(z_k,\xi_k),\partial_z u_{k-1}(z_k,\xi_k))$ for $i = 1,2,...,n$.
Case 7. Calculate $u_i(z,\xi) = \sum\limits_{k=1}^{i} B_k\overline{\psi}_k(z_k,\xi_k)$ for $i = 1,2,...,n$.

6.2. Numerical Applications

Example 1. *It will be examined that the following fractional-order Burgers' problem with Dirichlet boundary condition:*

$$ {}^{c}D_{\xi}^{\alpha}u + (1+z\xi)u_{zz} + z^2u + (z+1)u_z - \xi\sin(z)uu_z = f(z,\xi) \tag{60}$$

$$0 \le \xi \le 1, 0 \le z \le 1,\ 0 < \alpha \le 1,$$

$$u(z,0) = 0 = u(0,\xi) = u(1,\xi) = 0. \tag{61}$$

The exact solution of problem:

$$u(z,\xi) = (z^2 - z)\xi^{1+\alpha}, \tag{62}$$

and $f(z,\xi)$ is the function that provides the Equation (62). Taking $z_i = \frac{i}{a}, i = 1, 2, ..., a$, $\xi_i = \frac{i}{b}, i = 1, 2, ..., b$ and n-th term of approximate solution is selected as $n = a \times b$. Absolute error values for Example 1 is computed for $\alpha = 0.9$, $\alpha = 0.8$, $\alpha = 0.7$ and $n = 25$ $(a = b = 5)$. Error values are given in Tables 2–4 in order to observe of applicability and influence of method. The graphics of absolute errors are given for $\alpha = 0.7$, $\alpha = 0.8$, and $\alpha = 0.9$ in Figure 1.

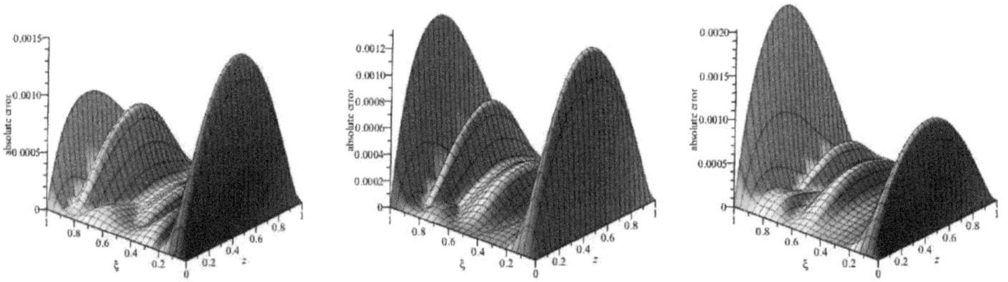

Figure 1. The surfaces show the absolute error of Example 1 with $n = 16$ $(a = b = 4)$ and for $\alpha = 0.7$, $\alpha = 0.8$, $\alpha = 0.9$ respectively on region Θ.

Table 2. Absolute error values of Example 1 for Burgers' equation with $\alpha = 0.9$.

z/ξ	0.1	0.2	0.3	0.4	0.5	0.6	0.7	0.8	0.9
0.1	1.31×10^{-4}	3.13×10^{-5}	3.36×10^{-5}	3.90×10^{-5}	5.67×10^{-5}	5.06×10^{-5}	6.67×10^{-5}	2.92×10^{-5}	1.31×10^{-4}
0.2	2.34×10^{-4}	5.74×10^{-5}	6.39×10^{-5}	7.70×10^{-5}	1.13×10^{-4}	1.08×10^{-4}	1.44×10^{-4}	1.55×10^{-5}	1.83×10^{-4}
0.3	3.07×10^{-4}	7.60×10^{-5}	8.59×10^{-5}	1.05×10^{-4}	1.55×10^{-4}	1.53×10^{-4}	2.07×10^{-4}	7.90×10^{-6}	1.96×10^{-4}
0.4	3.49×10^{-4}	8.65×10^{-5}	9.88×10^{-5}	1.22×10^{-4}	1.82×10^{-4}	1.81×10^{-4}	2.51×10^{-4}	3.54×10^{-5}	1.75×10^{-4}
0.5	3.62×10^{-4}	8.76×10^{-5}	1.00×10^{-4}	1.24×10^{-4}	1.87×10^{-4}	1.88×10^{-4}	2.66×10^{-4}	5.70×10^{-5}	1.33×10^{-4}
0.6	3.45×10^{-4}	8.13×10^{-5}	9.31×10^{-5}	1.16×10^{-4}	1.75×10^{-4}	1.76×10^{-4}	2.57×10^{-4}	7.18×10^{-5}	7.86×10^{-5}
0.7	2.99×10^{-4}	6.69×10^{-5}	7.60×10^{-5}	9.49×10^{-5}	1.45×10^{-4}	1.44×10^{-4}	2.19×10^{-4}	7.05×10^{-5}	3.03×10^{-5}
0.8	2.25×10^{-4}	4.73×10^{-5}	5.30×10^{-5}	6.56×10^{-5}	1.01×10^{-4}	9.98×10^{-5}	1.58×10^{-4}	5.56×10^{-5}	3.62×10^{-6}
0.9	1.25×10^{-4}	2.41×10^{-5}	2.63×10^{-5}	3.22×10^{-5}	5.09×10^{-5}	4.82×10^{-5}	8.20×10^{-5}	2.96×10^{-5}	1.49×10^{-5}

Table 3. Absolute error values of Example 1 for Burgers' equation with $\alpha = 0.8$.

z/ξ	0.1	0.2	0.3	0.4	0.5	0.6	0.7	0.8	0.9
0.1	1.26×10^{-4}	1.29×10^{-5}	2.37×10^{-5}	1.99×10^{-5}	4.07×10^{-5}	3.53×10^{-5}	6.82×10^{-5}	1.27×10^{-5}	8.96×10^{-6}
0.2	2.25×10^{-4}	2.58×10^{-5}	4.78×10^{-5}	4.48×10^{-5}	8.67×10^{-5}	8.28×10^{-5}	1.48×10^{-4}	5.90×10^{-5}	3.22×10^{-5}
0.3	2.96×10^{-4}	3.61×10^{-5}	6.66×10^{-5}	6.49×10^{-5}	1.23×10^{-4}	1.21×10^{-4}	2.13×10^{-4}	1.03×10^{-4}	8.09×10^{-5}
0.4	3.39×10^{-4}	4.36×10^{-5}	7.94×10^{-5}	7.88×10^{-5}	1.47×10^{-4}	1.48×10^{-4}	2.57×10^{-4}	1.40×10^{-4}	1.30×10^{-4}
0.5	3.53×10^{-4}	4.62×10^{-5}	8.30×10^{-5}	8.22×10^{-5}	1.54×10^{-4}	1.55×10^{-4}	2.72×10^{-4}	1.58×10^{-4}	1.67×10^{-4}
0.6	3.39×10^{-4}	4.54×10^{-5}	7.99×10^{-5}	7.82×10^{-5}	1.46×10^{-4}	1.47×10^{-4}	2.61×10^{-4}	1.60×10^{-4}	1.89×10^{-4}
0.7	2.96×10^{-4}	3.94×10^{-5}	6.77×10^{-5}	6.43×10^{-5}	1.22×10^{-4}	1.20×10^{-4}	2.21×10^{-4}	1.39×10^{-4}	1.85×10^{-4}
0.8	2.25×10^{-4}	2.95×10^{-5}	4.93×10^{-5}	4.46×10^{-5}	8.69×10^{-5}	8.34×10^{-5}	1.59×10^{-4}	1.01×10^{-4}	1.52×10^{-4}
0.9	1.26×10^{-4}	1.60×10^{-5}	2.59×10^{-5}	2.17×10^{-5}	4.40×10^{-5}	4.03×10^{-5}	8.22×10^{-5}	5.19×10^{-5}	8.97×10^{-5}

Table 4. Absolute error values of Example 1 for Burgers' equation with $\alpha = 0.7$.

z/ξ	0.1	0.2	0.3	0.4	0.5	0.6	0.7	0.8	0.9
0.1	1.29×10^{-4}	7.61×10^{-6}	2.09×10^{-5}	9.72×10^{-6}	3.07×10^{-5}	2.01×10^{-5}	4.75×10^{-5}	1.57×10^{-5}	4.67×10^{-5}
0.2	2.30×10^{-4}	9.60×10^{-6}	4.42×10^{-5}	2.82×10^{-5}	7.08×10^{-5}	5.80×10^{-5}	1.13×10^{-4}	6.51×10^{-5}	1.30×10^{-4}
0.3	3.03×10^{-4}	8.97×10^{-6}	6.33×10^{-5}	4.46×10^{-5}	1.04×10^{-4}	9.12×10^{-5}	1.69×10^{-4}	1.11×10^{-4}	2.07×10^{-4}
0.4	3.48×10^{-4}	5.73×10^{-6}	7.73×10^{-5}	5.69×10^{-5}	1.27×10^{-4}	1.15×10^{-4}	2.08×10^{-4}	1.48×10^{-4}	2.68×10^{-4}
0.5	3.64×10^{-4}	2.22×10^{-6}	8.27×10^{-5}	6.07×10^{-5}	1.35×10^{-4}	1.24×10^{-4}	2.23×10^{-4}	1.64×10^{-4}	3.03×10^{-4}
0.6	3.53×10^{-4}	2.36×10^{-6}	8.15×10^{-5}	5.87×10^{-5}	1.30×10^{-4}	1.20×10^{-4}	2.16×10^{-4}	1.64×10^{-4}	3.09×10^{-4}
0.7	3.11×10^{-4}	5.08×10^{-6}	7.10×10^{-5}	4.82×10^{-5}	1.10×10^{-4}	1.00×10^{-4}	1.84×10^{-4}	1.40×10^{-4}	2.80×10^{-4}
0.8	2.39×10^{-4}	6.20×10^{-6}	5.32×10^{-5}	3.31×10^{-5}	7.91×10^{-5}	7.04×10^{-5}	1.33×10^{-4}	1.01×10^{-4}	2.17×10^{-4}
0.9	1.35×10^{-4}	4.68×10^{-6}	2.90×10^{-5}	1.57×10^{-5}	4.05×10^{-5}	3.47×10^{-5}	6.90×10^{-5}	5.18×10^{-5}	1.22×10^{-4}

Example 2. *It will be examined that the fractional-order Burgers' equation with Neumann boundary condition as follow:*

$$ {}^{C}D_{\xi}^{\alpha}u - u_{zz} - uu_z = f(z,\xi) \tag{63} $$

$$ 0 \le z \le 1, 0 \le \xi \le 1, \ \frac{1}{2} < \alpha \le 1, $$

$$ u(z,0) = 0, u_z(0,\xi) = u_z(1,\xi) = 0. \tag{64} $$

The exact solution of problem is :

$$ u(z,\xi) = (\frac{z^3}{3} - \frac{z^2}{2})\xi^{2\alpha}, \tag{65} $$

and $f(z,\xi)$ is the function that provides the Equations (65). Taking $z_i = \frac{i}{a}$, $i = 1, 2, ..., a$, $\xi_i = \frac{i}{b}$, $i = 1, 2, ..., b$ and $n = a \times b$. Absolute error of Example 2 is computed for $\alpha = 0.9$, $\alpha = 0.8$, $\alpha = 0.7$ and $n = 64$ $(a = b = 8)$. Error values are given in Tables 5–7 in order to observe of applicability and influence of method. The graphics of absolute errors are given for $\alpha = 0.7$, $\alpha = 0.8$, and $\alpha = 0.9$ in Figure 2.

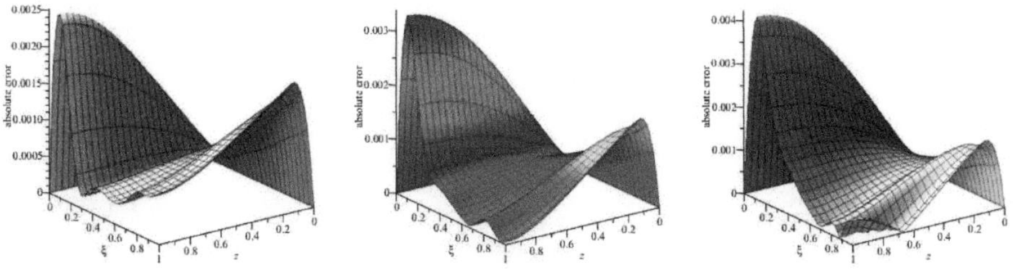

Figure 2. The surfaces show the absolute error of Example 2 with $n = 36$ $(a = b = 6)$ and for $\alpha = 0.7$, $\alpha = 0.8$, $\alpha = 0.9$ respectively on region Θ.

Table 5. Absolute error values of Example 2 for Burgers' equation with $\alpha = 0.9$.

z/ξ	0.1	0.2	0.3	0.4	0.5	0.6	0.7	0.8	0.9
0.1	4.76×10^{-4}	3.40×10^{-4}	2.88×10^{-4}	2.92×10^{-4}	3.24×10^{-4}	3.84×10^{-4}	4.64×10^{-4}	5.77×10^{-4}	6.89×10^{-4}
0.2	9.30×10^{-4}	6.16×10^{-4}	4.62×10^{-4}	4.00×10^{-4}	3.81×10^{-4}	4.03×10^{-4}	4.50×10^{-4}	5.49×10^{-4}	6.38×10^{-4}
0.3	1.36×10^{-3}	8.71×10^{-4}	6.16×10^{-4}	4.88×10^{-4}	4.16×10^{-4}	3.97×10^{-4}	4.09×10^{-4}	4.88×10^{-4}	5.54×10^{-4}
0.4	1.77×10^{-3}	1.10×10^{-3}	7.50×10^{-4}	5.58×10^{-4}	4.33×10^{-4}	3.72×10^{-4}	3.48×10^{-4}	4.06×10^{-4}	4.49×10^{-4}
0.5	2.15×10^{-3}	1.30×10^{-3}	8.62×10^{-4}	6.09×10^{-4}	4.34×10^{-4}	3.33×10^{-3}	2.74×10^{-4}	3.09×10^{-4}	3.30×10^{-4}
0.6	2.47×10^{-3}	1.46×10^{-3}	9.49×10^{-4}	6.42×10^{-4}	4.20×10^{-4}	2.82×10^{-4}	1.91×10^{-4}	2.02×10^{-4}	2.01×10^{-4}
0.7	2.74×10^{-3}	1.59×10^{-3}	1.01×10^{-3}	6.56×10^{-4}	3.94×10^{-4}	2.23×10^{-4}	1.01×10^{-4}	9.05×10^{-5}	6.96×10^{-4}
0.8	2.93×10^{-3}	1.68×10^{-3}	1.04×10^{-3}	6.56×10^{-4}	3.62×10^{-4}	1.63×10^{-4}	1.72×10^{-5}	1.43×10^{-5}	5.21×10^{-5}
0.9	3.05×10^{-3}	1.73×10^{-3}	1.06×10^{-3}	6.49×10^{-4}	3.32×10^{-4}	1.15×10^{-4}	4.78×10^{-5}	9.40×10^{-5}	1.43×10^{-4}

Table 6. Absolute error values of Example 2 for Burgers' equation with $\alpha = 0.8$.

z/ξ	0.1	0.2	0.3	0.4	0.5	0.6	0.7	0.8	0.9
0.1	3.88×10^{-4}	2.19×10^{-4}	2.12×10^{-4}	2.49×10^{-4}	3.02×10^{-4}	3.77×10^{-4}	4.63×10^{-4}	5.77×10^{-4}	6.84×10^{-4}
0.2	7.52×10^{-4}	3.60×10^{-4}	2.88×10^{-4}	2.86×10^{-4}	3.07×10^{-4}	3.59×10^{-4}	4.23×10^{-4}	5.31×10^{-4}	6.22×10^{-4}
0.3	1.10×10^{-3}	4.88×10^{-4}	3.52×10^{-4}	3.10×10^{-4}	2.96×10^{-4}	3.21×10^{-4}	3.61×10^{-4}	4.60×10^{-4}	5.34×10^{-4}
0.4	1.44×10^{-3}	6.01×10^{-4}	4.05×10^{-4}	3.23×10^{-4}	2.74×10^{-4}	2.73×10^{-4}	2.88×10^{-4}	3.74×10^{-4}	4.32×10^{-4}
0.5	1.75×10^{-3}	6.97×10^{-4}	4.45×10^{-4}	3.26×10^{-4}	2.43×10^{-4}	2.16×10^{-4}	2.07×10^{-4}	2.79×10^{-4}	3.21×10^{-4}
0.6	2.01×10^{-3}	7.75×10^{-4}	4.74×10^{-4}	3.19×10^{-4}	2.05×10^{-4}	1.53×10^{-4}	1.22×10^{-4}	1.79×10^{-4}	2.06×10^{-4}
0.7	2.23×10^{-3}	8.31×10^{-4}	4.90×10^{-4}	3.04×10^{-4}	1.62×10^{-4}	8.89×10^{-5}	3.63×10^{-5}	7.85×10^{-5}	9.18×10^{-5}
0.8	2.40×10^{-3}	8.68×10^{-4}	4.95×10^{-4}	2.85×10^{-4}	1.20×10^{-4}	2.81×10^{-5}	4.19×10^{-5}	1.33×10^{-5}	1.18×10^{-5}
0.9	2.50×10^{-3}	8.87×10^{-4}	4.94×10^{-4}	2.67×10^{-4}	8.76×10^{-5}	1.80×10^{-5}	1.00×10^{-4}	8.19×10^{-5}	8.88×10^{-4}

Table 7. Absolute error values of Example 2 for Burgers' equation with $\alpha = 0.7$.

z/ξ	0.1	0.2	0.3	0.4	0.5	0.6	0.7	0.8	0.9
0.1	2.86×10^{-4}	1.42×10^{-4}	1.89×10^{-4}	2.48×10^{-4}	3.17×10^{-4}	4.00×10^{-4}	4.88×10^{-4}	5.96×10^{-4}	6.96×10^{-4}
0.2	5.41×10^{-4}	1.88×10^{-4}	2.15×10^{-4}	2.53×10^{-4}	3.01×10^{-4}	3.73×10^{-4}	4.48×10^{-4}	5.53×10^{-4}	6.41×10^{-4}
0.3	7.93×10^{-4}	2.26×10^{-4}	2.34×10^{-4}	2.50×10^{-4}	2.77×10^{-4}	3.35×10^{-4}	3.95×10^{-4}	4.95×10^{-4}	5.71×10^{-4}
0.4	1.03×10^{-3}	2.57×10^{-4}	2.49×10^{-4}	2.42×10^{-4}	2.48×10^{-4}	2.91×10^{-4}	3.36×10^{-4}	4.30×10^{-4}	4.95×10^{-4}
0.5	1.26×10^{-3}	2.81×10^{-4}	2.58×10^{-4}	2.30×10^{-4}	2.16×10^{-4}	2.45×10^{-4}	2.75×10^{-4}	3.61×10^{-4}	4.16×10^{-4}
0.6	1.45×10^{-3}	2.98×10^{-4}	2.62×10^{-4}	2.14×10^{-4}	1.81×10^{-4}	1.96×10^{-4}	2.12×10^{-4}	2.91×10^{-4}	3.36×10^{-4}
0.7	1.62×10^{-3}	3.06×10^{-4}	2.60×10^{-4}	1.95×10^{-4}	1.45×10^{-4}	1.48×10^{-4}	1.52×10^{-4}	2.22×10^{-4}	2.58×10^{-4}
0.8	1.74×10^{-3}	3.09×10^{-4}	2.55×10^{-4}	1.76×10^{-4}	1.12×10^{-4}	1.04×10^{-4}	9.79×10^{-5}	1.59×10^{-4}	1.89×10^{-4}
0.9	1.82×10^{-3}	3.08×10^{-4}	2.50×10^{-4}	1.60×10^{-4}	8.69×10^{-5}	7.20×10^{-5}	5.79×10^{-5}	1.14×10^{-4}	1.38×10^{-4}

7. Conclusions

In this research, some special Hilbert spaces with inner products and the kernel function of these spaces are introduced. Then the iterative solution is obtained by reproducing kernel theory. Error estimation of the approximate solution and convergence analysis are verified with lemma and theorems. Numerical outcomes demonstrate that the iterative approximation is applicable, convenient, and powerful for fractional-order Burgers' equation with Dirichlet and Neumann conditions. Therefore, iterative RKM is successfully implemented for fractional-order Burgers' equation and so this study will contribute to the science.

Author Contributions: Resources, F.E.; Software, M.G.S.; Writing-original draft, O.S.; Writing-review & editing, O.S. and M.G.S. All authors have read and agreed to the published version of the manuscript.

Funding: This research received no funding.

Acknowledgments: We thank the reviewers for their positive remarks on our work.

Conflicts of Interest: The authors declare no conflict of interest.

Abbreviations

The following abbreviations are used in this manuscript:

RKM	Reproducing Kernel Method
RKHS	Reproducing Kernel Hilbert Space

References

1. Burgers, J.M. Mathematical examples illustrating relations occurring in the theory of turbulent fluid motion. In *Selected Papers of JM Burgers*; Verhandelingen Der Koninklijke Nederlandsche Akademle V An Wetenschappen, Afdeeling Natuurkunde; Springer: Dordrecht, The Netherlands, 1939; Volume 17, pp. 1–53.
2. Guesmia, A.; Daili, N. About the existence and uniqueness of solution to fractional Burgers Equation. *Acta Univ. Apulensis* **2010**, *21*, 161–170.
3. Lombard, B.; Matignon, D. Diffusive approximation of a time-fractional Burger's equation in nonlinear acoustics. *Siam J. Appl. Math.* **2016**, *76*, 1765–1791. [CrossRef]
4. Dong, Z.; Sun, X.; Xiao, H.; Zhai, J. Averaging principle for one dimensional stochastic Burgers equation. *J. Differ. Equ.* **2018**, *265*, 4749–4797. [CrossRef]
5. Nojavan, H.; Abbasbandy, S.; Mohammadi, M. Local variably scaled Newton basis functions collocation method for solving Burgers' equation. *Appl. Math. Comput.* **2018**, *330*, 23–41. [CrossRef]
6. Oruc, O.; Esen, A.; Bulut, F. A unified finite difference Chebyshev wavelet method for numerically solving time fractional Burgers' equation. *Discret. Contin. Dyn. Syst. Ser. S* **2019**, *12*, 533–542.
7. Rong-Pei, Z.; Xi-Jun, Y.; Guo-Zhong, Z. Modified Burgers' equation by the local discontinuous Galerkin method. *Chin. Phys. B* **2013**, *22*, 1–5.
8. Roshan, T.; Bhamra, K.S. Numerical solutions of the modified Burgers' equation by Petrov-Galerkin method. *Appl. Math. Comput.* **2011**, 218, 3673–3679. [CrossRef]
9. Ramadan, M.A.; Danaf, T.S.E. Numerical treatment for the modified Burgers equation. *Math. Comput. Simul.* **2005**, *70*, 90–98. [CrossRef]
10. Bahadir, A.R.; Saglam, M. A mixed finite difference and boundary element approach to one-dimensional Burgers' equation. *Appl. Math. Comput.* **2005**, *160*, 663–673. [CrossRef]
11. Dag, I.; Irk, D.; Saka, B. A numerical solution of the Burgers equation using cubic B-splines. *Appl. Math. Comput.* **2005**, *163*, 199–211.
12. Caldwell, J.; Wanless, P.; Cook, E. A finite element approach to Burgers' equation. *Appl. Math. Model.* **1981**, *5*, 189–193. [CrossRef]
13. Kutluay, S.; Bahadir, A.R.; Ozdes, A. Numerical solution of one-dimensional Burgers' equation: Explicit and exact-explicit finite-difference methods. *J. Comput. Appl.* **1999**, *103*, 251–261. [CrossRef]
14. Li, F.; Cui, M. A best approximation for the solution of one-dimensional variable-coefficient Burgers equation. *Numer. Methods Partial Differ. Equ.* **2009**, *25*, 1353–1365. [CrossRef]
15. Raza, N.; Awan, A.U.; Haque, E.U.; Abdullah, M.; Rashidi, M.M. Unsteady flow of a Burgers' fluid with Caputo fractional derivatives: A hybrid technique. *Ain Shams Eng. J.* **2019**, *10*, 319–325. [CrossRef]
16. Safdar, R.; Imran, M.; Khalique, C.M. Time-dependent flow model of a generalized Burgers' fluid with fractional derivatives through a cylindrical domain: An exact and numerical approach. *Results Phys.* **2018**, *9*, 237–245. [CrossRef]
17. Liu, J.; Hou, G. Numerical solutions of the space-and time-fractional coupled Burgers equations by generalized differential transform method. *Appl. Math. Comput.* **2011**, *217*, 7001–7008. [CrossRef]
18. Zhang, J.; Liu, F.; Lin, Z.; Anh, V. Analytical and numerical solutions of a multi-term time-fractional Burgers' fluid model. *Appl. Math. Comput.* **2019**, *356*, 1–12. [CrossRef]

19. Momani, S. Non-perturbative analytical solutions of the space-and time-fractional Burgers equations. *Chaos Solitons Fractals* **2006**, *28*, 930–937. [CrossRef]
20. Ajou, A.E.; Arqub, O.A.; Momani, S. Approximate analytical solution of the nonlinear fractional KdV-Burgers equation: A new iterative algorithm. *J. Comput. Phys.* **2015**, *293*, 81–95. [CrossRef]
21. Mittal, R.C.; Arora, G. Numerical solution of the coupled viscous Burgers' equation. *Commun. Nonlinear. Sci. Numer. Simulat.* **2011**, *16*, 1304–1313. [CrossRef]
22. Jiwari, R. A hybrid numerical scheme for the numerical solution of the Burgers' equation. *Comput. Phys. Commun.* **2015**, *188*, 59–67. [CrossRef]
23. Kutluay, S.; Esen, A.; Dag, I. Numerical solutions of the Burgers' equation by the least-squares quadratic B-spline finite element method. *J. Comput. Appl. Math.* **2004**, *167*, 21–33. [CrossRef]
24. Zaremba, S. Sur le calcul numérique des fonctions demandées dans le probléme de Dirichlet et le problème hydrodynamique. *Bull. Int. de l'Académie Sci. Cracovie* **1908**, *1908*, 125–195.
25. Aronszajn, N. Theory of reproducing kernels. *Trans. Am. Math. Soc.* **1950**, *68*, 337–404. [CrossRef]
26. Schwartz, L. Sous-espaces hilbertiens d'espaces vectoriels topologiques et noyaux associés (noyaux reproduisants). *J. Anal. Math.* **1964**, *13*, 115–256. [CrossRef]
27. Saitoh, S.; Sawano, Y. *Theory of Reproducing Kernels and Applications. Developments in Mathematics*; Springer: Singapore, 2016.
28. Akram, G.; Rehman, H. Numerical solution of eighth order boundary value problems in reproducing Kernel space. *Numer. Algor.* **2013**, *62*, 527–540. [CrossRef]
29. Jiang, W.; Lin, Y. Approximate solution of the fractional advection-dispersion equation. *Comput. Phys. Commun.* **2010**, *181*, 557–561. [CrossRef]
30. Arqub, O.A. Numerical algorithm for the solutions of fractional order systems of Dirichlet function types with comparative analysis. *Fundam. Inform.* **2019**, *166*, 111–137. [CrossRef]
31. Sakar, M.G.; Saldır, O.; Akgül, A. A novel technique for fractional Bagley–Torvik equation. *Proc. Natl. Acad. Sci. India Sect. A Phys. Sci.* **2019**, *89*, 539–545. [CrossRef]
32. Jiang, W.; Lin, Y. Representation of exact solution for the time-fractional telegraph equation in the reproducing kernel space. *Commun. Nonlinear Sci. Numer. Simulat.* **2011**, *16*, 3639–3645. [CrossRef]
33. Mohammadi, M.; Zafarghandi, F.S.; Babolian, E.; Jvadi, S. A local reproducing kernel method accompanied by some different edge improvement techniques: Application to the Burgers' equation. *Iran. J. Sci. Technol. Trans. Sci.* **2018**, *42*, 857–871. [CrossRef]
34. Arqub, O.A.; Al-Smadi, M. Numerical algorithm for solving time-fractional partial integrodifferential equations subject to initial and Dirichlet boundary conditions. *Numer. Methods Partial Differ. Equ.* **2018**, *34*, 1577–1597. [CrossRef]
35. Sakar, M.G. Iterative reproducing kernel Hilbert spaces method for Riccati differential equations. *J. Comput. Appl. Math.* **2017**, *309*, 163–174. [CrossRef]
36. Yao, H. Reproducing Kernel method for the solution of nonlinear hyperbolic telegraph equation with an integral condition. *Numer. Methods Partial Differ. Equ.* **2011**, *27*, 867–886. [CrossRef]
37. Arqub, O.A. Solutions of time-fractional Tricomi and Keldysh equations of Dirichlet functions types in Hilbert space. *Numer. Methods Partial Differ. Equ.* **2018**, *34*, 1759–1780. [CrossRef]
38. Akgül, A.; Inc, M.; Kilicman, A.; Baleanu, D. A new approach for one-dimensional sine-Gordon equation. *Adv. Differ. Equ.* **2010**, *8*, 1–20. [CrossRef]
39. Lin, Y.; Zhou, Y. Solving the reaction-diffusion equations with nonlocal boundary conditions based on reproducing kernel space. *Numer. Methods Partial Differ. Equ.* **2009**, *25*, 1468–1481. [CrossRef]
40. Arqub, O.A.; Maayah, B. Numerical solutions of integro differential equations of Fredholm operator type in the sense of the Atangana-Baleanu fractional operator. *Chaos Solitons Fractals* **2018**, *117*, 117–124. [CrossRef]
41. Arqub, O.A.; Al-Smadi, M.; Shawagfeh, N. Solving Fredholm integro-differentialequations using reproducing kernel Hilbert space method. *Appl. Math. Comput.* **2013**, *219*, 8938–8948.
42. Mohammadi, M.; Mokhtari, R. A reproducing kernel method for solving a class of nonlinear systems of PDEs. *Math. Model. Anal.* **2014**, *19*, 180–198. [CrossRef]
43. Wang, Y.; Du, M.; Tan, F.; Li, Z.; Nie, T. Using reproducing kernel for solving a class of fractional partial differential equation with non-classical conditions. *Appl. Math. Comput.* **2013**, *219*, 5918–5925. [CrossRef]
44. Arqub, O.A.; Al-Smadi, M. Atangana-Baleanu fractional approach to the solutions of Bagley–Torvik and Painlevéequations in Hilbert space. *Chaos Solitons Fractals* **2018**, *117*, 161–167. [CrossRef]

45. Mohammadi, M.; Mokhtari, R.; Panahipour, H. A Galerkin-reproducing kernel method: Application to the 2D nonlinear coupled Burgers equations. *Eng. Anal. Bound. Elem.* **2013**, *37*, 1642–1652. [CrossRef]
46. Sakar, M.G.; Saldır, O. Improving variational iteration method with auxiliary parameter for nonlinear time-fractional partial differential equations. *J. Optim. Theory Appl.* **2017**, *174*, 530–549. [CrossRef]
47. Cui, M.G.; Lin, Y.Z. *Nonlinear Numercal Analysis in the Reproducing Kernel Space*; Nova Science Publisher: New York, NY, USA, 2009.
48. Tanaka, K. Generation of point sets by convex optimization for interpolation in reproducing kernel Hilbert spaces. *Numer. Algor.* **2019**, *84*, 1049–1079. [CrossRef]
49. Sakar, M.G.; Saldır, O.; Erdogan, F. An iterative approximation for time-fractional Cahn-Allen equation with reproducing kernel method. *Comput. Appl. Math.* **2018**, *37*, 5951–5964. [CrossRef]
50. Lotfi, T.; Rashidi, M.; Mahdiani, K. A posteriori analysis: Error estimation for the eighth order boundary value problems in reproducing Kernel space. *Numer. Algor.* **2016**, *73*, 391–406. [CrossRef]
51. Saldır, O.; Sakar, M.G.; Erdogan, F. Numerical solution of time-fractional Kawahara equation using reproducing kernel method with error estimate. *Comp. Appl. Math.* **2019**, *38*, 198. [CrossRef]
52. Bakhtiari, P.; Abbasbandy, S.; Van Gorder, R.A. Solving the Dym initial value problem in reproducing kernel space. *Numer. Algor.* **2018**, *78*, 405–421. [CrossRef]
53. Sakar, M.G.; Saldır, O.; Erdogan, F. A hybrid method for singularly perturbed convection–diffusion equation. *Int. J. Appl. Comput. Math.* **2019**, *5*, 135. [CrossRef]
54. Sakar, M.G.; Saldır, O. A novel iterative solution for time-fractional Boussinesq equation by reproducing kernel method. *J. Appl. Math. Comput.* **2020**, in press. [CrossRef]
55. Gao, W.; Veeresha, P.; Prakasha, D.G.; Baskonus, H.M. Novel Dynamic Structures of 2019-nCoV with Nonlocal Operator via Powerful Computational Technique. *Biology* **2020**, *9*, 107. [CrossRef] [PubMed]
56. Goufo, E.F.D.; Toudjeo, I.T. Around chaotic disturbance and irregularity for higher order traveling waves. *J. Math.* **2018**, *2018*, 2391697.
57. Goufo, E.F.D. Application of the Caputo-Fabrizio fractional derivative without singular kernel to Korteweg-de Vries-Burgers equation. *Math. Model. Anal.* **2016**, *21*, 188–198. [CrossRef]
58. Podlubny, I. *Fractional Differential Equations*; Academic Press: New York, NY, USA, 1999.
59. Diethelm, K. *The Analysis of Fractional Differential Equations*; Lecture Notes in Mathematics; Springer: Berlin/Heidelberg, Germany, 2010.

fractal and fractional

MDPI

Article

On the Fractional Maximal Delta Integral Type Inequalities on Time Scales

Lütfi Akın

Department of Bussiness Administration, Mardin Artuklu University, Mardin 47100, Turkey; lutfiakin@artuklu.edu.tr

Received: 8 May 2020; Accepted: 15 June 2020; Published: 17 June 2020

Abstract: Time scales have been the target of work of many mathematicians for more than a quarter century. Some of these studies are of inequalities and dynamic integrals. Inequalities and fractional maximal integrals have an important place in these studies. For example, inequalities and integrals contributed to the solution of many problems in various branches of science. In this paper, we will use fractional maximal integrals to establish integral inequalities on time scales. Moreover, our findings show that inequality is valid for discrete and continuous conditions.

Keywords: operator theory; time scales; integral inequalities

MSC: 47B38; 34N05; 35A23

---

1. Introduction

The founder of the study of dynamic equations on time scales is Stefan Hilger [1]. Recently, the inequalities and dynamic equations on time scales have received great attention. Dynamic equations and inequalities have many applications in quantum mechanics, neural networks, heat transfer, electrical engineering, optics, economy and population dynamics [2–5]. It is possible to give an example from the economy, seasonal investments and income [6]. Many mathematicians have demonstrated various aspects of integral inequalities on time scales [7,8]. The most important examples of time scale studies are differential, difference and quantum calculus [9], i.e., when $\mathbb{T} = \mathbb{R}$, $\mathbb{T} = \mathbb{N}$ and $\mathbb{T} = q^{\mathbb{N}_0} = \left\{q^t : t \in \mathbb{N}_0\right\}$ where $q > 1$.

Fractional calculus is an extended version of non-integer integrals and derivatives. In time scales, Lebesgue spaces and different spaces, the subject of fractional integrals has been studied by many mathematicians [10–19]. We consider the functional [20]:

$$T(f,g) = \frac{1}{t-a}\int_a^t f(x)g(x)\Delta x - \left(\frac{1}{t-a}\int_a^t f(x)\Delta x\right)\left(\frac{1}{t-a}\int_a^t g(x)\Delta x\right)$$

where f and g are two synchronous integrable functions on $[a,t]_{\mathbb{T}}$, (i.e., $[a,t]_{\mathbb{T}} = [a,t] \cap \mathbb{T}$).

The main subject of our article is to create new fractional inequalities by using fractional maximal integral operators and synchronous functions on time scales. In addition, our findings include continuous inequalities and corresponding discrete analogs.

The organization of this article is as follows. In Section 2, we will give some definitions of the Δ-maximal type fractional integral operator on time scales. In Section 3, we will create new fractional inequalities by using fractional maximal integral operator and synchronous functions on time scales. In Section 4, we show a few applications of our results.

2. Preliminaries

Some basic concepts related to time scale are given below without proof. We recommend that the reader refer to the [2–25] monographs for details.

Definition 1. *[21] Given an open set $\Omega \subset \mathbb{R}^n$ and a, $0 < a < n$. Fractional maximal operator $M_a f$ is defined as follows*

$$M_a f(t) = \sup_{B \ni t} \frac{1}{|B|^{1-\frac{a}{n}}} \int_{B \cap \Omega} f(y) dy$$

where the supremum is again taken over all balls B which contain t. In the limiting case $a = 0$, the fractional maximal operator reduces to the Hardy–Littlewood maximal operator.

Definition 2. *[21] Let $\Phi \subset \mathbb{R}$ and $p : \Phi \to [1, \infty)$ a measurable function. $L^{p(\cdot)}$ is composed of all measurable functions f on Φ such that*

$$\int_{\Phi} \left(\frac{|f(x)|}{\lambda} \right)^{p(x)} dx \leq 1$$

for any $\lambda > 0$. The norm in $L^{p(x)}$ space is the generalization of the norm in L^p space (p is constant). The Luxemburg norm in $L^{p(x)}$ space is defined as follows.

$$||f||_{L^{p(\cdot)}} = \inf \left\{ \lambda > 0 : \int_{\Phi} \left(\frac{|f(x)|}{\lambda} \right)^{p(x)} dx \leq 1 \right\}$$

At the same time $L^{p(x)}$ becomes a Banach space.

Definition 3. *[22] Let f and g be two integrable functions on $[a, t]_{\mathbb{T}}$ (i.e., $[a, t]_{\mathbb{T}} = [a, t] \cap \mathbb{T}$). If for any $x, y \in [a, t]_{\mathbb{T}}$*

$$[f(x) - f(y)][g(x) - g(y)] \geq 0,$$

then f and g are called synchronous real-valued functions on $[a, t]_{\mathbb{T}} \subset \mathbb{R}$.

Definition 4. *[23] A time scale $\mathbb{T}$ is an arbitrary nonempty closed subset of the real numbers $\mathbb{R}$. We define the forward jump operator $\sigma : \mathbb{T} \to \mathbb{T}$ by $\sigma(t) = \inf\{s \in \mathbb{T} : s > t\}$ for $t \in \mathbb{T}$ and we define the backward jump operator $\rho : \mathbb{T} \to \mathbb{T}$ as defined by $\rho(t) = \sup\{s \in \mathbb{T} : s < t\}$ for $t \in \mathbb{T}$.*

If $\sigma(t) > t$, we say that t is right-scattered and if $\rho(t) < t$, we say that t is left-scattered. Moreover, if $\sigma(t) = t$, then t is called right-dense and if $\rho(t) = t$, then t is called left-dense. $\mu : \mathbb{T} \to \mathbb{R}^+$ such that $\mu(t) = \sigma(t) - t$ is called graininess mapping.

If $\mathbb{T}$ has a left-scattered maximum m, then $\mathbb{T}^k = \mathbb{T} - \{m\}$. Otherwise $\mathbb{T}^k = \mathbb{T}$. Briefly

$$\mathbb{T}^k = \begin{cases} \mathbb{T} \setminus (\rho \sup \mathbb{T}, \sup \mathbb{T}], & if \quad \sup \mathbb{T} < \infty, \\ \mathbb{T}, & if \quad \sup \mathbb{T} = \infty. \end{cases}$$

Along the same lines

$$\mathbb{T}_k = \begin{cases} \mathbb{T} \setminus [\inf \mathbb{T}, \sigma(\inf \mathbb{T})], & |\inf \mathbb{T}| < \infty, \\ \mathbb{T}, & \inf \mathbb{T} = -\infty. \end{cases}$$

Definition 5 *[23] A function f: $[a, b] \to \mathbb{R}$ is said to be right-dense continuous if it is right continuous at each right-dense point and there exists a finite left limit at all left-dense points, and f is said to be differentiable if its derivative exists.*

The space of rd-continuous functions is denoted by $C_{rd}(\mathbb{T}, \mathbb{R})$.

Definition 6. *[23] The generalized polynomials, that also occur in Taylor's formula are $g_k, h_k : \mathbb{T}^2 \to \mathbb{R}, k \in \mathbb{N}_0$ functions. The functions g_0, h_0 are $g_0(t,s) = h_0(t,s) \equiv 1, \forall s, t \in \mathbb{T}$. Given g_{k+1} and h_{k+1} are*

$$g_{k+1}(t,s) = \int_s^t g_k(\sigma(\tau), s)\Delta\tau, \forall s, t \in \mathbb{T}$$

and

$$h_{k+1}(t,s) = \int_s^t h_k(\tau, s)\Delta\tau, \forall s, t \in \mathbb{T}.$$

We claim that for $k \in \mathbb{N}_0$

$$g_k(t,s) = h_k(t,s) = \frac{(t-s)^k}{k!} \forall s, t \in \mathbb{R}.$$

Definition 7. *[24] If $f \in C_{rd}(\mathbb{T}, \mathbb{R})$ and $t \in \mathbb{T}^k$, then*

$$\int_t^{\sigma(t)} f(\tau)\Delta\tau = \mu(t)f(t).$$

For $\alpha \geq 1$ we can define the time scale Δ-maximal type fractional integral

$$M_a^\alpha f(t) = \sup_{B \ni t} \frac{1}{|B|^{\frac{n-a}{n}}} \int_a^t h_{\alpha-1}(t, \sigma(\tau)) f(\tau)\Delta\tau,$$

$$M_a^0 f(t) = \sup_{B \ni t} \frac{1}{|B|^{1-\frac{a}{n}}} f(t),$$

where $f \in L_1([a,t] \cap \mathbb{T})$ and $M_a^\alpha f \in L_1([a,t] \cap \mathbb{T})$ (for details on Lemma 2, see [25]) Lebesgue Δ-integrable functions on $[a,t] \cap \mathbb{T}$, $t \in [a,t] \cap \mathbb{T}$.

Lemma 1. *(Lemma 2, [25]) Let $\alpha \geq 1, f \in L_1([a,t] \cap \mathbb{T})$. Assume $h_{\alpha-1}(t, \sigma(\tau))$ is additionally Lebesgue Δ-measurable on $([a,t] \cap \mathbb{T})^2$; $a, t \in \mathbb{T}$. Then $M_a^\alpha f \in L_1([a,t] \cap \mathbb{T})$.*

3. Main Result

We now present the inequalities with respect to fractional maximal integral type operators and their norms in the variable exponential Lebesgue space.

Theorem 1. *Let f and g be two real-valued synchronous functions on $[0, \infty)_{\mathbb{T}} \subset \mathbb{R}$. For $\forall t > a$, $a > 0$, $\alpha \geq 1$ we have*

$$M_a^\alpha (fg)(t) \geq (h_\alpha(t,a))^{-1} (M_a^\alpha f)(t)(M_a^\alpha g)(t). \tag{1}$$

Proof. If f and g are two synchronous functions on $[0, \infty)_{\mathbb{T}}$, then, for $\forall \tau, \theta \geq 0$,

$$f(\tau)g(\tau) - f(\tau)g(\theta) - f(\theta)g(\tau) + f(\theta)g(\theta) \geq 0.$$

Hence

$$f(\tau)g(\tau) + f(\theta)g(\theta) \geq f(\tau)g(\theta) + f(\theta)g(\tau). \tag{2}$$

For $\tau \in (a,t)$ multiplying both sides of (2) by $h_{\alpha-1}(t, \sigma(\tau))$ we have

$$\begin{aligned} &h_{\alpha-1}(t, \sigma(\tau))f(\tau)g(\tau) + h_{\alpha-1}(t, \sigma(\tau))f(\theta)g(\theta) \geq h_{\alpha-1}(t, \sigma(\tau))f(\tau)g(\theta) + \\ &h_{\alpha-1}(t, \sigma(\tau))f(\theta)g(\tau). \end{aligned} \tag{3}$$

If we take the integral of both sides of (3) through (a,t) we get

$$\int_a^t h_{\alpha-1}(t,\sigma(\tau))f(\tau)g(\tau)\Delta\tau + \int_a^t h_{\alpha-1}(t,\sigma(\tau))f(\theta)g(\theta)\Delta\tau$$

$$\geq \int_a^t h_{\alpha-1}(t,\sigma(\tau))f(\tau)g(\theta)\Delta\tau + \int_a^t h_{\alpha-1}(t,\sigma(\tau))f(\theta)g(\tau)\Delta\tau.$$

Since $f(\theta), g(\theta)$ and $(f(\theta)g(\theta))$ are independent from τ, we can take them out of integral. Thus, the following is obtained

$$\int_a^t h_{\alpha-1}(t,\sigma(\tau))f(\tau)g(\tau)\Delta\tau + f(\theta)g(\theta)\int_a^t h_{\alpha-1}(t,\sigma(\tau))\Delta\tau$$

$$\geq g(\theta)\int_a^t h_{\alpha-1}(t,\sigma(\tau))f(\tau)\Delta\tau + f(\theta)\int_a^t h_{\alpha-1}(t,\sigma(\tau))g(\tau)\Delta\tau. \quad (4)$$

If we take $\alpha+1$ instead of k ($h_{k+1}(t,s) = \int_s^t h_k(\tau,s)\Delta\tau,\ \forall s,t \in \mathbb{T}$ and $g_{k+1}(t,s) = \int_s^t g_k(\sigma(\tau),s)\Delta\tau,\ \forall s,t \in \mathbb{T}$) in Definition 6, we get the following.

$$h_\alpha(t,s) = \int_s^t h_{\alpha-1}(\tau,s)\Delta\tau, \forall s,t \in \mathbb{T}.$$

Similarly,

$$g_\alpha(t,s) = \int_s^t g_{\alpha-1}(\sigma(\tau),s)\Delta\tau, \forall s,t \in \mathbb{T}.$$

We know that,

$$\sup_{B\ni t}\frac{1}{|B|^{\frac{n-a}{n}}}\int_a^t h_{\alpha-1}(t,\sigma(\tau))\Delta\tau \geq \int_a^t h_{\alpha-1}(t,\sigma(\tau))\Delta\tau = h_\alpha(t,a)\ ,\ \text{for}\ ,\ 0<a<n.$$

If we take the supremum of both sides of (4) over $B \ni t$, we get the following

$$\sup_{B\ni t}\frac{1}{|B|^{\frac{n-a}{n}}}\int_a^t h_{\alpha-1}(t,\sigma(\tau))f(\tau)g(\tau)\Delta\tau + f(\theta)g(\theta)\sup_{B\ni t}\frac{1}{|B|^{\frac{n-a}{n}}}\int_a^t h_{\alpha-1}(t,\sigma(\tau))\Delta\tau$$

$$\geq g(\theta)\sup_{B\ni t}\frac{1}{|B|^{\frac{n-a}{n}}}\int_a^t h_{\alpha-1}(t,\sigma(\tau))f(\tau)\Delta\tau + f(\theta)\sup_{B\ni t}\frac{1}{|B|^{\frac{n-a}{n}}}\int_a^t h_{\alpha-1}(t,\sigma(\tau))g(\tau)\Delta\tau$$

Due to ($M_a^\alpha f(t) = \sup_{B\ni t}\frac{1}{|B|^{\frac{n-a}{n}}}\int_a^t h_{\alpha-1}(t,\sigma(\tau))f(\tau)\Delta\tau$) Definition 7, we get following

$$M_a^\alpha(fg)(t) + f(\theta)g(\theta)(h_\alpha(t,a)) \geq g(\theta)(M_a^\alpha f)(t) + f(\theta)(M_a^\alpha g)(t). \quad (5)$$

For $\theta \in (a,t)$ multiplying both sides of (5) by $h_{\alpha-1}(t,\sigma(\theta))$ we have

$$h_{\alpha-1}(t,\sigma(\theta))M_a^\alpha(fg)(t) + h_{\alpha-1}(t,\sigma(\theta))f(\theta)g(\theta)(h_\alpha(t,a))$$

$$\geq h_{\alpha-1}(t,\sigma(\theta))g(\theta)(M_a^\alpha f)(t) + h_{\alpha-1}(t,\sigma(\theta))f(\theta)(M_a^\alpha g)(t). \quad (6)$$

If we take the integral of both sides of (6) through (a,t) we get

$$\int_a^t h_{\alpha-1}(t,\sigma(\theta))M_a^\alpha(fg)(t)\Delta\theta + \int_a^t h_{\alpha-1}(t,\sigma(\theta))f(\theta)g(\theta)(h_\alpha(t,a))\Delta\theta$$

$$\geq \int_a^t h_{\alpha-1}(t,\sigma(\theta))g(\theta)(M_a^\alpha f)(t)\Delta\theta + \int_a^t h_{\alpha-1}(t,\sigma(\theta))f(\theta)(M_a^\alpha g)(t)\Delta\theta.$$

Since $M_a^\alpha(fg)(t)$, $(M_a^\alpha f)(t)$, $(M_a^\alpha g)(t)$ and $(h_\alpha(t,a))$ are independent from θ, we can take them out of integral.

If we take $\alpha+1$ instead of k and if we take θ instead of τ ($h_{k+1}(t,s) = \int_s^t h_k(\tau,s)\Delta\tau,\ \forall s,t \in \mathbb{T}$ and $g_{k+1}(t,s) = \int_s^t g_k(\sigma(\tau),s)\Delta\tau,\ \forall s,t \in \mathbb{T}$ in the Definition 6), we get the following

$$\int_a^t h_{\alpha-1}(t,\sigma(\theta))\Delta\theta = h_\alpha(t,a).$$

Thus, the following is obtained

$$M_a^\alpha(fg)(t)\int_a^t h_{\alpha-1}(t,\sigma(\theta))\Delta\theta + (h_\alpha(t,a))\int_a^t h_{\alpha-1}(t,\sigma(\theta))f(\theta)g(\theta)\Delta\theta$$

$$\geq (M_a^\alpha f)(t)\int_a^t h_{\alpha-1}(t,\sigma(\theta))g(\theta)\Delta\theta + (M_a^\alpha g)(t)\int_a^t h_{\alpha-1}(t,\sigma(\theta))f(\theta)\Delta\theta.$$

Hence from Definitions 5 and 6 the following is obtained

$$M_a^\alpha(fg)(t)(h_\alpha(t,a)) + (h_\alpha(t,a))M_a^\alpha(fg)(t) \geq (M_a^\alpha f)(t)(M_a^\alpha g)(t) + (M_a^\alpha g)(t)(M_a^\alpha f)(t).$$

Finally we get

$$M_a^\alpha(fg)(t)(h_\alpha(t,a)) \geq (M_a^\alpha f)(t)(M_a^\alpha g)(t).$$

□

Theorem 2. *Let f and g be two real-valued synchronous functions on $[0,\infty)_\mathbb{T} \subset \mathbb{R}$. For $\forall t > a$, $a > 0$, $\alpha, \beta \geq 1$ we have*

$$h_\alpha(t,a)M_a^\beta(fg)(t) + h_\beta(t,a)M_a^\alpha(fg)(t) \geq (M_a^\alpha f)(t)(M_a^\beta g)(t) + (M_a^\beta f)(t)(M_a^\alpha g)(t).$$

Proof. If f and g are two synchronous functions on $[0,\infty)_\mathbb{T}$, then for $\forall \tau, \theta \geq 0$ we have

$$(f(\tau)-f(\theta))(g(\tau)-g(\theta)) \geq 0.$$

Hence

$$f(\tau)g(\tau) + f(\theta)g(\theta) \geq f(\tau)g(\theta) + f(\theta)g(\tau). \tag{7}$$

For $\tau \in (a,t)$ multiplying both sides of (7) by $h_{\alpha-1}(t,\sigma(\tau))$ we have

$$h_{\alpha-1}(t,\sigma(\tau))f(\tau)g(\tau) + h_{\alpha-1}(t,\sigma(\tau))f(\theta)g(\theta) \geq h_{\alpha-1}(t,\sigma(\tau))f(\tau)g(\theta) + h_{\alpha-1}(t,\sigma(\tau))f(\theta)g(\tau). \tag{8}$$

If we take the integral of both sides of (8) through (a,t) we get

$$\int_a^t h_{\alpha-1}(t,\sigma(\tau))f(\tau)g(\tau)\Delta\tau + \int_a^t h_{\alpha-1}(t,\sigma(\tau))f(\theta)g(\theta)\Delta\tau$$

$$\geq \int_a^t h_{\alpha-1}(t,\sigma(\tau))f(\tau)g(\theta)\Delta\tau + \int_a^t h_{\alpha-1}(t,\sigma(\tau))f(\theta)g(\tau)\Delta\tau. \tag{9}$$

We know that, $\sup_{B\ni t}\frac{1}{|B|^{\frac{n-a}{n}}}\int_a^t h_{\alpha-1}(t,\sigma(\tau))\Delta\tau \geq \int_a^t h_{\alpha-1}(t,\sigma(\tau))\Delta\tau = h_\alpha(t,a)$, for $0<a<n$.

If we take the supremum of both sides of (9) over $B \ni t$ we get the following

$$\sup_{B\ni t}\frac{1}{|B|^{\frac{n-a}{n}}}\int_a^t h_{\alpha-1}(t,\sigma(\tau))f(\tau)g(\tau)\Delta\tau + \sup_{B\ni t}\frac{1}{|B|^{\frac{n-a}{n}}}\int_a^t h_{\alpha-1}(t,\sigma(\tau))f(\theta)g(\theta)\Delta\tau$$

$$\geq \sup_{B\ni t}\frac{1}{|B|^{\frac{n-a}{n}}}\int_a^t h_{\alpha-1}(t,\sigma(\tau))f(\tau)g(\theta)\Delta\tau + \sup_{B\ni t}\frac{1}{|B|^{\frac{n-a}{n}}}\int_a^t h_{\alpha-1}(t,\sigma(\tau))f(\theta)g(\tau)\Delta\tau.$$

Due to $(M_a^{\alpha}f(t) = \sup_{B\ni t}\frac{1}{|B|^{\frac{n-a}{n}}}\int_a^t h_{\alpha-1}(t,\sigma(\tau))f(\tau)\Delta\tau)$ Definition 7, we get following

$$M_a^{\alpha}(fg)(t) + h_{\alpha}(t,\sigma(\tau))f(\theta)g(\theta) \geq g(\theta)(M_a^{\alpha}f)(t) + f(\theta)(M_a^{\alpha}g)(t). \tag{10}$$

For $\theta \in (a,t)$ multiplying both sides of (10) by $h_{\beta-1}(t,\sigma(\theta))$ we have

$$h_{\beta-1}(t,\sigma(\theta))M_a^{\alpha}(fg)(t) + h_{\beta-1}(t,\sigma(\theta))h_{\alpha}(t,\sigma(\tau))f(\theta)g(\theta)$$

$$\geq h_{\beta-1}(t,\sigma(\theta))g(\theta)(M_a^{\alpha}f)(t) + h_{\beta-1}(t,\sigma(\theta))f(\theta)(M_a^{\alpha}g)(t). \tag{11}$$

If we take the integral of both sides of (11) through (a,t) we get

$$\int_a^t h_{\beta-1}(t,\sigma(\theta))M_a^{\alpha}(fg)(t)\Delta\theta + \int_a^t h_{\beta-1}(t,\sigma(\theta))h_{\alpha}(t,\sigma(\tau))f(\theta)g(\theta)\Delta\theta$$

$$\geq \int_a^t h_{\beta-1}(t,\sigma(\theta))g(\theta)(M_a^{\alpha}f)(t)\Delta\theta + \int_a^t h_{\beta-1}(t,\sigma(\theta))f(\theta)(M_a^{\alpha}g)(t)\Delta\theta.$$

Hereby

$$M_a^{\alpha}(fg)(t)\int_a^t h_{\beta-1}(t,\sigma(\theta))\Delta\theta + h_{\alpha}(t,\sigma(\tau))\int_a^t h_{\beta-1}(t,\sigma(\theta))f(\theta)g(\theta)\Delta\theta$$

$$\geq (M_a^{\alpha}f)(t)\int_a^t h_{\beta-1}(t,\sigma(\theta))g(\theta)\Delta\theta + (M_a^{\alpha}g)(t)\int_a^t h_{\beta-1}(t,\sigma(\theta))f(\theta)\Delta\theta.$$

We get the following result from the above inequality

$$h_{\alpha}(t,a)M_a^{\beta}(fg)(t) + h_{\beta}(t,a)M_a^{\alpha}(fg)(t)$$

$$\geq (M_a^{\alpha}f)(t)(M_a^{\beta}g)(t) + (M_a^{\beta}f)(t)(M_a^{\alpha}g)(t).$$

Thus, the proof of Theorem 2 is completed. □

Theorem 3. *Let $(f_i)_{i=1,\dots,n}$ be n positive increasing functions on $[0,\infty)_{\mathbb{T}}$. For $\forall t > a$, $a \geq 0$, $\alpha \geq 1$ we have*

$$M_a^{\alpha}\Big(\prod_{i=1}^{n} f_i\Big)(t) \geq (h_{\alpha}(t,a))^{1-n}\prod_{i=1}^{n} M_a^{\alpha}f_i(t).$$

Proof. The induction method will be used to prove our theorem. For $n = 1$, and $\forall t > a$, $a \geq 0$, $\alpha \geq 1$ we have

$$M_a^{\alpha}(f_1)(t) \geq M_a^{\alpha}f_1(t).$$

For $n = 2$ and $\forall t > a$, $a \geq 0$, $\alpha \geq 1$ applying Theorem 1 we have

$$M_a^{\alpha}(f_1f_2)(t) \geq (h_{\alpha}(t,a))^{-1}M_a^{\alpha}f_1(t)M_a^{\alpha}f_2(t).$$

For $n = n - 1$ we assume that the following inequality holds.

$$M_a^\alpha\Big(\prod_{i=1}^{n-1} f_i\Big)(t) \geq (h_\alpha(t,a))^{2-n} \prod_{i=1}^{n-1} M_a^\alpha f_i(t). \tag{12}$$

For n we have to prove the following inequality

$$M_a^\alpha\Big(\prod_{i=1}^{n} f_i\Big)(t) \geq (h_\alpha(t,a))^{1-n} \prod_{i=1}^{n} M_a^\alpha f_i(t).$$

We know that $(f_i)_{i=1,\ldots,n}$ is a positive increasing function. Thus, $\big(\prod_{i=1}^{n-1} f_i\big)(t)$ is a positive increasing function.

Let $\prod_{i=1}^{n-1} f_i = f,\ f_n = g$ and applying Theorem 1 we have

$$\prod_{i=1}^{n} f_i = \prod_{i=1}^{n-1} f_i f_n = fg$$

and

$$M_a^\alpha\Big(\prod_{i=1}^{n} f_i\Big)(t) = M_a^\alpha\Big(\prod_{i=1}^{n-1} f_i f_n\Big)(t) \geq (h_\alpha(t,a))^{-1} M_a^\alpha\Big(\prod_{i=1}^{n-1} f_i\Big)(t) M_a^\alpha(f_n)(t).$$

Multiplying both sides of (12) by $(h_\alpha(t,a))^{-1} M_a^\alpha(f_n)(t)$ we have

$$(h_\alpha(t,a))^{-1} M_a^\alpha(f_n)(t) M_a^\alpha\Big(\prod_{i=1}^{n-1} f_i\Big)(t) \geq (h_\alpha(t,a))^{-1} M_a^\alpha(f_n)(t)(h_\alpha(t,a))^{2-n} \prod_{i=1}^{n-1} M_a^\alpha f_i(t).$$

Herewith, we get the following result from the above inequality

$$M_a^\alpha\Big(\prod_{i=1}^{n} f_i\Big)(t) \geq (h_\alpha(t,a))^{1-n} \prod_{i=1}^{n} M_a^\alpha f_i(t).$$

□

Theorem 4. *Let $\alpha > 2$, $f \in C_{rd}(\mathbb{T})$. Suppose $h_{\alpha-2}(t,\sigma(t))$ to be continuous on $([0,\infty)_{\mathbb{T}})^2$ with $p, q > 1$, $\frac{1}{p} + \frac{1}{q} = 1$. Then we have*

$$\int_0^\infty \left|M_0^\alpha f(t)\right|^q \Delta t \leq \left(\int_0^\infty \sup_{B \ni t} \frac{1}{|B|}\left(\int_0^t \left|h_{\alpha-2}(t,\sigma(\tau))\right|^p \Delta\tau\right)^{\frac{q}{p}} \Delta t\right)\left(\int_0^\infty |f(t)|^q \Delta t\right).$$

Proof. By Definition 6 we know that

$$M_0^\alpha f(t) = \sup_{B \ni t} \frac{1}{|B|} \int_0^t h_{\alpha-2}(t,\sigma(\tau)) f(\tau) \Delta\tau.$$

Hence, by Hölder's inequality, we have

$$\left|M_0^\alpha f(t)\right| \leq \sup_{B \ni t} \frac{1}{|B|} \int_a^t \left|h_{\alpha-2}(t,\sigma(\tau)) f(\tau)\right| \Delta\tau$$

$$\leq \sup_{B \ni t} \frac{1}{|B|}\left(\int_0^t \left|h_{\alpha-2}(t,\sigma(\tau))\right|^p \Delta\tau\right)^{\frac{1}{p}}\left(\int_0^t |f(\tau)|^q \Delta\tau\right)^{\frac{1}{q}}$$

$$\leq \sup_{B \ni t} \frac{1}{|B|}\left(\int_0^t \left|h_{\alpha-2}(t,\sigma(\tau))\right|^p \Delta\tau\right)^{\frac{1}{p}}\left(\int_0^\infty |f(\tau)|^q \Delta\tau\right)^{\frac{1}{q}}$$

Herewith, the following result is obtained

$$\left|M_0^{\alpha} f(t)\right|^q \leq \sup_{B \ni t} \frac{1}{|B|} \left(\int_0^t \left|h_{\alpha-2}(t, \sigma(\tau))\right|^p \Delta\tau \right)^{\frac{q}{p}} \left(\int_0^{\infty} \left|f(\tau)\right|^q \Delta\tau \right). \tag{13}$$

If we take the integral of both sides of (13) through $\forall t \in [0, \infty)_{\mathbb{T}}$ we get

$$\int_0^{\infty} \left|M_0^{\alpha} f(t)\right|^q \Delta t \leq \left(\int_0^{\infty} \sup_{B \ni t} \frac{1}{|B|} \left(\int_0^t \left|h_{\alpha-2}(t, \sigma(\tau))\right|^p \Delta\tau \right)^{\frac{q}{p}} \Delta t \right) \left(\int_0^{\infty} \left|f(t)\right|^q \Delta t \right).$$

Now, we present a few applications of our results. □

4. Applications

Example 1. *Let* $f(t) = \left\{ \begin{array}{c} t+1,\ 1 \leq t < \frac{5}{2} \\ 2t-1,\ 3 \leq t < 8 \end{array} \right\}$, $g(t) = \left\{ \begin{array}{c} t^2+1,\ 1 \leq t < \frac{5}{2} \\ 3t^3-2,\ 3 \leq t < 8 \end{array} \right\}$; $t \in \mathbb{T} = \mathbb{N}_0 = \{n : n \in \mathbb{N}_0\}$ *be two synchronous functions on* $[0, \infty)_{\mathbb{T}}$. *From Definition 3*

$$[f(t) - f(z)][g(t) - g(z)] = [t+1-z-1]\left[t^2+1-z^2-1\right] = [t-z]\left[t^2-z^2\right] = [t-z]^2[t+z] \geq 0$$

and

$$[f(t) - f(z)][g(t) - g(z)] = [2t-1-2z+1]\left[3t^2-2-3z^2+2\right] = 6[t-z]^2[t+z] \geq 0.$$

Then, for $\forall t > a$, $a = 1$, $\alpha = 2$ *we have*

$$M_1^2(fg)(t) \geq (h_2(t,1))^{-1}(M_1^2 f)(t)(M_1^2 g)(t).$$

Example 2. *Let* $f(t) = t+1$, $g(t) = t^2-1$; $t \in \mathbb{T} = \mathbb{N}_0 = \{n : n \in \mathbb{N}_0\}$ *be two synchronous functions on* $[0, \infty)_{\mathbb{T}}$. *Then* $\forall t > a$, $a = 1$, $\alpha = 2$, $\beta = 3$ *we have*

$$h_2(t,1)M_1^3(fg)(t) + h_3(t,1)M_1^2(fg)(t) \geq (M_1^2 f)(t)(M_1^3 g)(t) + (M_1^3 f)(t)(M_1^2 g)(t).$$

Example 3. *Let* $\left(f_i\right)_{i=1,\ldots,9}$ $f_i(t) = \left(2t^i + 12\right)$; $t \in \mathbb{T} = \mathbb{N}_0 = \{n : n \in \mathbb{N}_0\}$ *be a synchronous function on* $[0, \infty)_{\mathbb{T}}$. *Then, for* $\forall t > a$, $a = 2$, $\alpha = 3$ *we have*

$$M_2^3\left(\prod_{i=1}^{9} f_i\right)(t) \geq (h_3(t,2))^{-8} \prod_{i=1}^{9} M_2^3 f_i(t).$$

Remark 1. *Let* $p : \Phi \to [1, \infty)$ *be a measurable function for* $\Phi \subset \mathbb{R}$. *Using Definition 2, we can easily see that the following norm inequalities are provided in the variable exponential Lebesgue space.*

(I) $\|M_a^{\alpha}(fg)(t)\|_{L^{p(x)}([0,\infty)_{\mathbb{T}})} \geq \|(h_{\alpha}(t,a))^{-1}(M_a^{\alpha} f)(t)(M_a^{\alpha} g)(t)\|_{L^{p(x)}([0,\infty)_{\mathbb{T}})}$

(II) $\|h_{\alpha}(t,a)M_a^{\beta}(fg)(t) + h_{\beta}(t,a)M_a^{\alpha}(fg)(t)\|_{L^{p(x)}([0,\infty)_{\mathbb{T}})}$
$\geq \|(M_a^{\alpha} f)(t)(M_a^{\beta} g)(t) + (M_a^{\beta} f)(t)(M_a^{\alpha} g)(t)\|_{L^{p(x)}([0,\infty)_{\mathbb{T}})}$

(III) $\|M_a^{\alpha}\left(\prod_{i=1}^{n} f_i\right)(t)\|_{L^{p(x)}([0,\infty)_{\mathbb{T}})} \geq \|(h_{\alpha}(t,a))^{1-n} \prod_{i=1}^{n} M_a^{\alpha} f_i(t)\|_{L^{p(x)}([0,\infty)_{\mathbb{T}})}$

5. Discussion and Conclusions

Recently, the concept of inequalities and dynamic equations in time scales has gained an important place in the scientific literature. Mathematicians have emphasized many aspects of integral inequalities and integral equation, for example, transformations, inverse conversions, extensions, etc. However, these studies did not work on time scales. Moreover, the contribution of these studies to science has been weak. In particular, apart from the science of mathematics, we see very little the effect of the concept of time scales in different science fields. This study motivated us to find solutions to problems in these areas. In this paper, we examined fractional maximal integral inequalities on time scales. Furthermore, we demonstrated that different results can be obtained. These results can be examined in two or more dimensions. Moreover, they can be extended to nabla and diamond alpha derivatives.

Funding: This research received no external funding.

Acknowledgments: The author is grateful to the editor and the referees for their careful reading of the manuscript and their valuable comments.

Conflicts of Interest: The author declares no conflict of interest.

References

1. Hilger, S. Analysis on measure chains-a unified approach to continuous and discrete calculus. *Results Math.* **1990**, *18*, 18–56. [CrossRef]
2. Tassaddiq, A.; Rahman, G.; Nisar, K.S.; Samraiz, M. Certain fractional conformable inequalitiesfor the weighted and the extended Chebyshev functionals. *Adv. Differ. Equ.* **2020**, *2020*, 1–9. [CrossRef]
3. Singh, J.; Kumar, D.; Hammouch, Z.; Atangana, A. A fractional epidemiological model for computer viruses pertaining to a new fractional derivative. *Appl. Math. Comput.* **2018**, *316*, 504–515. [CrossRef]
4. Dananea, J.; Allalia, K.; Hammouch, Z. Mathematical analysis of a fractional differential model of HBV infection with antibody immune response. *Chaos Solut. Fractals* **2019**, *136*, 109787. [CrossRef]
5. Ghanbari, B.; Günerhan, H.; Srivastava, H.M. An application of the Atangana-Baleanu fractional derivative in mathematical biology: A three-species predator-prey model. *Chaos Solut. Fractals* **2020**, *138*, 109910. [CrossRef]
6. Bohner, M.; Peterson, A. *Dynamic Equations on Time Scales, An İntroduction with Applications*; Birkhauser: Boston, MA, USA, 2001. [CrossRef]
7. Akin-Bohner, E.; Bohner, M.; Akin, F. Pachpatte inequalities on time scales. *J. Inequal. Pure Appl. Math.* **2005**, *6*, 1–23.
8. Li, W.N. Nonlinear Integral Inequalities in Two Independent Variables on Time Scales. *Adv. Differ. Equ.* **2011**, 283926. [CrossRef]
9. Kac, V.; Cheung, P. *Quantum Calculus*; Universitext Springer: New York, NY, USA, 2002.
10. Chen, Q.; Yang, B. On a new reverse Hardy-Littlewood's type inequality. *Appl. Math. Sci.* **2012**, *6*, 6553–6561.
11. Bohner, M.; Heim, J.; Liu, A. Qualitative analysis of Solow model on time scales. *J. Concrete Appl. Math.* **2015**, *13*, 183–197.
12. Agarwal, R.P.; Bohner, M.; Peterson, A. Inequalities on time scales: A survey. *Math. Inequal. Appl.* **2001**, *4*, 535–555. [CrossRef]
13. Belarbi, S.; Dahmani, Z. On some new fractional integral inequalities. *J. Inequal. Pure Appl. Math.* **2009**, *10*, 1–12.
14. Bohner, M.; Guseinov, G.S. Multiple Lebesgue integration on time scales. *Adv. Differ. Equ.* **2006**, 026391. [CrossRef]
15. Agarwal, R.P.; Otero–Espinar, V.; Perera, K.; Vivero, D.R. Basic properties of Sobolev's spaces on time scales. *Adv. Differ. Equ.* **2006**, 038121. [CrossRef]
16. Chen, G.; Wei, C. A functional generalization of diamond-α integral Dresher's inequality on time scales. *Adv. Differ. Equ.* **2014**, *2014*, 324. [CrossRef]
17. Rahman, G.; Nisar, K.S.; Abdeljawad, T. Certain Hadamard Proportional Fractional Integral Inequalities. *Mathematics* **2020**, *8*, 504. [CrossRef]

18. Rahman, G.; Nisar, K.S.; Abdeljawad, T. Tempered Fractional Integral Inequalities for Convex Functions. *Mathematics* **2020**, *8*, 500. [CrossRef]
19. Ucar, S.; Ucar, E.; Ozdemir, N.; Hammouch, Z. Mathematical analysis and numerical simulation for a smoking model with Atangana-Baleanu derivative. *Chaos Solut. Fractals* **2019**, *118*, 300–306. [CrossRef]
20. Chebyshev, P.L. Sur les expressions approximatives des integrales definies par les autres prises entre les memes limites. *Proc. Math. Soc. Charkov.* **1882**, *2*, 93–98.
21. Akin, L. Compactness of Fractional Maximal Operator in Weighted and Variable Exponent Spaces. *Erzincan Univ. J. Sci. Technol.* **2019**, *12*, 185–190. [CrossRef]
22. Uçar, D.; Hatipoğlu, V.F.; Akincali, A. Fractional Integral Inequalıties On Tıme Scales. *Open J. Math. Sci.* **2018**, *2*, 361–370. [CrossRef]
23. Agarwal, R.P.; O'Regan, D.; Saker, S.H. *Dynamic Inequalities on Time Scales*; Springer: Cham, Switzerland, 2014.
24. Bohner, M.; Agarwal, R.P. Basic calculus on time scales and some of its applications. *Result. Math.* **1999**, *35*, 3–22. [CrossRef]
25. Anastassiou, G.A. Principles of delta fractional calculus on time scales and inequalities. *Math. Comput. Model.* **2010**, *52*, 556–566. [CrossRef]

MDPI
St. Alban-Anlage 66
4052 Basel
Switzerland
Tel. +41 61 683 77 34
Fax +41 61 302 89 18
www.mdpi.com

Fractal and Fractional Editorial Office
E-mail: fractalfract@mdpi.com
www.mdpi.com/journal/fractalfract

Lightning Source UK Ltd.
Milton Keynes UK
UKHW050624070223
416551UK00004B/422

9 783036 519685